DC ELECTRONICS

TEXT BOOK

Revised and edited by:

Greg V. Michalski, M.S.
Senior Educational Media Designer

EB-6101A
595-3402-07

Contents

Most educational programs in the electronic field begin with the study of DC electronics. This Heathkit/Zenith Educational program is no exception. The EB-6101A DC Electronics course presents the basic principles in the study of electronics.

In the Heathkit/Zenith Educational courses we use the convention of electron flow as current flow. Therefore, current always flows from negative to positive unless otherwise specifically stated.

Later in your studies the term "hole flow and conventional current flow" will be introduced.

Remember as you read this course that in the Heathkit Basic Electronic courses, the terms "electron flow and current flow" are used interchangeably.

Course Objectives

When you have completed this course, you will be able to do the following:

1. Solve basic electronic problems involving current, voltage, resistance, and power.

2. Explain the relationship between current, voltage, resistance, and power.

3. Discuss the relationship between electricity and magnetism.

4. Using a schematic diagram as a guide, construct DC circuits with components such as resistors, relays, switches, lamps, batteries, and capacitors.

5. Given a wiring diagram of a circuit containing components such as resistors, relays, switches, lamps, batteries, and capacitors, draw an equivalent schematic diagram.

6. Use a multimeter to measure current, voltage and resistance.

7. Describe the construction, operation, and purpose of resistors, potentiometers, switches, fuses, relays, capacitors, inductors, and batteries.

8. State the basic safety procedures designed to protect you and your test equipment.

9. Build and experiment with basic DC circuits of your own design.

Course Outline

UNIT 1
CURRENT

Contents

Introduction

Electronics is the branch of science that studies the behavior of electrons. In fact, the word electronics is derived from the word electron. Obviously then, to understand electronics, we must first understand the nature of the electron. In this unit, you will see what the electron is, how it behaves, and how you can use it to do work. You will also learn how to measure the flow of electrons.

The unit objectives state exactly what you are expected to learn from this unit. Study this list now and refer to it often as you study the text.

Unit Objectives

When you have completed this unit, you will be able to:

1. Define the following terms: Direct current (DC), molecule, element, atom, proton, neutron, electron, nucleus, ion, coulomb, ampere, conductor, insulator, valence, current, directed drift, battery, polarity, balanced state, neutral state, normal state, electrostatic induction, short circuit, open, and compound.

2. State Coulomb's Law and the effects of the behavior of like and unlike charges.

3. State the electrical charge that is associated with the following: Atom, electron, proton, neutron, nucleus, and ion.

4. Given a simple diagram of Bohr's atomic model, identify the three basic atomic particles.

5. Name the three basic parts of an electrical circuit.

6. Given a simple circuit schematic diagram, indicate the direction of current flow.

7. Draw a schematic of a circuit using the resistor, battery, and conductor schematic symbols.

8. State the correct method for connecting an ammeter in a circuit.

9. Identify materials most likely to become positive or negative ions.

Composition of Matter

Controlling the behavior of electrons is what electronics is all about. Therefore, an understanding of the electron is vitally important to an understanding of electronic fundamentals. **Electrons** are tiny particles which carry the energy to light our homes, cook our food, and do much of our work. To understand what an electron is, we must investigate the make-up of matter.

Matter is generally described as anything which has weight and occupies space. Thus, the earth and everything on it are classified as matter. Matter exists in three different states — solid, liquid, and gas. Examples of solid matter are gold, sand, and wood. Some liquid examples are water, milk, and gasoline. Helium, hydrogen, and oxygen, are examples of gaseous forms of matter.

Elements and Compounds

Elements are the basic building materials from which all matter is constructed. Some examples of elements are iron, carbon, hydrogen, and gold. Just over one hundred elements are presently known. Of these, only 92 occur in nature. These are called natural elements. Figure 1-1A lists the names of the 92 natural elements. In addition, there are about a dozen man-made elements that are listed in Figure 1-1B.

As you look around, it becomes obvious that there are many more types of matter than there are elements. For example, substances like salt, steel, water, and protein do not appear in the list of elements. The reason for this is that these substances are not elements but compounds. A **compound** is composed of two or more elements. Just as the letters of the alphabet can be arranged in various combinations to form millions of different words, the elements can be arranged in various combinations to form millions of different compounds. For example, water is a compound that is made up of the elements hydrogen and oxygen. On the other hand, sugar is composed of hydrogen, carbon, and oxygen and salt is composed of sodium and chlorine.

To better understand how the compound is related to its elements, let's investigate the structure of a compound with which you are familiar — water. Suppose you divide a drop of water into two parts. Next, suppose you divide each part again and again. After a few dozen divisions, you have a drop so small that it can be seen only with a microscope. If you divide it even further into smaller and smaller particles, you will eventually get a particle so small that it can not be divided further and **still be water**. This smallest particle of water that still retains the characteristics of water is called a **molecule**. The water molecule can be broken into still smaller pieces but the pieces will not be water. Thus, if you break up the water molecule, you find that the pieces are the elements hydrogen and oxygen.

Atoms

The smallest particle to which an element can be reduced is called an **atom**. Molecules

THE NATURAL ELEMENTS

Atomic Number	Name	Symbol	Atomic Number	Name	Symbol	Atomic Number	Name	Symbol
1	Hydrogen	H	32	Germanium	Ge	63	Europium	Eu
2	Helium	He	33	Arsenic	As	64	Gadolinium	Gd
3	Lithium	Li	34	Selenium	Se	65	Terbium	Tb
4	Beryllium	Be	35	Bromine	Br	66	Dysprosium	Dy
5	Baron	B	36	Krypton	Kr	67	Holmium	Ho
6	Carbon	C	37	Rubidium	Rb	68	Erbium	Er
7	Nitrogen	N	38	Strontium	Sr	69	Thulium	Tm
8	Oxygen	O	39	Yttrium	Y	70	Ytterbium	Yb
9	Fluorine	F	40	Zirconium	Zr	71	Lutetium	Lu
10	Neon	Ne	41	Niobium	Nb	71	Hafnium	Hf
11	Sodium	Na	42	Molybdenum	Mo	73	Tantalum	Ta
12	Magnesium	Mg	43	Technetium	Tc	74	Tungsten	W
13	Aluminum	Al	44	Ruthenium	Ru	75	Rhenium	Re
14	Silicon	SI	45	Rhodium	Rh	76	Osmium	Os
15	Phosphorus	P	46	Palladium	Pd	77	Iridum	Ir
16	Sulfur	S	47	Silver	Ag	78	Platinum	Pt
17	Chlorine	Cl	48	Cadmium	Cd	79	Gold	Au
18	Argon	A	49	Indium	In	80	Mercury	Hg
19	Potassium	K	50	Tin	Sn	81	Thallium	Tl
20	Calcium	Ca	51	Antimony	Sb	82	Lead	Pb
21	Scandium	Sc	52	Tellurium	Te	83	Bismuth	Bi
22	Titanium	Ti	53	Iodine	I	84	Polonium	Po
23	Vanadium	V	54	Xenon	Xe	85	Astatine	At
24	Chromium	Cr	55	Cesium	Cs	86	Radon	Rn
25	Manganese	Mn	56	Barium	Ba	87	Francium	Fr
26	Iron	Fe	57	Lanthanum	La	88	Radium	Ra
27	Cobalt	Co	58	Cerium	Ce	89	Actinium	Ac
28	Nickel	Ni	59	Praseodymium	Pr	90	Thorium	Th
29	Copper	Cu	60	Neodymium	Nd	91	Protactinium	Pa
30	Zinc	Zn	61	Promethium	Pm	92	Uranium	U
31	Gallium	Ga	62	Samarium	Sm			

THE ARTIFICIAL ELEMENTS

Atomic Number	Name	Symbol	Atomic Number	Name	Symbol	Atomic Number	Name	Symbol
93	Neptunium	Np	97	Berkelium	Bk	101	Mendelevium	Mv
94	Plutonium	Pu	98	Californium	Cf	102	Nobelium	No
95	Americium	Am	99	Einsteinium	Es	103	Lawrencium	Lr
96	Curium	Cm	100	Fermium	Fm	104	Rutherfordium	Rf

Figure 1-1 Table of elements.

are made up of atoms that are bound together. The water molecule is shown in Figure 1-2 as three atoms. The two smaller atoms represent hydrogen while the large one represents oxygen. Therefore, a molecule of water consists of two atoms of hydrogen (H) and one atom of oxygen (O). This is why the chemical formula for water is H_2O.

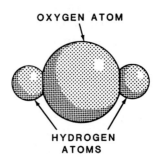

Figure 1-2 The water molecule.

Electrons, Protons, and Neutrons

As small as the atom is, it can be broken up into even smaller particles. If you investigate the structure of the atom, you'll find that it contains three distinct types of particles; **electrons**, **protons**, and **neutrons**. These are the three basic building blocks that make up all atoms and, therefore, all matter. Electrons, protons, and neutrons have very different characteristics. However, as far as is known, all electrons are exactly alike. By the same token, all protons are exactly alike and, in the same manner, all neutrons are identical.

Bohr Model of the Atom

Figure 1-3 shows how electrons, protons, and neutrons are combined to form an atom. This particular one is a helium atom. Two protons and two neutrons are bunched together near the center of the atom. The center of the atom, which is composed of protons and neutrons, is called the **nucleus**. Depending on the type of atom, the nucleus will contain from one to about 100 protons. Also, in all atoms except hydrogen, the nucleus contains neutrons. The neutrons and protons have approximately the same weight and size. Because they are much heavier than electrons, the overall weight of the atom is determined primarily by the number of protons and neutrons in the nucleus.

Rotating around the nucleus are the electrons. Notice that the helium atom has two electrons. The electrons are extremely light and they travel at fantastic speeds. The atom can be compared to the solar system with the nucleus representing the sun and the electrons representing the planets. The electrons orbit the nucleus in much the same way that the planets orbit the sun.

Any picture of an atom must be based on assumptions rather than actual observation. Figure 1-3 is a very simple model of the atom based on these assumptions. Today, much more complex models of the atom have been proposed. However, all these models have several things in common. They all assume that the basic structure is that of electrons orbiting a nucleus that is composed largely of protons and neutrons. Thus, the model shown in Figure 1-3 is adequate for our purposes even though it may be somewhat simplified. This model of the atom is called the Bohr model after the man who proposed it.

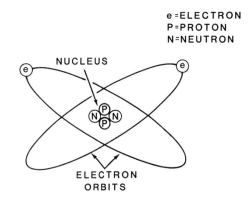

Figure 1-3 Bohr model of the helium atom.

The Difference Between Elements

At present there are 104 known elements although only 92 of these commonly occur in nature. The difference between these elements is their atomic structure. Each is made up of atoms that contain a unique number of protons, electrons, and, with the exception of hydrogen, neutrons. Let's look at Figure 1-4 to see exactly what we mean.

The simplest of all elements, hydrogen, is shown in Figure 1-4A. It consists of a single electron orbiting a single proton. This is the only atom that contains no neutrons. Because it is made up of the fewest number of particles, hydrogen is the lightest element.

Figure 1-4B represents the carbon atom. Notice, this atom is made up of 6 electrons that orbit a nucleus of 6 protons and 6 neutrons.

The heaviest element shown in Figure 1-4 is copper. It consists of 29 electrons, 29 protons, and 35 neutrons. However, the most complex atom commonly found in nature is the uranium atom. It has 92 electrons, 92 protons and 146 neutrons.

The Balanced Atom

In the examples shown, you may have noticed that the number of electrons is always equal to the number of protons. This is normally true of any atom. When this is the case, the atom is said to be in its **normal**, **balanced**, or **neutral state**. As you will see later, this state can be upset by an external force. However, normally the atom is considered to contain equal numbers of electrons and protons.

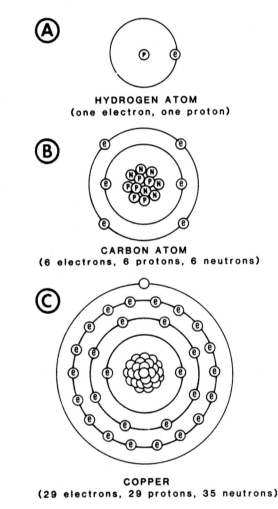

HYDROGEN ATOM
(one electron, one proton)

CARBON ATOM
(6 electrons, 6 protons, 6 neutrons)

COPPER
(29 electrons, 29 protons, 35 neutrons)

Figure 1-4 The difference between atoms is the number of electrons, protons and neutrons that they have.

Self-Test Review

1. Anything that has weight and occupies space is called _____.

2. Water is composed of two _____ called hydrogen and oxygen.

3. A substance that is composed of two or more elements is called a _____.

4. Salt, steel, and sugar are all called compounds because they are composed of two or more _____.

5. The 92 natural elements can be combined in millions of different combinations to form all the _____ known to man.

6. The smallest particle of water that is still water is a _____.

7. While the molecule is the smallest particle of a compound, the atom is the smallest particle of an _____.

8. Just as a compound is made up of molecules, an element is made up of _____.

9. Since there are only 92 natural elements, there are only 92 different types of _____ found in nature.

10. The three basic building blocks from which all atoms are made are _____, _____, and _____.

11. If you compare the atom to the solar system, the sun is equivalent to the _____ of the atom.

12. All atoms, except hydrogen, have both protons and _____ in their nucleus.

13. A uranium atom has 92 protons and _____ electrons.

Electrostatics is the branch of physics dealing with electrical charges at rest, or **static electricity**. On the other hand, electronics deals largely with moving electrical charges. However, before you can fully understand the action of electrical charges in motion, you must first have some basic knowledge of their behavior at rest.

The Electrical Charge

You have examined the structure of the atom and learned about some of the characteristics of the electron, proton, and neutron. However, you have not yet learned the most important characteristic of these particles. This characteristic is their **electrical charge**. An electrical charge is a property associated with the electron and the proton. It is this electrical charge that makes the electron useful in electrical and electronic work.

The electrical charge is difficult to visualize because it is not an object, like a molecule or an atom. Rather, it is a property or characteristic that electrons and protons have that causes these particles to behave in certain predictable ways.

There are two distinct types of electrical charges. Because these two types of charges have opposite characteristics, they have been given the names **positive** and **negative**. The electrical charge associated with the **electron** has been arbitrarily given the name **negative**. On the other hand, the electrical charge associated with the proton is considered to be **positive**. The neutron has no electrical charge at all. It is electrically neutral and, therefore, plays no known role in electricity or electronics.

The electron revolves around the nucleus of the atom in much the same way that the earth orbits the sun. You can compare this action to that of a ball that is attached to the end of a string and twirled in a circle. If the string breaks, the ball flies off in a straight line. Thus, it is the restraining action of the string that holds the path of the ball to a circle. In the case of the earth rotating around the sun, it is the gravitational attraction of the sun that prevents the earth from flying off into space. The gravitational attraction of the sun exactly balances the centrifugal force of each planet. Therefore, the planets travel in more or less circular paths around the sun.

Electrons orbit around the nucleus of the atom at a fantastic speed. What force keeps them from flying off into space? It is not gravity because the gravitational force exerted by the nucleus is much too weak. Instead, the force at work here results from the charge on the electron in orbit and the charge on the proton in the nucleus. The negative charge of the electron is **attracted** by the positive charge of the proton. We call this force of attraction an **electrostatic force**.

To explain this force, science has adopted the concept of an **electrostatic field**. Every charged particle is assumed to be surrounded by an electrostatic field that extends for a distance outside the particle itself. It is the interaction of the fields surrounding the charged particles that causes the electron and proton to attract each other.

Figure 1-5A shows a diagram of a proton. The plus sign in the center of the illustration represents the positive electrical charge. The arrows that extend outward represent the lines of force that make up the electrostatic field surrounding the proton. Notice that the lines are arbitrarily assumed to extend outward away from the positively charged particle. Compare this to the electron shown in Figure 1-5B. Here, the minus sign represents the negative charge while the arrows that point inward represent the lines of the electric field.

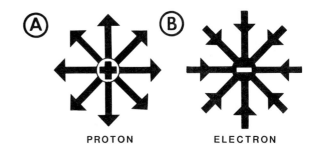

Figure 1-5 Fields associated with protons and electrons.

Law of Electrical Charges

There is a basic law that describes the action of electrical charges. It is called Coulomb's Law after Charles A. de Coulomb, who discovered this relationship.

Quite simply, Coulomb's Law states that:

1. Like charges repel.
2. Unlike charges attract.

Because like charges repel, two electrons will repel each other. In a like manner, two protons will also repel each other. Figure 1-6A illustrates how the lines of force interact between two electrons. The directions of the lines of force are such that the two fields cannot interconnect. The net effect is that the electrons attempt to move apart. That is, they repel each other. Figure 1-6B shows that the same is true of two protons. In Figure 1-6C, an electron and a proton are shown. Here, the two fields do interconnect. As a result, the two charges attract and tend to move together.

These examples show only individual charged particles. However, Coulomb's Law holds true for concentrations of charges as well. In fact, it holds true for any two charged bodies. An important part of Coulomb's Law is the equation that allows you to determine the force of attraction or repulsion between charged bodies. The equation states that:

$$F = \frac{q_1 \times q_2}{d^2}$$

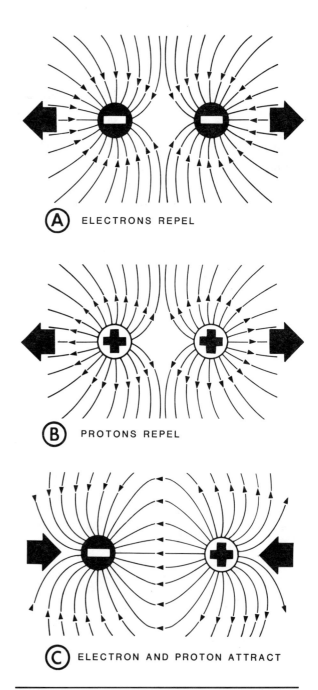

Figure 1-6 Action of like and unlike charges.

Where:

F = the force of attraction between un-like charges or the force of repul-sion between like charges.

q_1 = the charge on one body.

q_2 = the charge on the second body.

d^2 = the square of the distance between the two bodies.

While you do not need to work problems to determine the force between charges, you can see some interesting relationships if you examine the equation. If you experiment with the equation by substituting some sim-ple arbitrary numbers for q_1, q_2, and d^2, you can determine how the force changes as the quantities change. For example, if the value of either charge doubles, the force between the charges also doubles. If both charges double, the force between them increases by a factor of four. On the other hand, increas-ing the distance between charges decreases the force by the square of the increase in distance. If the distance between charges is doubled, the force is reduced to one fourth its former value.

The magnitude of the electron's negative charge is exactly equal to the magnitude of the proton's positive charge. Figure 1-7 de-picts a hydrogen atom consisting of one electron in orbit around one proton. Notice that the negative charge of the electron is exactly offset by the positive charge of the proton. Thus, the atom as a whole has no charge at all. That is, overall this atom has neither a negative nor a positive charge. It is electrically neutral.

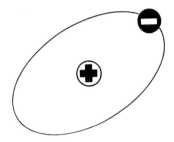

Figure 1-7 Hydrogen atom.

Atoms that are electrically neutral have no net charge. Therefore, they neither attract nor repel each other. By the same token, they are neither attracted nor repelled by charged particles such as electrons and pro-tons. We have seen that atoms normally contain the same number of electrons (nega-tive charges) as protons (positive charges). Since the neutrons add no charge, all atoms are normally neutral as far as their electrical charge is concerned. However, this **normal** condition can be easily upset by external forces.

The Ion

Atoms are affected by many outside forces such as heat, light, electrostatic fields, chemical reactions, and magnetic fields. Quite often the balanced state of the atom is upset by one or more of these forces. As a result, an atom can lose or gain one or more electrons. When this happens, the number of negative charges is no longer exactly offset by the number of positive charges. Thus, the atom ends up with a net charge. An atom that is no longer in its neu-tral state is called an **ion**. The process of changing an atom to an ion is called **ionization**.

There are both negative and positive ions. Figure 1-8 compares a neutral atom of carbon with negative and positive ions of carbon. Figure 1-8A shows the balanced or neutral carbon atom. Notice that the six negatively charged electrons are exactly offset by the six positively charged protons. The neutrons are ignored in this example since they contribute nothing to the overall electrical charge.

Figure 1-8B shows the condition that exists when the carbon atom loses an electron. Notice that the carbon atom now has a greater number of protons than electrons. Thus, there is one positive charge that is not cancelled by a corresponding negative charge. The atom now has a net positive charge and is called a **positive ion**.

Figure 1-8C shows a carbon atom that has picked up a stray electron. In this case, there is one negative charge that is not offset by a corresponding positive charge. The atom, therefore, has a net negative charge and is called a **negative ion**.

It is important to note that the ion still has all the basic characteristics of carbon because the nucleus of the atom has not been disturbed. Therefore, an atom can give off or pick up electrons without changing its basic characteristics.

Changing atoms to ions is an easy thing to do and everything you see around you con-tains ions as well as atoms. The material around you also contains a large number of **free** or **stray electrons**. These are electrons that have escaped from atoms leaving behind positive ions. As you will see later, the electrical characteristics of different types of material are determined largely by the number of free electrons and ions within the material.

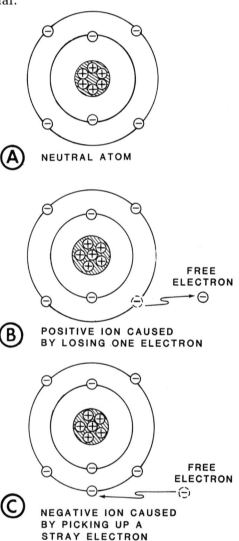

Figure 1-8 Carbon atom and ions.

Action of Electrostatic Charges

At one time or another you have seen or felt the effects of an electrostatic charge. One spectacular effect is lightning. Less spectacular examples are often seen when you remove clothes from a dryer, comb your hair, or touch a metal object after scuffing your feet on a rug. In each of these cases, two different bodies receive opposite electrical charges. This occurs when one of the bodies gives up a large number of electrons to the other. The body that gives up the electrons becomes positively charged while the body receiving the electrons becomes negatively charged.

When you comb your hair vigorously with a hard rubber comb, your hair gives up electrons to the comb. This causes the comb to become negatively charged while your hair becomes positively charged. That is, the comb collects a large number of free electrons from your hair. This is an example of **charging by friction**.

There are other ways in which an object can become charged. For example, the charge on the comb can be partially transferred to another body simply by touching the comb to the uncharged body. When the charged comb comes into contact with the uncharged object, many of the excess electrons leave the comb and collect on the other object. If you now remove the comb, the object will have a charge of its own. This is called **charging by contact**.

You can also charge an object by **induction** or **electrostatic induction**. This method uses the electrostatic field which exists in the space surrounding a charged body. In this way, you can charge an object without actually touching it with a charged body. Figure 1-9 shows a negatively charged comb placed close to an aluminum rod. The excess electrons in the comb repel the free electrons in the rod. Consequently, the free electrons gather at the end of the rod away from the charged comb. This causes that end of the rod to acquire a negative charge. The other end of the rod acquires a positive charge because of the deficiency of electrons. If you now touch the negative end of the rod with a neutral body, some of the electrons leave the rod and enter the neutral body. This leaves the rod with a net positive charge. Thus, you have induced a positive charge into the rod without touching it with a charged body.

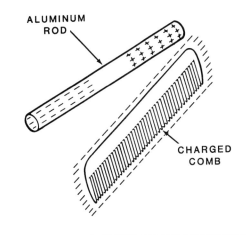

Figure 1-9 Charging by induction.

It is also possible to neutralize electrical charges. When a glass rod is rubbed with a silk cloth, the glass gives up electrons to the silk. As a result, the glass becomes positively charged while the silk becomes negatively charged. This is shown in Figure 1-10A. If the rod is now brought back into contact with the cloth, the negative electrons in the silk are attracted by the positive charge in the glass. The force of this attraction pulls the electrons back out of the silk so that the charge is neutralized as shown in Figure 1-10B. Thus, if two objects having equal but opposite charges are brought into contact, electrons flow from the negatively charged object into the positively charged object. The flow of electrons continues until both charges have been neutralized.

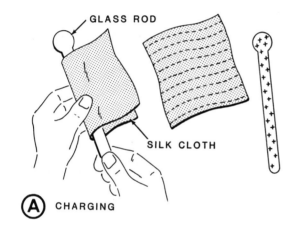
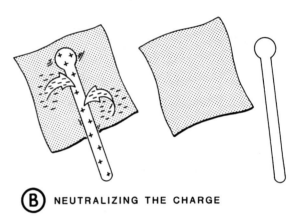

Figure 1-10 Charging and discharging a glass rod.

14. The proton is said to have a positive charge, while the electron has a _____ charge.

15. The charges on the electron and the proton have opposite _____.

16. The particle in the atom that has no electrical charge is the _____.

17. The negatively charged electrons are held in orbit around the nucleus by the attraction of the positively charged _____ in the nucleus of the atom.

18. According to Coulomb's Law, unlike charges _____.

19. Again, according to Coulomb's Law, like charges _____.

20. According to Coulomb's Law, two electrons should _____ each other.

21. Also, any two positively charged bodies should _____.

22. A negatively charged body should be attracted by a _____ charged body.

23. An atom has no net charge when it has the same number of protons as _____.

24. Since electrons are negatively charged, an atom that picks up an extra electron becomes a _____ ion.

25. On the other hand, an atom that loses an electron becomes a _____ ion.

26. One way to produce free electrons and positive ions, is to rub a glass rod with a silk cloth. The glass rod gives up many electrons to the silk cloth. Thus, the glass rod becomes _____ charged.

27. Simultaneously, the silk cloth becomes _____ charged.

28. Developing an electrical charge by rubbing a glass rod with a piece of silk is an example of charging by _____.

29. Charging an object without actually touching it is called charging by _____.

In electronics, **current** is defined as the flow of electrical charge from one point to another. You have already learned something about this. You will remember that when a negatively charged body is touched to a positively charged body, electrons flow from the negatively charged object to the positively charged object. Since electrons carry a negative charge, this is an example of electrical charges flowing. Before an electron can flow from one point to another, it must first be freed from the atom. The following is a discussion of the mechanism by which electrons are removed from an atom.

Freeing Electrons

You have learned that electrons revolve around the atom's nucleus at very high speeds. Two forces hold the electron in a precarious balance. The centrifugal force of the electron that thrusts it away from the nucleus is exactly offset by the attraction of the protons in the nucleus. This balanced condition can be upset very easily so that the electron is dislodged from its orbit.

Not all electrons can be freed from the atom with the same ease. Some are dislodged more easily than others. To see why, you must study the concept of **orbital shells**. It has been proven that electrons orbit the atom's nucleus according to a certain pattern. For example, in all atoms that have two or more electrons, two of the electrons orbit relatively close to the nucleus. The area in which these electrons travel is called a

shell. The shell closest to the nucleus contains two electrons. This area can support only two electrons and all other electrons must orbit in shells further from the nucleus.

A second shell somewhat further from the nucleus can hold up to eight electrons. There is a third shell that can contain up to 18 electrons and a fourth shell that can hold up to 32 electrons. The first four shells are illustrated in Figure 1-11. Although not shown, there are also additional shells in the heavier atoms.

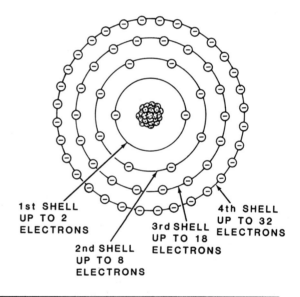

Figure 1-11 Arrangement of orbital shells in an atom.

It is possible to predict the number of electrons in each shell using the equation $2N^2$ where N is the number of the shell. For example, in the third shell there may be as many as $2 \times (3)^2$ or 18 electrons.

Of particular importance in the study of electronics is the outer electron shell of the atom. Hydrogen has one electron in its outer shell while helium has two. In this case, the outer shell is the first, and only, shell. For atoms that have three to ten electrons, the outer shell is the second shell. Regardless of which shell it happens to be, the outer shell is called the **valence shell** and electrons in this shell are called **valence electrons**.

Electrons are arranged in such a way that the valence shell never has more than eight electrons. This may be confusing since the third shell can contain up to 18 electrons. The following example shows why both statements are true.

An atom of argon contains 18 electrons — 2 in the first shell, 8 in the second shell, and 8 in the third shell. It might seem that the next heavier element, potassium, would have 9 electrons in its third shell. However, this would violate the valence rule stated above. Actually, what happens is that the extra electron is placed in a fourth shell. Thus the 19 electrons are distributed in this manner — 2 in the first shell, 8 in the second shell, 8 in the third shell, and 1 in the fourth shell. Notice that the outer or valence shell becomes the fourth shell rather than the third. Once the fourth shell is established as the valence shell, the third shell can fill to its full capacity of 18 electrons.

The valence electrons are extremely important in electronics. These are the electrons that can be easily freed and used to perform work. To understand why the valence electrons are easy to free, consider the structure of an atom of copper. Figure 1-12A shows how the electrons are distributed in the various shells in the copper atom. Notice that the valence shell contains only one electron. This electron is further from the nucleus than any of the other electrons. From Coulomb's Law you know that the force of attraction between charged particles decreases dramatically as the distance between the particles increases. Therefore, the valence electrons experience less attraction from the nucleus. For this reason, these electrons can be easily separated from the atom.

Since you are only concerned with the valence electrons, the atom can be depicted in the simplified form shown in Figure 1-12B. Figures 1-12C and 1-12D use this simplified form to illustrate one way in which a valence electron can be freed. Here, two copper atoms are shown as they might appear in a copper wire. Each valence electron is held in orbit by the attraction of the nucleus. However, the force of attraction is quite weak because the orbits are so far from the nucleus. If these two atoms are close together, the electrons in the valence shells may be closer to each other than either electron is to its nucleus. At certain points in their orbits, the two electrons may come very close together. When this happens the force of repulsion between the two electrons is stronger than the force of attraction exerted by the nucleus. Thus, one or both

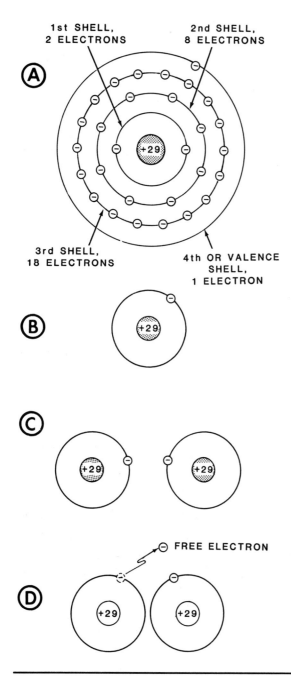

1st SHELL,
2 ELECTRONS

2nd SHELL,
8 ELECTRONS

Ⓐ

+29

3rd SHELL,
18 ELECTRONS

4th OR VALENCE
SHELL,
1 ELECTRON

Ⓑ   +29

Ⓒ   +29   +29

⊖ FREE ELECTRON

Ⓓ   +29   +29

Figure 1-12 Freeing an electron from a copper atom.

of the electrons may be forced out of orbit to wander as a free electron. Notice that when the electron leaves, the atom becomes a positive ion.

As the free electron wanders around the atomic structure, it may be eventually captured by another positive ion or it may come close enough to other valence electrons to force them from orbit. The point is that events like these occur frequently in many types of material. Thus, in a piece of copper wire containing billions and billions of atoms, there are bound to be billions of free electrons wandering around the atomic structure.

Conductors and Insulators

The importance of the valence electrons cannot be emphasized too strongly. Both the electrical and chemical characteristics of the elements depend on the action of the valence electrons. An element's electrical and chemical stability are determined to a great extent by the number of electrons in the valence shell. You have seen that the valence shell can contain up to eight electrons. Those elements that have valence shells that are filled or nearly filled tend to be stable. That is, they tend to maintain their atomic structure rather than give up or accept electrons.

For example, the elements neon, argon, krypton, xenon, and radon have 8 electrons in their valence shell. The valence shell is completely filled and, as a result, these elements are so stable that they resist any sort of chemical activity. They will not even combine with other elements to form compounds. Furthermore, atoms of these elements are very reluctant to give up electrons. Because they do not react with other elements, these elements are called inert gases.

Elements that have their valence shells almost filled also tend to be stable, although they are not as stable as those whose valence shells are completely filled. These elements strive to fill their valence shell by capturing free electrons. Consequently, elements of this type have very few free electrons in their atomic structure.

Substances that have very few free electrons in their atomic structure are called **insulators**. In addition to certain elements that act as insulators, there are many compounds that exhibit the same characteristic. Thus, they act as insulators also. By opposing the production of free electrons, these substances resist certain electrical actions. Insulators are important in electrical and electronics work for this reason. The plastic material on electrical wires is an insulator that protects you from electrical shock.

Elements in which the valence shell is almost empty behave quite differently than insulators. Elements that have only one or two electrons tend to give them up very easily. For example, copper, silver, and gold each have one valence electron. In these elements, the valence electrons are easily removed. Consequently, a bar of any one of these elements has a great number of free electrons.

Substances that have a large number of free electrons are called **conductors**. In addition to silver, copper, and gold, some other good conductors are iron, nickel, and aluminum. Notice that all of these elements are metals. Most metals are good conductors. Conductors are important because they act as current paths and allow electrical current to move from one place to another.

Some elements have four electrons in their valence shell. Silicon and germanium are examples of elements whose valence shell is half filled. Elements of this type are neither good conductors nor good insulators. Because of this, these elements are called **semiconductors**. Later in your studies you will learn more about semiconductors. However, in this course the discussions will be limited to conductors and insulators.

The Battery

Current flow is the movement of free electrons from one place to another. Thus, to have current flow you must first have free electrons. You have learned that valence electrons can be separated from atoms thereby resulting in the formation of free electrons and positive ions. This occurs when you comb your hair or rub a glass rod with a silk cloth. However, to perform a useful function, you must free tremendous numbers of electrons and concentrate them in one area. This requires more sophisticated techniques. One device for doing this is the ordinary battery. There are many different types of batteries. Figure 1-13 shows two familiar examples. These are the dry cell, or flash-light battery, and the wet cell, or automobile battery.

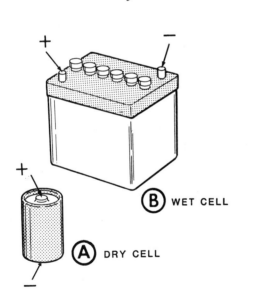

Figure 1-13 Types of batteries.

While these two types of batteries are quite different in construction, they do have several points in common. Both have two terminals or poles to which an electrical circuit can be connected. In addition, both employ a chemical reaction that produces an excess of electrons at one terminal and a deficiency of electrons at the other. The terminal at which the electrons congregate is called the **negative terminal**. It is indicated by the minus sign in Figure 1-13. The other terminal, indicated by a plus sign, has a deficiency of electrons and is called the **positive terminal**. Because the battery has terminals that are polarized, it has a specific effect on the movement of electrons through a conductor. The following discussion examines that effect.

Random Drift and Directed Drift

A conductor is a substance that contains a large number of free electrons. These free electrons do not stand still. Instead, they drift about in random motion. Figure 1-14A shows a small section of a conductor containing many free electrons. At any instant, the free electrons move randomly through the conductor. This is referred to as **random drift**. This occurs in all conductors but it has little practical use. To do work, the free electrons must be forced to drift in the same direction rather than at random.

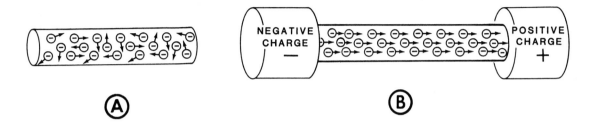

Figure 1-14 Comparison of random and directed drift.

You can influence the drift of electrons so that all or most electrons move in the same direction through the conductor. This is done by placing electrical charges at opposite ends of the conductor. Figure 1-14B shows a negative charge placed at one end of the conductor while a positive charge is placed at the other. The negative charge repels the free electrons while the positive charge attracts them. As a result, all of the free electrons move or drift in the same general direction. The direction of movement is from the negative charge to the positive charge.

Here, the application of the electrical charges at the ends of the conductor changes random drift to directed drift. The directed drift of free electrons is called **current flow** because electric current is flowing through the conductor. If the electrical charges shown in Figure 1-14B are small in magnitude, the flow of electrons will quickly cancel both charges and only a momentary current will flow. However, if the two electrical charges are maintained by the chemical action of a battery, the current will flow for quite some time. Therefore, it can be said that a battery can maintain a continuous current through a circuit for an extended period of time.

Copper wire is a good example of a conductor. Figure 1-15 shows a length of copper wire connected between the terminals of a battery. When this is done, heavy current flows from the negative terminal of the battery to the positive terminal. Recall that the negative terminal is a source of free electrons. An electron at this point is repelled by the negative charge and is attracted by the positive charge at the opposite terminal. Thus, the electrons flow through the wire as shown. When they enter the positive terminal of the battery, they are captured by positive ions. The chemical reaction of the battery is constantly releasing new free electrons and creating positive ions to make up for the ones lost by recombination.

It should be pointed out that in practice you never connect a conductor directly across the terminals of the battery as shown in Figure 1-15. The heavy current would quickly exhaust the battery and could cause the battery to rupture or explode. This is an example of a "short circuit" and is normally avoided at all cost. This example is shown here merely to illustrate the concept of current flow.

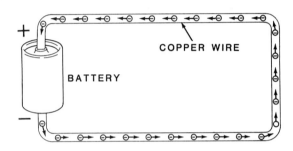

Figure 1-15 Current flows from the negative terminal to the positive terminal of the battery.

30. Since electrons carry electrical charges, current can also be defined as the flow of _____.

31. When an electron is dislodged from an atom, the atom becomes a positive _____.

32. Electrons in the outer shell of an atom are called _____ electrons.

33. The difference between conductors and insulators results from the number of electrons in their _____ shell.

34. The ease with which an electron can be dislodged from an atom depends largely on the _____ of electrons in the valence shell.

35. Elements that have only one or two electrons in their valence shell normally are good _____.

36. Elements with four electrons in their valence shell are called:

    _____

37. Elements with 6 or 7 valence electrons make good _____.

38. In a battery, the terminal with the deficiency of electrons is called the _____ terminal.

39. When a battery is connected to a conductor, electrons will always flow from the _____ terminal to the _____ terminal.

40. The flow of electrons through a conductor is called _____.

The Electric Circuit

In its simplest form, an electric circuit consists of a power source, a load, and conductors that connect the power source to the load. Often the power source is a battery. The power source provides the force necessary to direct the flow of electrons. As you will see in the next unit, this force is called **voltage**. Power sources produce voltage by creating a positive charge at one terminal and a negative charge at the other.

The **load** is generally some kind of electrical device that performs a useful function. It might be a lamp that produces light, a motor that produces physical motion, a horn that produces sound, or a heating element that produces heat. Regardless of the type of load used, it performs a useful function only when electric current flows through it.

The third part of the circuit is the conductor that connects the power source to the load. It provides a path for current flow. The conductor may be a length of copper wire, a strip of aluminum, or the metal frame of an automobile.

Figure 1-16 shows an electric circuit consisting of a battery, a lamp, and connecting copper wires. The battery produces the force (voltage) necessary to cause the directed flow of electrons. The force developed by the battery causes the free electrons in the conductor to flow through the lamp in the direction shown. The free electrons are repelled by the negative charge and are attracted by the positive charge. Thus, the electrons flow from negative to positive. The negative and positive charges in the battery are constantly being replenished by the chemical action of the battery. Therefore, the battery maintains a current flow for a long period of time. As the electrons flow through the lamp, they heat up the wire within the lamp. As the wire becomes hotter, the lamp emits light. The lamp will glow as long as a fairly strong current is maintained.

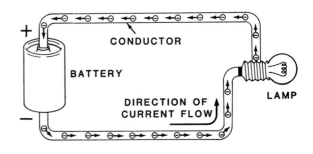

Figure 1-16 Simple electric circuit.

You know from your experience with flashlights that a battery cannot maintain a constant current flow forever. As time passes, the chemical reaction within the battery slows down, and eventually, the battery produces no current at all. At this time, it is said to be dead, or run down. For this reason, it is necessary to add a component to your simple electrical circuit.

The circuit in Figure 1-16 can be made much more practical by adding a control. In this case, the control is a switch that provides an easy way to start and stop current flow. Since some type of control is necessary, it can be said that a practical elementary circuit consists of four parts; the power source, the load, the conductor, and the control.

Figure 1-17 shows the circuit after the switch has been added. For simplicity, a "knife" switch is shown. It consists of two metal contacts to which conductors may be connected, a metal arm that can be opened and closed, and a base. Current does not flow through the base of the switch because it is made from an insulator material. Current can flow only through the arm and then only if the arm is closed.

Figure 1-17A shows the switch in a closed position. With the switch closed, there is a path for current flow from the negative terminal of the battery through the switch and lamp to the positive terminal. The lamp lights because current flows through it.

When the switch is opened, as shown in Figure 1-17B, the path for current flow is broken or open. Thus, the lamp does not glow because there is no current flowing through it.

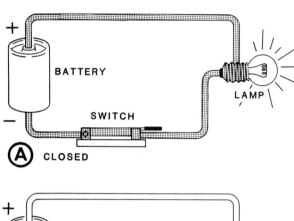

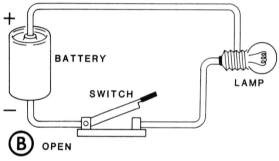

Figure 1-17 Circuit with switch.

While simple circuits can be drawn as shown in Figures 1-16 and 1-17, it is very difficult to draw complex circuits in this manner. For this reason, the **schematic diagram** was developed. A schematic diagram is a drawing in which symbols are used to represent circuit components. The first step to understanding the schematic diagram is to learn the symbols used to represent the various components.

Figure 1-18 compares the schematic symbol with the pictorial representation of the circuit components used up to this point. The conductor is represented by a single line. The picture of the battery is replaced by a series of long and short lines. The long line represents the positive terminal while the short line represents the negative terminal. The same symbol can be used regardless of the type of battery. The symbols for the lamp, switch, and resistor are also shown. Resistors are discussed in detail in Unit 3.

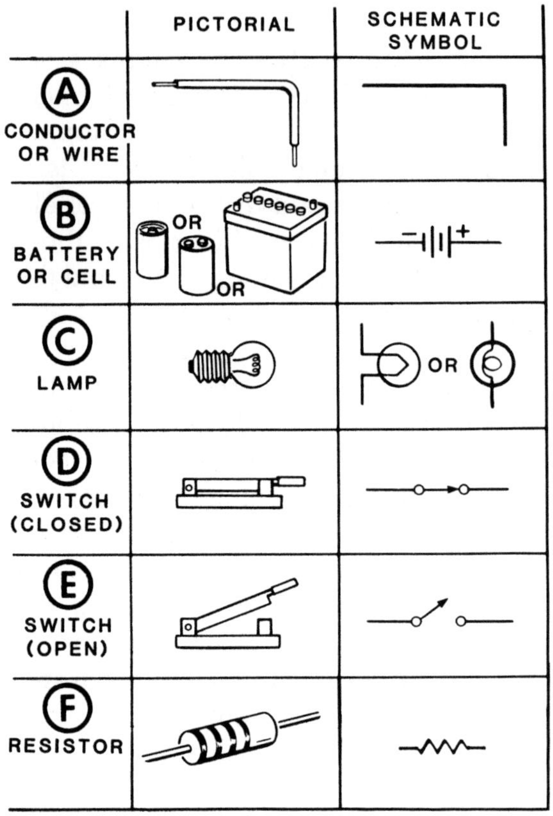

	PICTORIAL	SCHEMATIC SYMBOL
(A) CONDUCTOR OR WIRE		
(B) BATTERY OR CELL		
(C) LAMP		
(D) SWITCH (CLOSED)		
(E) SWITCH (OPEN)		
(F) RESISTOR		

Figure 1-18 Pictorial representations compared with the schematic symbols.

In Figure 1-19 several schematic symbols are combined to form a schematic diagram. Figure 1-19A is the schematic diagram for the pictorial drawing shown earlier in Figure 1-17A while Figure 1-19B is a schematic diagram of the pictorial shown in Figure 1-17B.

The circuit shown in Figure 1-19 is the schematic diagram of a flashlight. It is also the diagram for the headlight system in an automobile. In fact it can represent any system which contains a battery, a lamp, and a switch. If the lamp is replaced with a motor, the circuit becomes that of the starter system in a car. In this case, the switch is operated by the ignition key. Other circuits which operate in a similar manner are a doorbell and an automobile horn. In the first case, the bell is the load while the switch is operated by a push button at the door.

In the second case, the horn is the load and the switch is located on the steering wheel.

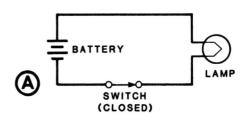

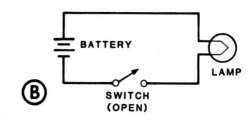

Figure 1-19 Schematic diagram of a simple circuit.

41. A simple electric circuit consists of a _____ connected to a _____.

42. The _____ is a device in a circuit that performs some useful function.

43. Since most circuits are not expected to operate continuously, the current is turned on and off by some kind of _____.

44. The schematic diagram differs from a pictorial presentation in that the components are drawn as _____ .

45. Shown in Figure 1-20 are four different schematic symbols. Identify each one.

    A. _____
    B. _____
    C. _____
    D. _____

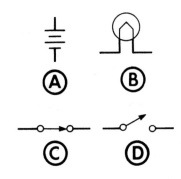

Figure 1-20 Identify these symbols.

46. In a battery symbol, the short line at one end represents the _____ terminal.

47. Figure 1-19 shows a complete electrical circuit. When the switch is closed, electrons flow from the _____ terminal of the battery through the lamp to the _____ terminal.

Measuring Current

Current is the flow of electrons from a negative to a positive charge. To measure current flow, you must measure the number of electrons flowing past a point in a specific length of time. Before you learn how current is measured, you must first learn how the unit of electrical charge and the unit of current are defined.

The Coulomb

You have seen that the charge on an object is determined by the number of electrons that the object loses or gains. If the object loses electrons, the charge is positive. However, an object that gains electrons has a negative charge. In order to measure the magnitude of the charge, you must have a unit of measure.

The unit of measure for electrical charge is called the **coulomb**. The coulomb is equal to a charge of 6.25×10^{18} electrons. For those who are not used to expressing numbers in this way, the number is:

$$6,250,000,000,000,000,000.$$

An object that has gained 6.25×10^{18} electrons has a negative charge of one coulomb. On the other hand, an object that has given up 6.25×10^{18} electrons has a positive charge of one coulomb.

Powers of Ten and Scientific Notation

A word about powers of ten and scientific notation may be helpful at this point. The number 6,250,000,000,000,000,000 can be expressed as 6.25×10^{18}. This number is read "six point two five times ten to the eighteenth power." The expression "ten to the eighteenth power" means that the decimal place in 6.25 must be moved 18 places to the right in order to convert to the decimal number. This is done because it is easier to write and remember 6.25×10^{18} than it is to write and remember 6,250,000,000,000,000,000.

This shorthand method of expressing numbers is known as **powers of ten**, or **scientific notation**. It is often used in electronics to express very large and very small numbers. Very small numbers are expressed by using negative powers of ten. For example, 3.2×10^{-8} is scientific notation for the number 0.000000032. Here, "ten to the minus eight power" means "move the decimal place in 3.2 eight places to the left." To be sure you have the idea, look at the following examples of both positive and negative powers of ten:

Positive Powers of Ten

$7.9 \times 10^4 = 79,000$
$9.1 \times 10^8 = 910,000,000$
$1.0 \times 10^{12} = 1,000,000,000,000$

Negative Powers of Ten

$7.9 \times 10^{-4} = 0.00079$
$9.1 \times 10^{-8} = 0.000\,000\,091$
$1.0 \times 10^{-12} = 0.000\,000\,000\,001$

If after studying these examples you do not understand this system of numerical notation, read Appendix A at the end of this text. It is a programmed instruction sequence designed to teach powers of ten and scientific notation in much greater detail.

The Ampere

The unit of measurement for current is the **ampere**. The ampere indicates the rate at which electrons move past a given point. As previously mentioned, 1 coulomb is equal to 6.25×10^{18} electrons. An ampere is equal to **1 coulomb per second**. That is, if 1 coulomb (6.25×10^{18} electrons) flows past a given point in one second then the current past that point is equal to 1 ampere. Coulombs indicate numbers of electrons; amperes indicate the number of electrons per second or the rate of electron flow.

When 6.25×10^{18} electrons flow through a wire each second, the current flow is 1 ampere. If twice this number of electrons flows through a conductor each second, the current is 2 amperes. This relationship is expressed by the equation:

$$\text{amperes} = \frac{\text{coulombs}}{\text{seconds}}$$

If 10 coulombs flow past a point in two seconds, then the current flow is 5 amperes.

The name ampere is often shortened to **amp** and is abbreviated **A**. Many times the ampere is too large a unit to use to conveniently specify a rate of current flow. In these cases metric prefixes are used to denote smaller units. The milliampere (mA) is one thousandth (.001) of an ampere. The microampere μ(A) is one millionth (.000 001) of an ampere. In other words, there are 1000 milliamperes or 1,000,000 microamperes in an ampere.

You convert amperes to milliamperes by multiplying by 10^3. Thus 1.7 amperes is equal to 1.7×10^3 milliamperes. You can also convert amperes to microamperes by multiplying by 10^6. Therefore, 1.7 amperes is equal to 1.7×10^6 microamperes.

For those who need it, a more detailed explanation of metric prefixes is given in Appendix A at the end of this text.

The Ammeter

The **ammeter** is a device for measuring current flow. The name ammeter is a shortened form of the name ampere meter. Figure 1-21 shows an ammeter. It has a pointer that moves in front of a calibrated scale. In this figure, the scale is calibrated from 0 to 10 amperes. The movement of the pointer is proportional to the amount of current flowing through the meter. Therefore, an accurate indication of the amount of current flowing in a circuit is obtained by reading the position of the pointer on the ammeter face. The meter is presently displaying a reading of just over 6 amperes.

Figure 1-22A shows a circuit in which an unknown amount of current is flowing. You can measure the current in this circuit by inserting an ammeter into the circuit as shown in Figure 1-22B. Notice that the schematic symbol for the ammeter is a circle with the letter A. Before the ammeter can measure current, it must be connected to the circuit in such a way that the current you wish to measure flows through the meter. To do this, the ammeter is connected in series with the circuit elements. Incidentally, a circuit like the one shown in Figure 1-22B is called a series circuit. A **series circuit** has only one current path. That is, the current flows through all the elements in one continuous loop.

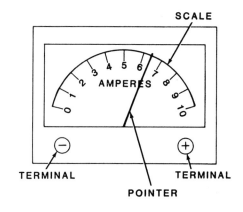

Figure 1-21 Ammeter.

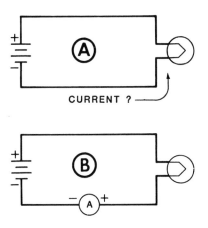

Figure 1-22 Measuring current.

The maximum current that an ammeter can safely measure is indicated by the highest number on the scale. The highest current that the ammeter in Figure 1-21 can safely measure is 10 amperes. This is called its full scale reading. Many ammeters are much more sensitive. Some have a full scale reading of 1 milliampere. Others provide a full scale reading with only 50 microamperes flowing through them.

Ammeters are delicate instruments and can be destroyed if the current applied greatly exceeds the full scale reading of the meter. For this reason, you must exercise some precautions when using the ammeter.

To protect yourself and the ammeter, there is a definite procedure that you must follow when using an ammeter. The first step is to select an ammeter that can safely measure the current in the circuit. You must be sure that the amount of current in the circuit does not exceed the maximum rating of your meter. As mentioned above, if you exceed the current rating, the meter may be damaged.

The second step is to remove power from the circuit under test. In battery powered circuits this is done by removing the battery or by disconnecting one of the battery leads. The purpose of this step is to protect your-self from electrical shock as you connect the ammeter.

The third step is to break the circuit at the point where you want to measure the current. The circuit must be broken in order to connect the ammeter in series with the rest of the circuit.

Fourth, the ammeter is connected to the circuit while **observing polarity**. The ammeter has two terminals labeled negative and positive. Current must flow through the ammeter from the negative terminal to the positive terminal. Thus, the wire from the negative terminal of the battery must lead to the negative terminal of the ammeter. If the ammeter is connected backwards, the pointer will attempt to deflect backwards. This may damage the meter.

Observing polarity simply means that the negative terminal of the ammeter is connected to the conductor that leads to the negative terminal of the battery. Naturally, the positive terminal of the ammeter is connected to the conductor that leads to the positive side of the battery.

Finally, power is reapplied to the circuit and a current reading is obtained from the ammeter scale. Figure 1-23 illustrates this step-by-step procedure.

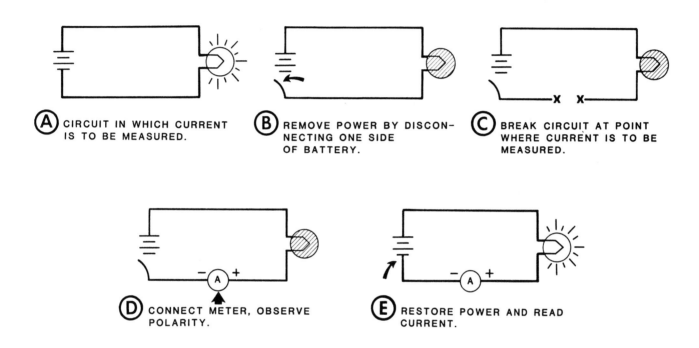

A) CIRCUIT IN WHICH CURRENT
IS TO BE MEASURED.

B) REMOVE POWER BY DISCON-
NECTING ONE SIDE
OF BATTERY.

C) BREAK CIRCUIT AT POINT
WHERE CURRENT IS TO BE
MEASURED.

D) CONNECT METER, OBSERVE
POLARITY.

E) RESTORE POWER AND READ
CURRENT.

Figure 1-23 Procedure for measuring current.

48. If an object has an excess of 6.25×10^{18} electrons, it has a negative charge of one _____.

49. An object that has given up 6.25×10^{18} electrons has a (positive/negative) charge of one coulomb.

50. If one coulomb per second flows through a conductor, the current in the conductor is one _____.

51. The milliampere is one-thousandth of an ampere while the microampere is one – _____ of an ampere.

52. The ammeter must be connected in _____ with the circuit being tested.

53. The positive lead must be connected to the wire that leads to the _____ side of the battery.

Summary

The following is a summary of the important points discussed in Unit 1. If you have a question on any point presented here, re-read that portion of the text that covered that particular point.

Matter is anything which has weight and occupies space.

All matter is composed of one or more of the elements.

A compound is a substance composed of two or more elements. The smallest particle of a compound is a molecule. A molecule consists of two or more atoms bound together.

The atom is the smallest particle into which an element can be divided. There are 92 different types of atoms occurring in nature. Another dozen or more have been artificially made by man.

Atoms are composed of electrons, protons, and neutrons. The nucleus contains protons and neutrons. Electrons orbit the nucleus.

The type of atom is determined by the number of electrons, protons, and neutrons.

Electricity is a property that electrons and protons have which causes them to behave in certain predictable ways.

The electron has a negative electrical charge.

The proton has a positive electrical charge.

An electrostatic field surrounds every charged particle. Coulomb's Law describes the action of charged particles. It states that like charges repel, while unlike charges attract.

An atom has a neutral charge when it contains the same number of electrons and protons. An atom which has a net electrical charge is called an ion.

Electrical charges can be produced in certain materials by friction.

An electrical charge can be partially transferred from a charged object to an uncharged object by touching the two objects together.

An electrical charge can be induced into a neutral object by bringing a charged object near it.

In its simplest form, a circuit consists of a power source, a load, and conductors that connect the power source to the load.

In electronics, current is defined as the flow of electrical charge from one point to another.

Before an electron can participate in current flow, it must be freed from its atom.

The centrifugal force of the orbiting electron is exactly offset by the attraction of the positive charge in the nucleus.

Electrons are distributed in shells. The outer shell is called the valence shell and valence electrons are important in electronics because they can be freed to contribute to current flow. The number of valence electrons determines if an element is a conductor or an insulator.

A conductor is a substance that has a large number of free electrons.

An insulator is a substance that has very few free electrons.

Most metals are good conductors.

A battery is a two-terminal device that produces an excess of electrons at one terminal and a deficiency of electrons at the other.

Free electrons normally drift around in a random pattern. However, they can be forced to flow in a desired direction. Current flow is the directed drift of free electrons. Electrons flow from negative to positive charges.

A schematic diagram uses symbols to represent electronic components.

The unit of electrical charge is the coulomb. The coulomb is equal to 6.25×10^{18} electrons.

Current is the rate at which electrons flow past a point. The ampere is the unit of current. The ampere is equal to one coulomb per second. A microampere is one millionth of an ampere.

A device for measuring current is the ammeter. The ammeter must be connected in series with the circuit under test. Polarity must be observed when connecting an ammeter to a circuit.

Unit 2
Voltage

Contents

Introduction

In the previous unit, you learned that a battery produces a force that causes electrons to flow in a closed circuit. You did not learn very much about the force except that it results from electrical charges at the battery terminals. That is, the force is produced by an excess of electrons at one terminal and a deficiency of electrons at the other. This force is called an **electromotive force**. Literally, electromotive force means the force that **moves electrons**. The unit of measure of this force is the **volt**. In fact the terms **electromotive force** and voltage are frequently used interchangeably although, strictly speaking, they do have slightly different meanings.

In this unit, you will learn about voltage or electromotive force in detail. You will also learn several ways in which this force is produced and used. Furthermore, you will learn how voltage is measured and several important laws concerning voltage.

Unit Objectives

When you have completed this unit, you will be able to:

1. Define the following terms: Electromotive force (EMF), potential difference, voltage, volt, cell, primary cell, secondary cell, voltage drop, voltage rise, ground, short, open, battery, alternating current (AC), triboelectric effect, thermoelectric effect, piezoelectric effect, and photoelectric effect.

2. List six different ways that electromotive force can be produced.

3. Describe the proper method for connecting a voltmeter to a circuit and measuring voltage.

4. Determine the output voltage from batteries connected in series aiding, series opposing, parallel, or series parallel configurations.

5. Given the magnitude and polarity of the two charges, state whether a potential difference exists between them.

6. Given the magnitude and polarity of the two charges, state the direction of electron movement between them.

7. Name the factors that determine the voltage and current capacity of a cell.

8. Given a list of applications, match them with the effect produced by an EMF.

9. Name the three main parts of a cell.

10. State the output voltage of a dry cell and a wet cell.

11. State the relationship between a voltage rise and a voltage drop.

Electrical Force

You've already learned that current will not flow in a circuit unless an external force is applied. In the circuits discussed in the previous unit, this force was provided by batteries. The battery does this by changing chemical energy to electrical energy and separating negative charges (electrons) from positive charges (ions). These charges produce the force or pressure that causes electrons to flow and do work. This force is given several different names that are used more or less interchangeably. In the following sections you will learn about the three most popular names and see what each name implies.

Electromotive Force (EMF)

One popular name for electrical force is **electromotive** force which is abbreviated **EMF** or **emf**. This name is very descriptive since it literally means a force that moves electrons. Thus, EMF is the force or pressure that sets electrons in motion.

You will recall that Coulomb's law states that like charges repel while unlike charges attract. The battery, by chemical action, produces a negative charge at one terminal and a positive charge at the other. The negative charge is simply an excess of electrons while the positive charge is an excess of positive ions. If a circuit is connected across a battery as shown in Figure 2-1A, a path for electron flow exists between the battery terminals. Free electrons are repelled by the charge on the negative terminal and are at-

tracted by the charge on the positive terminal. The two opposite charges exert a pressure that forces the electrons to move. That is, the force or pressure results from the attraction of the unlike charges. To summarize, EMF is the force that sets electrons in motion in a closed circuit.

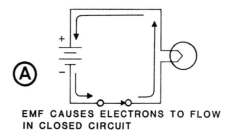

EMF CAUSES ELECTRONS TO FLOW
IN CLOSED CIRCUIT

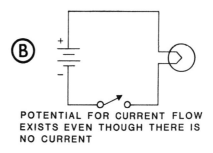

POTENTIAL FOR CURRENT FLOW
EXISTS EVEN THOUGH THERE IS
NO CURRENT

Figure 2-1 EMF and potential difference.

Potential Difference

Another name for electrical force is potential difference. This name describes the characteristics of EMF in an open circuit. EMF is the force that causes electrons to move as shown in Figure 2-1A. However, consider the situation shown in Figure 2-1B. Here, electrons cannot flow because the switch is open. Nevertheless, the battery still produces the same electrical pressure or force as before. Thus, the **potential** for producing current flow exists even though no current is presently flowing. As used here, **potential** means the possibility of doing work. If the switch is closed, current flows, the lamp lights, and work is done. Therefore, whether a battery is connected to a circuit or not, it has the **potential** for doing work.

Actually, any charge has the potential for doing work. For example, a charge can move another charge either by attraction or repulsion. Even a single electron can repel another electron. If one electron moves as the result of the action of another electron, some small amount of work is done. In the battery, you are concerned with two different types of charges rather than a single charge. The electrons at the negative terminal are straining to rush to the positive terminal and cancel out the positive charge there. In the same way, the positive ions at the other terminal are straining to draw the electrons. We call this force **potential difference**. It is the **potential** for doing work that exists between two **different** charges.

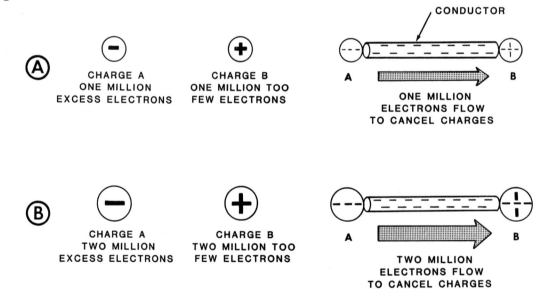

Figure 2-2 Static charges have the potential for doing work.

The amount of work that can be done must be related in some way to the characteristics of the charges. You can better understand this point by considering some static charges. Figure 2-2A shows a small negative charge separated from a small positive charge. Now, assume that charge A has an excess of one million electrons while charge B has a deficiency of one million electrons. If a conductor is connected between the two charges, electrons will flow from the negative to the positive charge. The work done here is the moving of electrons. To cancel the two charges, one million electrons must flow from charge A to charge B.

Now consider what happens if the magnitude of the two charges is doubled as shown in Figure 2-2B. Here charge A has an excess of two million electrons while charge B has a deficiency of two million electrons. If a conductor is connected between the two charges, then two million electrons will rush from charge A to charge B. Thus, twice as much work is done.

However, the magnitude of the charges is not the important consideration. It is the difference between the two charges that is important. Figure 2-3 illustrates that no work can be done if both charges have the same polarity and magnitude.

In Figure 2-3A two charges are shown. Each is the result of an excess of ten million electrons. How much work is done if these two charges are connected by a conductor? The answer, of course, is that no work is done. Because the two objects have exactly the

same charge, no electrons can flow from one to the other. Thus, there is no potential for doing work. Figure 2-3B shows that the same is true for equal positive charges.

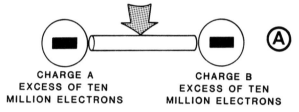

NO ELECTRONS FLOW BECAUSE
THE TWO CHARGES ARE EQUAL

CHARGE A
EXCESS OF TEN
MILLION ELECTRONS

CHARGE B
EXCESS OF TEN
MILLION ELECTRONS

Ⓐ

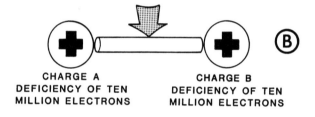

NO ELECTRONS FLOW BECAUSE
THE TWO CHARGES ARE EQUAL

CHARGE A
DEFICIENCY OF TEN
MILLION ELECTRONS

CHARGE B
DEFICIENCY OF TEN
MILLION ELECTRONS

Ⓑ

Figure 2-3 No potential for doing work exists between equal charges.

The potential to move electrons exists between any two unlike charges. That is, when two charges are different, electrons will flow from one charge to the other if given the chance. Charges can differ in two ways. First, they can be of opposite **polarity**. This simply means that one is positive and the other is negative as shown in Figure 2-2. Second, they can have different **magnitudes**. For example, Figure 2-4A shows two charges that have the same polarity but different magnitudes. Charge A is more negative because it has more excess electrons than charge B.

If a conductor is connected between the two charges as shown in Figure 2-4B, electrons will flow from the greater negative charge to the less negative charge. The number of electrons will be exactly the right amount to equalize the two charges. In this example, charge A originally has three million excess electrons while charge B has an excess of only one million electrons. To equalize the two charges, one million electrons will flow from charge A to charge B. Electron flow ceases as soon as the two charges become equal. Notice that the direction of current flow is from the more negative charge to the less negative charge.

Figure 2-5A shows two positive charges of different magnitudes. A potential exists here because one charge is greater than the other and electrons will flow if given the chance. Figure 2-5B shows a conductor connecting the two charges. Notice that electrons flow from the less positive (more negative) to the more positive potential. Again, the number of electrons that flow is the amount necessary to exactly balance the two charges.

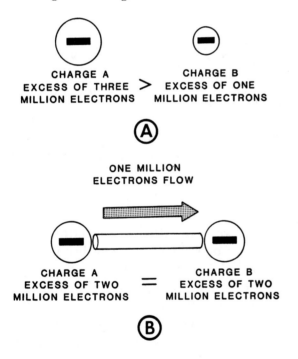

Figure 2-4 A potential exists between two charges of the same polarity if they have different magnitudes.

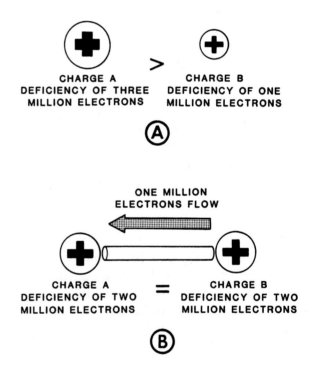

Figure 2-5 Electrons flow from the less positive to the more positive charge.

Figure 2-6 shows five terminals at various levels of charge. Since no two are of the same magnitude and polarity, a difference of potential exists between any two terminals. Consequently, if a conductor is placed between any two terminals, electrons will flow until those two charges are balanced. Notice that terminal C has no charge. It contains the same number of electrons as protons. Nevertheless, if terminal C is connected to any other terminal, electrons will still flow. If it is connected to one of the negative terminals, electrons will flow into terminal C. If it is connected to one of the positive terminals, electrons will flow from terminal C. Remember that electrons always flow from the more negative to the more positive terminal.

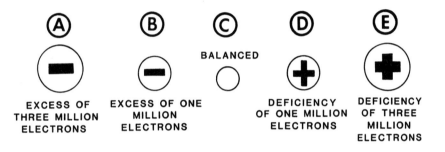

Figure 2-6 Five levels of charge.

Voltage

Another term that is often used interchangeably with EMF and potential difference is **voltage**. Strictly speaking, there is a difference between voltage and EMF. Voltage is the measure of EMF or potential difference. For example, the battery in your car has an EMF of 12 volts. The EMF supplied by wall outlets is 115 volts while that required by most electric stoves is 220 volts. A large screen color TV receiver produces an EMF at one point which may be 25,000 volts or higher. High tension power lines often have a difference of potential as high as 500,000 volts.

The unit of measure for EMF or potential difference is the **volt**. At this point, it is difficult to visualize exactly how much EMF constitutes one volt. However, as you work with electronics, this point will become clearer. One volt is the magnitude of EMF that will cause one unit of energy to move one coulomb of charge from one point to another.

The metric unit of energy is the **joule**. This unit is equally difficult to visualize since it is defined in other unfamiliar terms such as newtons. However, joules can be expressed in the more familiar English units. For example, one joule is equal to 0.738 foot-pounds. A foot-pound is the amount of work required to lift one pound a distance of one foot. Thus, a joule is approximately the amount of work required to lift 3/4 of a pound one foot off the ground.

Using this information, let's return to the volt. One volt is the EMF required to cause one joule (or 0.738 foot-pounds) of work to move one coulomb of charge (6.25×10^{18} electrons) from one point to another. To look at it another way, when the movement of one coulomb of charge between two points produces one joule (or 0.738 foot-pounds) of work, the EMF between the two points is 1 volt. Later on, after you have studied resistance, the volt will be defined the volt in terms of current and resistance. It will be much easier to visualize then.

The abbreviation of volt is V. Thus, 1.5 volts is abbreviated 1.5 V. As with amperes, metric prefixes are attached to indicate smaller and larger units of voltage. Thus, one millivolt equals 1/1000 volt, while one microvolt equals 1/1,000,000 volt. Also, one kilovolt equals 1000 volts while one megavolt equals 1,000,000 volts.

Self-Test Review

1. Electrons are repelled by negative charges and are attracted by ___+___ charges.

2. The general name given to the force that moves electrons is _electro motive force_ and is abbreviated EMF.

3. A battery that is not connected to a circuit retains the ability to move electrons. In this case, the battery's EMF is referred to as _____ difference.

4. Charges can differ in two ways. There can be a difference in _____ or a difference in _____.

5. Figure 2-6 shows five terminals each of which is at a different potential or state of charge. The greatest difference of potential exists between terminals A and _____.

6. Refer again to Figure 2-6. If a conductor is connected from charge A to charge E, _____ electrons will flow from A to E.

7. In Figure 2-6, terminal C is more positive than terminals _____ and _____.

8. In Figure 2-6, charge B is more (Positive/negative) charge A.

9. Again in Figure 2-6, if a conductor is connected from A to B, electrons will flow from terminal _____ to _____.

10. In Figure 2-6, charge D and E are both positive but charge _____ is more positive.

11. E is measured in volts. Thus, voltage is a measure of potential difference or _____.

EMF is produced when an electron is forced from its orbit around the atom. An electric pressure exists between the free electron and the resulting positive ion. Thus, any form of energy that can remove electrons from atoms can be used to produce an EMF. In no case is energy actually created. It is simply changed to electrical energy from other forms. For example, a battery converts chemical energy to electrical energy while a generator converts mechanical energy to electrical energy.

There are six common methods of producing EMF. Each has its own applications. The following section contains discussions of these methods.

Magnetism

This is the most widely used method of producing electrical power. At present, it is the only practical method that can produce enough electrical power to run an entire city. Well over 99 percent of all electrical power available today is produced by this method.

The method for producing an EMF with magnetism is quite simple. When a conductor is moved through a magnetic field, an EMF is produced. This is called **magnetoelectricity**. The force of the magnetic field and the movement of the conductor provide the energy necessary to free electrons in the conductor. If the conductor forms a closed loop, then the electrons will flow through the conductor. If the conductor does not form a closed loop, a potential difference is still present.

The basic requirements for producing an EMF using this method are a magnetic field, a conductor, and relative motion between the two. Figure 2-7 illustrates how this is done. Here, the magnetic field is produced by a permanent magnet. The field is represented by the lines drawn from the north to the south poles of the magnet. If a conductor is moved up so that it moves across the field as shown in Figure 2-7A, electrons flow in the direction indicated. The same effect can be obtained if the conductor is held still and the magnet is moved down. All that is required is relative motion between the magnetic field and the conductor.

Figure 2-7B shows that electrons flow in the opposite direction if the relative motion is reversed. When the conductor is moved up and down in the magnetic field, the direction of electron flow changes each time the motion reverses. In generators, a reciprocal motion like this occurs. Thus, the current produced alternately flows in one direction then the other. This is known as **alternating current** or simply **AC**.

In power generating stations the reciprocal motion occurs 60 times each second. Thus, the power supplied to your home is often referred to as 60 cycle AC. This is an alternating current that goes through the forward-and-reverse current cycle 60 times each second. In this course, you will not be concerned with alternating current although you will learn about magnetism in some detail later.

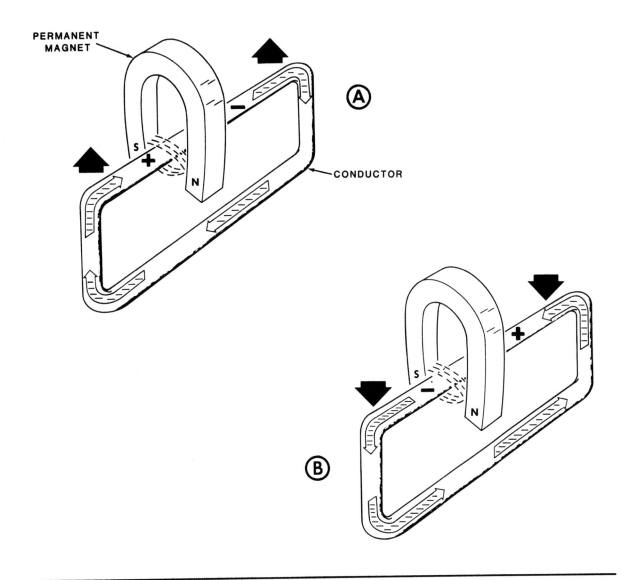

Figure 2-7 Electricity from magnetism.

Chemical

The second most popular method of generating an EMF is by chemical means sometimes called **electrochemistry**. Automobile and flashlight batteries are two examples of producing an EMF through chemical action. There are many chemical reactions that will transfer electrons to produce an EMF. Some of these will be discussed in more detail later in this unit.

Figure 2-8 illustrates how a basic battery or cell is made. A glass beaker is filled with a solution of sulfuric acid and water. This solution is called the **electrolyte**. In the electrolyte, the sulfuric acid breaks down into hydrogen and sulfate. Because of the chemical action involved, the hydrogen atoms give up electrons to the molecules of sulfate. Thus, the hydrogen atoms exist as positive ions while the sulfate molecules act as negative ions. Even so, the solution has no net charge since there are the same number of negative and positive charges.

Next, two bars called **electrodes** are placed in the solution. One bar is copper while the other is zinc. The positive hydrogen ions

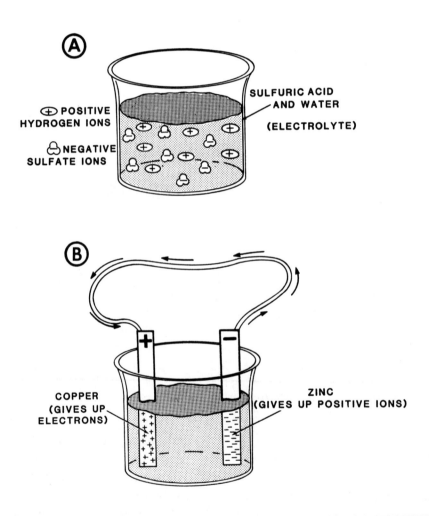

Figure 2-8 Electricity from chemicals.

attract the free electrons in the copper. This causes the copper bar to give up electrons to the electrolyte. Thus, the copper bar is left with a net positive charge.

The zinc reacts with the sulfate in much the same way. The sulfate molecules have a negative charge. Thus, positive zinc ions are pulled from the bar. This leaves the zinc bar with a surplus of electrons and a net negative charge.

If a conductor is connected between the zinc and copper bars, electrons will flow from the negative to the positive terminal. Because current flow is always in the same direction, the current flow is called direct current or DC and the EMF supplied by the battery is referred to as a DC voltage or volts DC. Compare this to the AC voltage produced by magnetism in Figure 2-7.

Friction

The oldest known method for producing electricity is by friction. Some examples of this were discussed in the previous unit. Rubbing a glass rod with silk, as shown in Figure 2-9A, results in friction between the two materials. This produces a positive charge on the glass rod and a negative charge on the silk as shown in Figure 2-9B. Different materials can also produce a charge. Figure 2-9C shows that fur rubbed on a hard rubber rod becomes positively charged while the rubber becomes negatively charged.

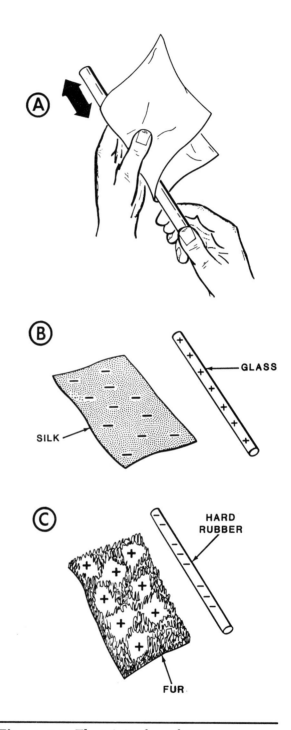

Figure 2-9 Electricity from friction.

You have probably experienced this phenomenon yourself many times. When you scuff your feet across a nylon or wool rug, your shoes develop a charge that is transferred to your body. When you touch a neutral object such as a metal door knob or another person, a discharge occurs. Frequently, there is a tiny arc between your finger and the neutral body. The arc is the visible movement of electrons between two objects.

In many cases, static electricity produced by friction is troublesome or annoying. However, there is a device used in physics laboratories that uses friction to develop very high voltages. It is called the Van de Graff generator and some models produce 10 million volts or more. Producing electricity from friction is called the **triboelectric effect**.

Light

Light energy can be converted to electrical energy in large enough quantities to provide limited amounts of power. A familiar example of this is the solar cells frequently used on spacecraft. Although solar cells are relatively expensive, recent scientific advances have significantly reduced their cost. In fact, solar cells are already used in applications such as microwave towers in remote locations.

Figure 2-10 shows how one type of solar- or photocell is constructed. It consists of a

photosensitive material sandwiched between two plates that act as electrodes. A photosensitive material is one that develops a charge when it is subjected to light. Some substances that behave in this way are cesium, selenium, germanium, cadmium, and sodium. When the photosensitive material is struck by light, some of its atoms absorb the light energy and release electrons. This is known as the **photoelectric effect**.

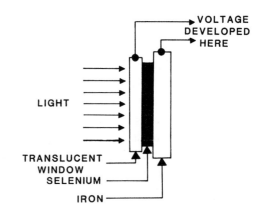

Figure 2-10 Electricity from light.

In Figure 2-10, light passes through the translucent window and strikes the selenium alloy underneath. Some of the selenium atoms give up electrons and a charge develops between the two plates. When exposed to sunlight, a single cell can provide a fraction of a volt charge and deliver a few milliamperes of current. When used as a power source, hundreds of the cells may be connected so that they produce larger voltage and current levels.

Pressure

A small electrical charge develops in some materials when they are subjected to pressure. This is referred to as the **piezoelectric effect**. It is especially noticeable in substances such as quartz, tourmaline, and Rochelle salts, all of which have a crystalline structure. Figure 2-11 illustrates how the charge is produced. In the normal structure, negative and positive charges are distributed so that no overall charge can be measured. However, when the material is subjected to pressure, electrons leave one side of the material and accumulate on the other side. Thus, a charge develops. When the pressure is relieved, the electrons are again distributed so that there is no net charge.

This effect is put to good use in crystal microphones, phonograph pickups, and precision oscillators. In all of these examples, the crystals are subjected to varying

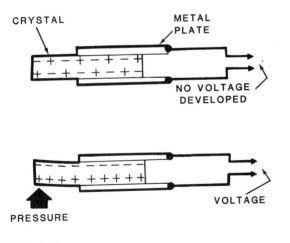

Figure 2-11 Electricity from pressure.

pressure. The pressure can be supplied by sound waves travelling through the air as is the case with the microphone, or, as with the phonograph pickup, some type of direct pressure can be applied. At any rate, the voltage produced is very small and it must be amplified before it is used.

Heat

As with most other forms of energy, heat can be converted directly into electricity. The device used to do this is called a **thermocouple**. A thermocouple consists of two dissimilar metals joined together. A typical example of these metals is copper and zinc.

You have seen that copper will readily give up electrons. This is especially true when the copper is heated. As shown in Figure 2-12, the free electrons from the copper are transferred to the zinc. Thus, the copper develops a positive charge while the zinc develops a negative charge.

Since more heat will cause more electrons to transfer, the charge developed is directly proportional to the heat applied. This characteristic allows the thermocouple to be used as a thermometer in places that are too hot for conventional thermometers. A specific voltage across the thermocouple corresponds to a specific temperature. Therefore, the voltage can be measured and compared to a chart to find the corresponding temperature. The process by which heat is converted directly to electricity is called **thermoelectric effect**.

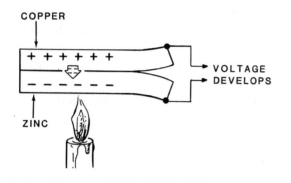

Figure 2-12 Electricity from heat.

Effects of EMF

You have learned that an EMF can be produced by light, heat, magnetism, pressure, and chemical activity. It is interesting to note that the reverse is also true. That is, an EMF can be used to produce light, heat, magnetism, pressure, and chemical activity.

The electric light is an example of light produced by electricity. Current flowing through the light's filament causes it to glow. The light is a result of the EMF applied to the circuit. Here, the electrical energy is converted to light.

The toaster and electric stove are examples of electricity producing heat. In both of these, current flowing through the heating elements produces a great amount of heat. In these instances, the energy applied to the components is given off as heat.

Whenever current flows through a wire, a magnetic field is produced. This field surrounds the wire and can be put to many practical uses. Some examples of these uses are motors, loud speakers, and solenoids.

Recall that a crystal produces a voltage when it is bent or twisted. The reverse is also true. When a voltage is applied to a crystal, the structure bends or twists. It can therefore be said that an EMF can produce pressure.

Finally, you already know that an EMF can be produced by chemical activity. It is also possible to produce chemical activity by applying an EMF to some materials. An example of this is the electrolysis of water. When an electric current flows through water, the water is broken down into its component parts of hydrogen and oxygen. Electroplating is another example of chemical activity caused by electricity. Here, ions of the plating material are removed from a solution and "plated" on the desired surface by the application of an electrical potential.

12. The most widely used method to produce an EMF is the _electro_ effect. _magnetic_

13. In order to produce an EMF with magnetism, you must have a magnetic field a conductor, and relative _motion_ between the two.

14. In a battery, the solution that reacts with the metal electrodes is called the _electrolyte_

15. Another device that can produce an EMF is the solar cell. It utilizes the _photoelectric_ effect to produce a voltage.

16. Electricity produced by _friction_ is attributed to the triboelectric effect.

17. Producing an EMF through pressure is called the _piezoelectric_ effect.

18. The thermocouple converts _heat_ to electricity.

19. Match each of the following applications of electricity with the effect that causes it:

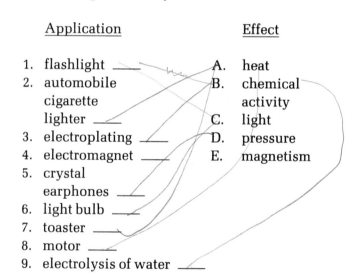

Application	Effect
1. battery	A. magnetoelectric
2. generator	B. piezoelectric
3. crystal microphone	C. thermoelectric
	D. electrochemical
4. thermocouple	E. photoelectric
5. solar cell	

20. Match each of the following with the effect produced by the EMF.

Application	Effect
1. flashlight	A. heat
2. automobile cigarette lighter	B. chemical activity
3. electroplating	C. light
4. electromagnet	D. pressure
5. crystal earphones	E. magnetism
6. light bulb	
7. toaster	
8. motor	
9. electrolysis of water	

One type of battery or cell was discussed in the previous section. It consisted of zinc and copper electrodes inserted into an electrolyte of sulfuric acid and water. This section presents the construction and operation of several more common types of batteries. But first, you should know the difference between a battery and a cell.

A cell is a single unit that contains negative and positive electrodes immersed in an electrolyte. A battery is a combination of two or more electrochemical cells. Thus, what you call a flashlight battery is really a cell since it contains only one unit for producing an EMF. In spite of this technical definition the word battery is loosely used to describe a single cell.

There are two basic types of cells. One type can be **recharged** and is called a **secondary cell**. The other type, called a **primary cell**, can **not** be **recharged**. No matter which type of cell you examine, they all store energy in a chemical form that can be released as electricity.

Dry Cell

Figure 2-13 shows the components of a flashlight battery or dry cell. The positive terminal is the steel top at the end of the carbon electrode. The negative terminal is the zinc can or container that holds the rest of the cell. A plastic jacket protects the zinc container and insulates the negative terminal from the positive terminal.

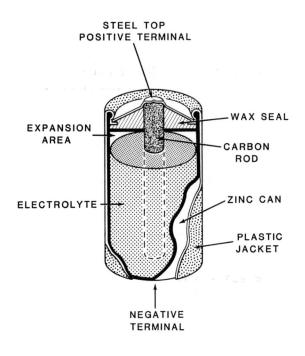

Figure 2-13 Construction of the dry cell.

Even though this type of cell is referred to as a "dry cell," it is not dry on the inside but contains a moist electrolyte paste. A wax seal closes off the open end of the zinc container. This prevents any paste from oozing out when the battery is turned upside down or placed on its side. Thus, this type of cell can be used in any position without the electrolyte escaping.

The electrolyte used in this cell is a solution of ammonium chloride and zinc chloride. The electrolyte gradually dissolves the zinc by stripping away positive ions. This process leaves behind an excess of electrons. Thus, the remaining zinc acts as the negative electrode. If it were not for the carbon rod, the electrolyte would develop a positive charge by virtue of the positive ions pulled from the zinc. However, the positive charge is neutralized by electrons pulled from the carbon rod. Thus, the carbon rod developes a deficiency of electrons resulting in a positive charge.

The cell just described is referred to as the Lelanche cell and it produces just over 1.5 volts when new. As it is used, the chemical action slows and the voltage output gradually decreases. Because this type of cell cannot be recharged, it is considered a primary cell. Furthermore, because the paste gradually dries out, the dry cell slowly loses its ability to produce an EMF. This occurs even if the battery is not in use. For this reason, the dry cell must be used within about two years of the time it is manufactured. That is, it has a shelf life of about two years.

The voltage produced by this type of cell is determined strictly by the types of material used as the electrodes and the electrolyte. Thus, the voltage is determined by the chemical reaction and not the size of the cell. For this reason, a small pen light cell produces the same voltage as a much larger D cell. However, since the larger battery has larger electrodes and a greater volume of electrolyte, it can deliver a greater amount of electrons per period of time. In other words, the larger battery has a higher current rating. The size D cell can deliver 50 milliamperes of current for approximately 60 hours. A small penlight cell becomes exhausted much sooner at the same current.

Lead-Acid Battery

The primary disadvantage of the dry cell is that it cannot be recharged. Other cells, called secondary cells, can be recharged. The most popular of the secondary cells is the lead-acid battery. In this type of cell, a reversible chemical reaction takes place. It is this reaction that produces EMF between the battery terminals.

In Figure 2-14A you see a typical lead-acid battery. The positive electrode consists of a plate of lead dioxide (PbO_2) and the negative electrode is a plate of spongy lead (Pb) are submersed in a solution of sulfuric acid (H_2SO_4) and water (H_2O).

The sulfuric acid in the solution separates into positive hydrogen ions (H^+) and negative sulfate (SO_4^-) ions. (Here the H^+ indicates that the hydrogen has lost 1 electron while the SO_4^- indicates that the sulfate has gained 2 electrons.) While this is happening, the lead plate begins to give up electrons and form Pb^{++} positive ions. Some of the negative sulfate ions in the solution combine with the positive lead ions on the surface of the negative electrode and form a coating of lead sulfate. The electrons given up by the lead plate travel through the conductor to the positive electrode.

Meanwhile, the atoms on the surface of the lead dioxide plate give up negatively charged oxygen ions (O^-) into the solution. The loss of the electrons that the oxygen carries into the solution gives the lead dioxide

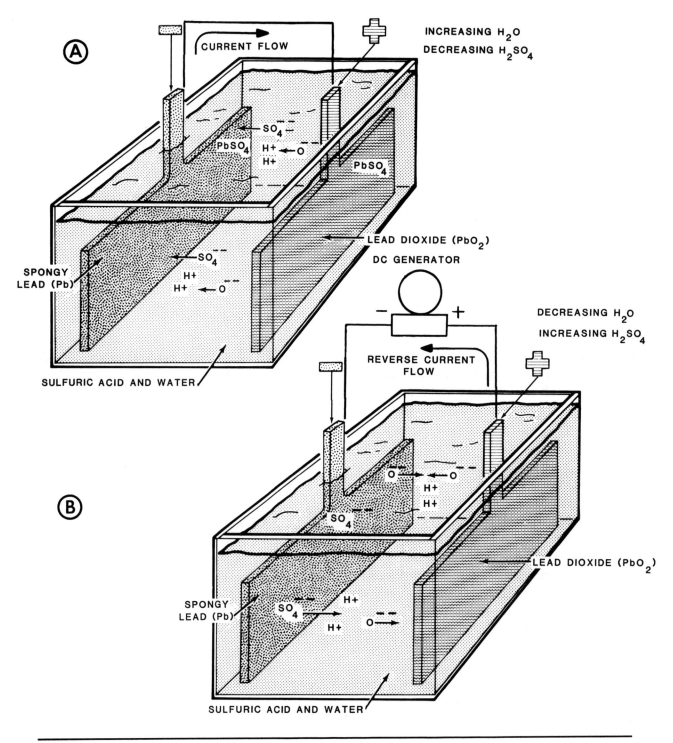

Figure 2-14 The basic lead-acid cell.

plate an overall positive charge. That is, Pb^{+++} ions are formed on the surface of the plate. Again, as with the negative electrode, some of the negative sulfate ions combine with the positive lead ions to form a coating of lead sulfate on the positive electrode. However, this does not completely neutralize the charge of the lead ions. In fact, each of the lead ions on the plate is still Pb^{++}. It is this positive charge that attracts the electrons from the negative electrode through the conductor.

The negatively charged oxygen ions in the solution now combine with the positively charged hydrogen ions that resulted from the separation of the sulfuric acid and form water (H_2O). As the cell discharges, the amount of water increases while the amount of acid decreases.

This entire process can be reversed by reversing the ion flow through the battery. This is done by connecting a source of DC voltage greater than that produced by the lead-acid cell as shown in Figure 2-14B. However, during the recharging process, some of the oxygen and hydrogen in the solution will escape into the air. Since hydrogen in its pure form is highly explosive and oxygen aids combustion, you should be extremely careful when charging a lead-cell battery.

The amount of EMF produced by a cell is determined by the chemical reaction that occurs within the cell. The lead-acid cell just described produces an EMF of about 2.1 volts. Cells made of other materials will produce different voltages.

The amount of current that a cell can deliver is determined by the size of the cell or, to state it more correctly, by the physical size of the electrodes and the amount of sulfuric acid in the solution.

The Nickel-Cadmium (NICAD) Battery

The plates or electrodes in the nickel-cadmium battery are made of nickel powder heat bonded to a metal screen. This results in an extremely porous plate that is then impregnated with electrically active materials. It is the active materials that actually produce the EMF. The active material in the positive plate is nickel hydroxide while the active material in the negative plate is cadmium hydroxide.

A typical nickel-cadmium battery is shown in Figure 2-15. It consists of a number of positive and negative plates, each forming a cell, held apart by a separator. The filler cap is removed to place the potassium hydroxide and distilled water electrolyte into the battery. This cap also serves as a safety valve in the event that there is a pressure buildup inside the battery during charging.

The electrodes in the NICAD battery become positive or negative through electron/ion transfer in essentially the same manner as in other batteries. Therefore, the actual chemical reaction within the battery is not as important as certain unique characteristics of the NICAD battery.

First, the NICAD battery is completely sealed and rechargeable. This means that during charging no explosive gasses escape as with the lead-acid battery. This feature makes the battery safer and greatly increases the potential uses.

Second, unlike the other batteries discussed thus far, the NICAD's voltage remains relatively constant throughout most of its discharge period. Only when the battery is almost completely discharged does the voltage begin to drop off significantly.

Finally, charging and discharging the NICAD battery involves little or no change in the concentration of the electrolyte. This is because the electrolyte does not react with the battery but, rather, acts only as a conductor of ions and electrons. For this reason, the plates do not deteriorate as do those in a lead-acid battery. This increases the useful life of the battery.

To achieve full benefit from a recharged NICAD Battery. All of the cells should first be completely discharged. Then, when the battery is recharged, all of the cells will charge at a uniform rate. Once fully recharged, the charge will last for a longer period of time.

Despite all of its advantages, the expense of the NICAD battery is a limiting factor in some applications.

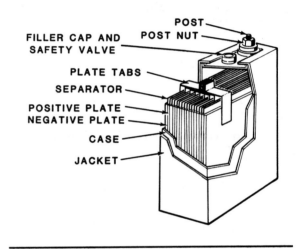

Figure 2-15 Large nickel-cadmium cell using liquid electrolyte.

21. A cell or battery is a device which stores energy in __chemical__ form.

22. A battery is composed of two or more __cells__ connected together for a specific current and voltage rating.

23. The main parts of a cell are its two electrodes and an __electrolyte__, which separates them.

24. A secondary cell is one that can be __recharged__.

25. The dry cell is a (Primary/Secondary) cell.

26. When new, the dry cell produces an EMF of about __1.5__ volts.

27. In a lead-acid battery, the positive plate is lead dioxide while the negative plate is pure __Pb__.

28. The lead-acid cell produces an EMF of approximately __2.1__ volts.

29. In the lead-acid cell, recharging reverses the chemical reaction and converts the lead-sulfate and water back to __Sulfuric__ acid and lead.

30. One advantage of the __dry cell__ battery is that it can be used in any position.

31. To create a lead-acid battery with an output of 6.3 volts you need __3__ lead-acid cells.

32. In the same way, a 12.6 volt battery must consist of __6__ cells connected in a series aiding configuration.

Cells can be connected together to increase either the voltage or current rating. There are four different ways that cells or batteries can be connected. These are series aiding, series opposing, parallel, and series parallel. Each of these configurations has its own advantages and uses. The following is a discussion of these configurations.

Series Aiding Connection

The 12-volt automobile battery consists of six cells connected together so that the individual cell voltages are additive. In the 6-volt battery, three cells are connected in the same way. This arrangement is called a **series aiding** connection and is shown in

Figure 2-16A as it occurs in a three-cell flashlight.

The cells are connected so that the positive terminal of the first cell connects to the negative terminal of the second; the positive terminal of the second cell connects to the negative terminal of the third; and so on. This type of connection forms a single current path through all three cells. Thus, it is called a series connection. It is an aiding connection because the EMF of each cell moves current in the same direction. Hence, the cells aid each other in current movement. Since the individual EMF of each cell is 1.5 volts, and the cells aid each other, the overall EMF is 4.5 volts. The schematic drawing for this connection is shown on the right of Figure 2-16A.

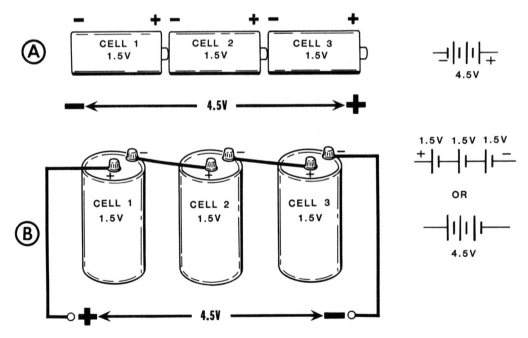

Figure 2-16 The series aiding connection.

Figure 2-16B shows a different type of cell in a series configuration. As before, the voltages add together because the cells work together or aid one another in current movement. That is, the negative terminal of the first cell connects to the positive terminal of the next and so on. Thus, the three 1.5 volt cells provide a total EMF of 4.5 volts. The schematic symbol for this configuration is shown on the right of Figure 2-16B.

With the series aiding connection, the total voltage across the battery is equal to the sum of the individual values of each cell. However, the current capacity of the battery does not increase. Since the total circuit current flows through each cell, the current capacity is the same as for one cell.

Series Opposing Connections

The series aiding connection just discussed is extremely important and is widely used. The **series opposing** connection of cells is just the opposite. It has little practical use and is usually avoided. It is mentioned here because an inexperienced person may inadvertently connect cells in this way. The series opposing connection of two cells is shown in Figure 2-17A. Notice that the two cells are connected in series, but the like terminals of the cells are connected together. Here, the cells provide EMF in opposite directions with the result that the two voltages cancel each other and the overall EMF is 0 volts. Because the two voltages

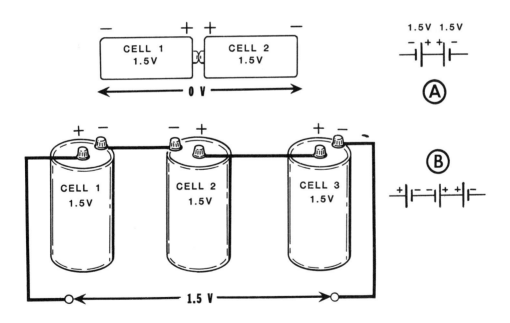

Figure 2-17 The series opposing connection.

cancel, this arrangement cannot produce current flow.

Figure 2-17B shows another example of a series opposing connection. Here three cells are connected in series but cell number 2 is connected backwards. Consequently, its voltage is subtracted from the voltage of the two cells connected series aiding. The total voltage for cells 1 and 2 is 0 volts. This leaves the output voltage of cell 3. Therefore, the total output of the three cells is only 1.5 volts.

Parallel Connection

You have learned that the series aiding connection of cells increases the output voltage but not the current capabilities of the cells. There is a way to connect cells so that their current capabilities add together. This is called a parallel connection and is shown in Figure 2-18A. Here, like terminals are connected. That is, all the positive terminals are connected together as are all of the negative terminals.

Figure 2-18B shows why the current capacities of the cells are added together. Notice that the total current through the lamp is the sum of the individual cell currents. Each cell provides one third of the total current. Thus, the total current capacity is three times that of any one cell. However, connecting cells in this way does not increase the voltage. That is, the total voltage is the same as that for any one cell. If 1.5-volt cells are used, then the total voltage is 1.5 volts.

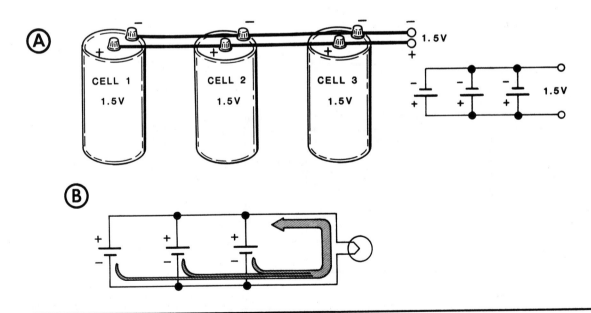

Figure 2-18 The parallel connection.

Series-Parallel Connection

When both a higher voltage and an increased current capacity are required, cells can be connected in series-parallel. For example, suppose you have four 1.5-volt cells and you wish to connect them so that the EMF is 3 volts and the current capacity is twice that of any one cell. This is achieved by connecting the four cells as shown in Figure 2-19. To get 3 volts, connect cells 1 and 2 in series. However, this does not increase the current capacity. To double the current capacity, you must connect a second series string (cells 3 and 4) in parallel with the first. The result is the series-parallel arrangement shown.

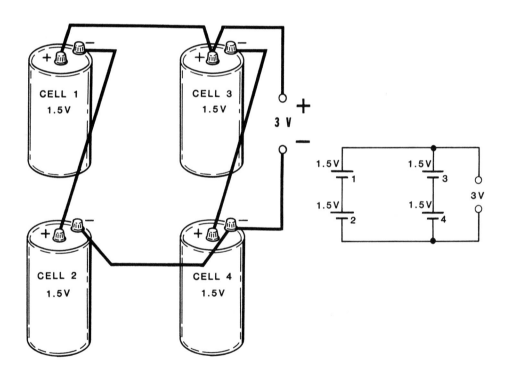

Figure 2-19 The series-parallel connection.

To be certain that you have the idea, consider the following example. Suppose that you have a number of identical 1.5 volt cells from which you want to construct a battery with an EMF of 4.5 volts and current capacity three times that of the individual cells.

Figure 2-20 shows that nine cells are required. Cells 1, 2, and 3 are connected in a series string to provide 4.5 volts. However, to achieve the higher current, three of these strings are connected in parallel.

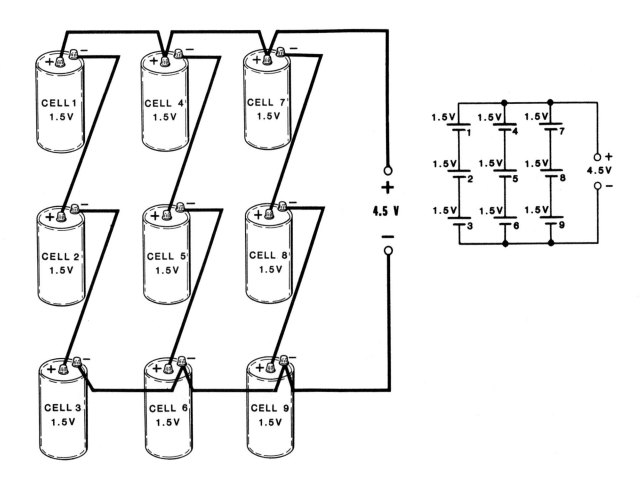

Figure 2-20 Nine cells connected in series parallel.

Self-Test Review

33. Four cells, each having an EMF of 2.1 volts, can be connected in a series aiding configuration to produce an EMF of ___8.4___ volts.

34. When connecting cells in the series aiding connection, the negative terminal of one cell is connected to the ___positive___ terminal of the next.

35. If three 1.5 V batteries with a maximum current capacity of 100 milliamperes are connected series aiding, the resulting battery will have an EMF of ___4.5___ volts and a current capacity of ___100___ milliamperes.

36. If, in a series string of four 1.5 V batteries, one battery is connected backwards, the total circuit voltage will be ___3.0___ volts.

37. If two identical batteries are connected series opposing, the output voltage will be ___0___ volts.

38. Thus, if a single cell has a current capacity of 1/4 amp, then three of the cells in parallel will have a current capacity of ___3/4___ amp.

39. If five 2.1 V cells are connected in parallel the total output voltage is ___2.1___ volts.

40. In a series-parallel configuration, the current capacity is determined by the ___number___ of series strings connected in parallel.

41. If you have a number of identical 1.5 V cells each with a current capacity of 200 milliamperes, to construct a 7.5 V battery you would need ___5___ cells connected in ___seris aiding___

42. If you have a string of batteries identical to the one described in the previous question, to obtain a current capacity of 800 milliamperes you would have to connect ___4___ of these strings in parallel.

43. To construct the configuration described in the preceding question you would need a total of ___20___ cells.

Voltage Rises and Voltage Drops

In electronics and electrical work there are two kinds of EMF or potential difference. Both are expressed in volts but they have somewhat different characteristics. One type of EMF is called a voltage rise. The other is called a voltage drop. The following sections discuss voltage rises and drops in detail.

Voltage Rise

You know that a battery provides an EMF or voltage. It does this by chemically producing an excess of electrons at the negative terminal and an excess of positive ions at the positive terminal. When a load is connected across the battery, electrons flow through the load. Each electron that leaves the negative terminal is replaced by an electron from the battery. At the positive terminal, each electron arriving from the load cancels one positive ion. However, for each ion that is cancelled, the battery produces a replacement ion. Thus, the voltage between the two terminals remains constant even though electrons are constantly flowing from the negative terminal and into the positive terminal.

Energy is required to move the electrons through the load. The battery gives each electron the energy required to make the trip. As you know, the energy (in joules) is related to the EMF of the battery (in volts) and the number of electrons moved (in coulombs).

The energy comes from the chemical reaction within the battery that is converted to electrical energy. This energy has a capacity to do work, and the amount of work is determined by the voltage of the battery. After all, it is the EMF or voltage of the battery that causes the electrons to flow in the first place. The battery is a source of EMF. This type of EMF is referred to as a voltage rise. Thus, in an electrical circuit a voltage rise is an EMF that is provided by a **voltage source**.

Earlier, several different types of voltage sources were presented. As previously stated, the two most common are the generator and the battery. However, solar cells and thermocouples also produce an EMF and may be considered as voltage sources. Any EMF introduced into a circuit by a voltage source is called a **voltage rise**. Thus, a 10 V battery has a **voltage rise** of ten volts.

Voltage Drop

Electrons that leave the negative terminal of a battery have been given energy by the battery. As the electrons flow through the load, they give up their energy to the load. Often, the energy is given up as heat. However, if the load is a light bulb, both heat and light are given off or, in the case of a motor, the energy is given off as heat and motion. The point is that the electrons release to the circuit the energy given to them by the battery.

Since the energy introduced into the circuit is called a voltage rise, the energy removed from the circuit by the load is called a voltage drop. A voltage drop is expressed in volts like a voltage rise. In fact, the same equation expresses the relationship between volts, joules, and coulombs in both cases. The equation is:

$$\text{volts} = \frac{\text{joules}}{\text{coulombs}}$$

Using this equation, you can determine the voltage drop across a load if you know the energy consumed by the load (in joules) and the number of electrons flowing through the load (in coulombs). For example, assume that a light bulb releases 10 joules of energy in one second when a current of two amperes flows through it. With a current of two amperes, two coulombs flow through the bulb each second. Using the above equation, you can determine the voltage drop:

$$\text{volts} = \frac{\text{joules}}{\text{coulombs}}$$

$$\text{volts} = \frac{10 \text{ joules}}{2 \text{ coulombs}}$$

$$\text{volts} = 5$$

Thus, the voltage drop of the light bulb is 5 volts. It is important to realize that this voltage exists between the two terminals of the bulb and that it can be measured with a voltmeter. In fact, the meter cannot tell the difference between a voltage rise produced by a battery and a voltage drop produced by a load. This is the reason that a

battery and a light bulb may both have a rating of 12 volts. In the case of the battery it means that the battery supplies 12 volts. This is a voltage rise. However, for the light bulb, it means that a voltage drop of 12 volts is required to make it work.

One difference between a voltage drop and a voltage rise is that the voltage drop occurs only when current flows through the load. A battery, on the other hand, has a voltage rise whether or not it is connected to a circuit.

Voltage Drops Equal Voltage Rises

Figure 2-21A shows a 10 V battery with a light bulb connected across it. The battery provides a voltage rise of 10 volts. As electrons flow through the lamp, a voltage drop develops across it. Since the lamp consumes the same amount of energy as the battery provides, the voltage drop across the lamp is equal to the voltage rise across the battery. That is, the voltage drop is 10 volts.

In Figure 2-21B, two light bulbs are connected in series across a 10-volt battery. Each bulb drops part of the 10 volts supplied. If the two lamps are identical, each will drop half of the supplied voltage as indicated in Figure 2-21B. If the two lamps are not identical, one bulb will drop more voltage than the other. However, the sum of the voltage drops will always equal the sum of the voltage rises.

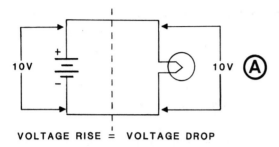

VOLTAGE RISE = VOLTAGE DROP

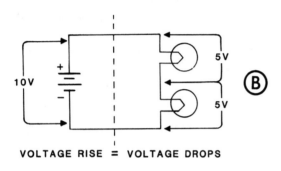

VOLTAGE RISE = VOLTAGE DROPS

Figure 2-21 The voltage drops are equal to the voltage rises.

To be certain that you have the idea, consider the example shown in Figure 2-22A. Here, three batteries are connected series aiding across a single lamp. The sum of the voltage rises is equal to 12 volts. Hence, the lamp, since it is the only load, must drop 12 volts.

Now look at Figure 2-22B. In this case, two 4.5 V batteries are connected in series with three identical lamps. The total voltage rise in the circuit is 9 V. Since the lamps are identical, each drops one-third of the applied voltage or 3 V. Once again, the sum of the voltage rises equals the sum of the voltage drops.

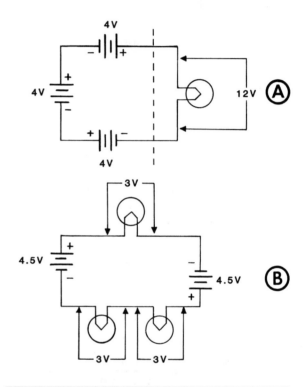

Figure 2-22 The sum of the voltage drops equals the sum of the voltage rises.

44. In any circuit in which current is flowing, there are two types of EMF. One is called a voltage rise while the other is called a voltage __drop__.

45. Any device which produces EMF is a voltage source and can provide a voltage (rise)/drop).

46. As with all forms of EMF, the voltage rise is measured in __volts__.

47. Unlike the voltage rise, a voltage drop is present across a load only when __current__ is flowing through the load.

48. Since current flow is caused by a voltage rise, a voltage drop cannot exist unless there is an accompanying voltage __rise__.

49. If the voltage rise in a circuit is 10 volts, then the voltage drop will also be __10__ volts.

50. No matter how many loads are connected across a 10 volt battery, the sum of the voltage drops must equal __10__ volts.

51. If two identical lamps are connected in series across a voltage source, each will drop __1/2__ of the applied voltage.

Concept of Ground

One of the most important points in the study of electricity and electronics is the concept of **ground**. Originally ground was just what the name implies – the earth. In fact, in some countries the name **earth** is used instead of **ground**. Earth is considered to have zero potential. Thus, ground or earth can be used as a reference point to which voltages, either positive or negative, are compared.

Many electrical appliances in your home are grounded. This is especially true of air conditioning units, electric clothes dryers, and washing machines. Often this is done by connecting a heavy wire directly to a cold water pipe that is buried deep in the earth (ground). In other cases, a third prong on the power plug connects the metal frame through a third line in your house wiring to ground. The purpose of this is to protect you in case a short circuit develops in the appliance. It also places the grounded metal parts of different appliances at the same potential so that you are not in danger of receiving an electrical shock from a difference in potential between two appliances. This type of ground is sometimes called **earth ground**. The schematic symbol for earth ground shown in Figure 2-23A.

In some electronic equipment, the zero reference point, or ground point, is the metal frame or chassis on which the various circuits are constructed. In your automobile, the chassis or metal body of the automobile is considered as ground. If you look closely at the straps leaving the battery you will see that one connects directly to the metal frame of the car. This point is considered to be ground as is every other point on the metal frame. When working on pieces of equipment like these, all voltages are measured with respect to this **chassis ground**. In a schematic, chassis grounds are depicted as shown in Figure 2-23B. In many instances, the schematic symbols shown in Figures 2-23A and 2-23B are used interchangeably.

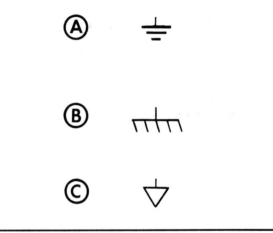

Figure 2-23 Ground reference.

There is another method of reference or ground used in electronics. For example, a certain point in a circuit is called **ground** although no point on the circuit connects to earth in any way. In this case, ground is simply a zero reference point within an electronic circuit called a **circuit ground**. Usually, in a piece of electronic equipment the various circuit grounds are connected together. At any rate, all voltages measured within the circuit are measured with respect to circuit ground. The schematic symbol for a circuit ground is shown in Figure 2-23C.

In electronics, ground is important because it provides you with a reference. This, in turn, enables you to use and measure both negative and positive voltages. Up to now you have studied only with relative voltages between two points. For example, a 6 V battery has an EMF between its two terminals of 6 volts. You have not yet learned to think of this as +6 volts or −6 volts but rather simply 6 volts.

However, the concept of ground allows you to express negative and positive voltages. Remember ground is merely a reference point that is considered zero or neutral. If you assume that the positive terminal of a 6 V battery is ground, then the negative terminal is 6 volts more negative. Thus, the voltage at this terminal with respect to ground is −6 volts.

On the other hand, if you assume that the negative terminal of the battery is ground, then the positive terminal with respect to ground is +6 volts. Notice that the battery can produce −6 volts or +6 volts depending on which terminal you assign as a ground or reference.

The schematic symbol for earth ground is once again shown in Figure 2-24A. Figure 2-24B shows how it is used in a circuit. Point A is at ground or zero potential. Now, since this is a 10 V battery, point B is at a plus 10 volt potential with respect to ground. We say that point B is ten volts above ground or that the voltage at this point with respect to ground is +10 volts.

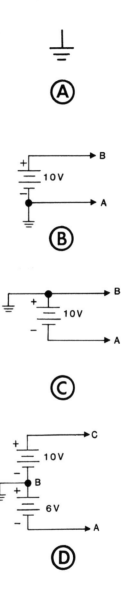

Figure 2-24 The polarity of the voltage depends upon the connection to ground.

Figure 2-24C shows why it is so important to have a ground or reference. Here the same battery is shown but with the positive terminal connected to ground. In this case, the positive terminal is the zero volt point in this circuit. Because the negative terminal is ten volts more negative, the voltage at point A with respect to ground is − 10 volts. Thus, we can use the battery as a + 10 volt source or as a − 10 volt source depending on which terminal is connected to ground.

Another example is shown in Figure 2-24D. Here two batteries are connected in series, with the ground connection between them.

Thus, the zero reference is at point B. Since the top battery has an EMF of 10 volts, the voltage at point C with respect to ground is + 10 volts. The lower battery has an EMF of 6 volts. Because the positive terminal is connected to ground, the EMF at point A with respect to ground is − 6 volts.

Remember, voltage is always the measure of the potential difference between two points. Thus, in Figure 2-24D, when you speak of the voltage at point A, what you really mean is the voltage between point A and ground.

52. The common point in any circuit that acts as a zero reference is called __ground__.

53. If a piece of electronic equipment is grounded to a metal pipe driven deep into the earth or through the third prong in its plug, this type of ground is sometimes called __earth__ ground.

54. Some electronic devices use their frame as a reference point. In this case, the reference is referred to as a __chassis__ ground.

55. In any circuit, the ground acts as a __neutral__ point.

56. A 12 V battery becomes a +12 volt source when the __negative__ terminal is connected to ground.

57. On the other hand, the same battery becomes a −12 volt source when the __positive__ terminal is connected to ground.

58. When you say that the voltage at point A is +12 volts, you mean that +12 volts of EMF exists between point A and __grnd__.

Measuring Voltage

The device most often used for measuring voltage is the voltmeter. There are many different types of voltmeters in use today. Some use a mechanical meter movement like the one shown in Figure 2-25A. Here the voltage is read from a scale behind the moving pointer. Another type, called the digital voltmeter, is extremely popular. It is shown in Figure 2-25B. Here the voltage is read from a numeric display. This type of meter is usually more accurate and always easier to read. Generally speaking, it is also more expensive.

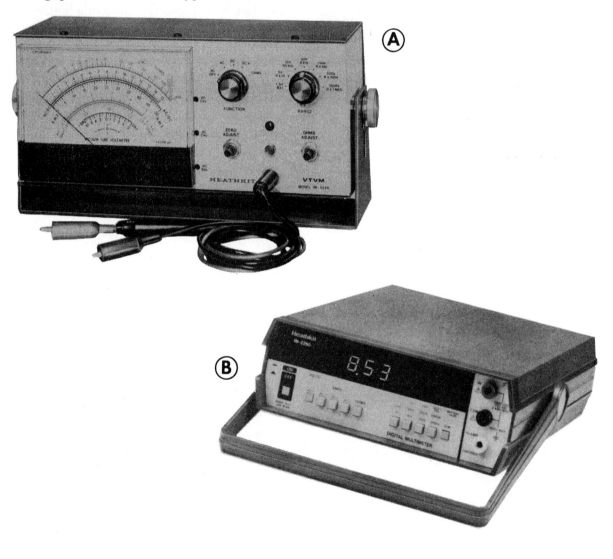

Figure 2-25 Typical Meters

Regardless of the type of voltmeter, certain precautions must be taken to ensure accurate readings. To begin with, voltage is always measured **between two points**. The schematic symbol for the voltmeter is shown in Figure 2-26A. Notice that one of the leads is marked negative while the other is marked positive. As with the ammeter discussed earlier, polarity must be observed when using the voltmeter. This means that the negative lead must be attached to the more negative of the two points across which the voltage is to be measured.

Fortunately, the voltmeter is much easier to use than the ammeter. When using the voltmeter, the circuit under test need not be broken nor disturbed in any way. To measure the voltage between two points, simply touch the two leads of the voltmeter to the two points. However, remember that you must observe polarity.

Figure 2-26B shows how the voltmeter is connected to measure the voltage drop across the lower lamp. Notice that the negative lead is connected to the more negative point. Also note that the meter is connected directly across the lower bulb. In this case, the meter is measuring a voltage drop. If the switch is opened so that current flow stops, the voltage drop disappears and the meter reading falls to zero.

Figure 2-26C shows a different circuit with the meter connected to measure the voltage rise of the battery at the bottom of the illustration. Once again, polarity is observed and the meter is connected directly across the

component. Here, the meter is used to measure a voltage rise rather than a voltage drop. Therefore, the voltage remains constant when the switch is opened. Notice that the voltage rise does not depend on current flow.

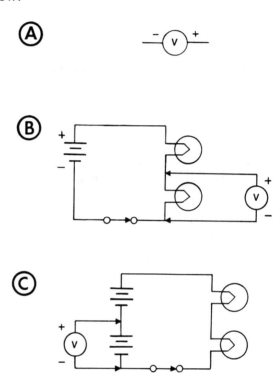

Figure 2-26 Connecting the voltmeter.

A couple of precautions must be taken when using a voltmeter. First, you should always make certain that the voltage you are going to measure is not higher than the meter can measure. If it is, the high voltage may damage the meter. Also, you should be certain the meter is on the proper range. For example, you should not attempt to measure 100 volts with the meter set to the 1 volt range. This, too, may damage the meter. When you are unsure of the value of voltage to be measured, you should make your first measurement with the meter on a high range. This will prevent the unknown voltage from **pegging** the meter.

For your own safety there are some other precautions that you must observe. You should hold the meter leads only by the insulated portions. Otherwise, you may receive an electrical shock.

As you have seen, in most electronic devices voltages are measured with respect to ground. Therefore, when working on electronic equipment, it is a good idea to connect one lead to ground and leave it there. This way only one hand is required to make voltage measurements. The other hand can be held away from the equipment. This greatly reduces your chances of receiving an electrical shock.

59. The device used for measuring voltage is the _voltmeter_.

60. If a voltmeter is connected across a voltage source then the EMF measured represents a voltage _rise_.

61. When the meter is connected across a load, the EMF measured represents a voltage _drop_.

62. As when using an ammeter, when you use a voltmeter you must observe _polarity_.

Summary

The following is a point-by-point summary of Unit 2. If you are in doubt about any of the facts given here, you should review the appropriate portion of the text.

EMF is the force that moves electrons. This force is a natural result of Coulomb's law.

Potential difference is another name for the same force. It represents the potential for moving electrons.

EMF or potential difference exists between any two charges that are not exactly alike. A difference of potential exists between any uncharged body and any charged body. An EMF exists between two unequal positive charges, between unequal negative charges, and between any negative charge and any positive charge.

Voltage is the unit of measure of EMF or potential difference. The unit of voltage is the volt. One volt is equal to one joule of energy or work per coulomb of transferred charge.

The joule is the metric unit of work and is equal to 0.738 foot pounds.

The millivolt is 1/1000 volt. The microvolt is 1/1,000,000 volt. The kilovolt is 1000 volts. The megavolt is 1,000,000 volts.

EMF can be produced in several different ways. The most common method uses magnetism and mechanical motion. Other methods use chemical reactions, friction, light, pressure, or heat.

A cell is an electrochemical device that contains negative and positive electrodes separated by an electrolyte.

A battery is a combination of two or more cells.

There are two basic types of cells — the primary cell and the secondary cell. The primary cell cannot be recharged. The secondary cell can be recharged.

The dry cell uses a paste-like electrolyte and can be used in any position.

The wet cell uses a liquid electrolyte.

The most common type of dry cell uses an electrolyte of ammonium chloride and zinc chloride. The positive electrode is carbon and the negative electrode is zinc. It produces an emf of about 1.5V when new. It is a primary cell.

The most common type of wet cell is used in the lead-acid battery. This is the type of battery used in almost all automobiles.

The electrolyte is sulfuric acid and water. The positive electrode is lead dioxide and the negative electrode is pure lead. It produces an emf of about 2.1V. It is a secondary cell which can be recharged repeatedly.

The voltage produced by a cell is determined by the chemical reaction and not by the size of the cell. However, current capacity is determined by the size.

When two or more cells are connected in a series aiding configuration, the individual voltages add. Thus, a 6 volt battery can be formed by connecting four 1.5 volt cells in the series aiding arrangement.

When two cells are connected in a series opposing configuration, the voltage produced by one cell is subtracted from that produced by the other. This connection is normally avoided.

When two or more cells are connected in parallel, the output voltage is the same as that for any one cell. That is, the voltages do not add. However, the current capacity does increase.

Cells can be connected in a series-parallel arrangement so that both the voltage and the current capacity increase.

A voltage can exist at two different points in a circuit: where it is produced and again where it is used. A voltage that exists because EMF is being produced is called a voltage rise. A voltage that exists because energy is being used is called a voltage drop.

A voltage rise can exist with or without current flow. A voltage drop exists across a component only when current flows through the component.

If one joule of energy is consumed by a load when one coulomb of charge flows through it, then the voltage drop across the load is one volt.

In a circuit in which current is flowing, the sum of the voltage drops is equal to the sum of the voltage rises.

Ground is the name given to the point in a circuit that is used as the zero reference. Often this is the metal chassis or frame of the electronic device.

Voltages may be negative or positive with respect to ground. A battery can be connected as a negative voltage rise or as a positive voltage rise depending on how it is connected to ground.

The device used to measure voltage is called the voltmeter.

Voltage is measured between two points that have a difference of potential.

You must observe polarity when connecting a voltmeter to a circuit.

The voltmeter is connected across the voltage rise or voltage drop to be measured. Thus, you need not break the circuit under test when measuring voltage.

A short offers no opposition to current flow. If a short is placed across a component, all current will pass through the short and no current will pass through the component. The voltage drop across a short is zero.

An open offers infinite opposition to current flow. In a series circuit, the voltage measured across an open is equal to the voltage rise in the circuit.

Unit 3
Resistance

Contents

Introduction

In this unit, you will study resistance. Resistance is the name given to that property of any substance that causes it to oppose current flow. All materials have this property to some extent. Some materials such as glass and rubber offer a great deal of opposition to current flow. They allow almost no current to flow through them. Thus, they are said to have a very high resistance. Other materials such as silver and copper offer very little opposition to current flow. Therefore, they have a very low resistance.

This unit deals with the characteristics of resistance. It describes what resistance is, how it is measured, and how it is used.

Unit Objectives

When you have completed this unit, you will be able to:

1. Define the following terms: Resistivity, resistance, conductance, ohm, thermistor, potentiometer, LDR, positive temperature coefficient, negative temperature coefficient, specific resistance, and rheostat.

2. Name four factors that determine the resistance of a substance and state the relationship that these factors have to the resistance of a substance.

3. State the difference between a conductor and an insulator, in terms of resistance.

4. Given the gauge and type of wire, calculate the resistance of a length of wire.

5. Determine a resistor's value and tolerance by examining its color code.

6. Determine a resistor's power rating by examining its size.

7. Calculate the total resistance of resistors in series, parallel, and series-parallel configurations.

8. State the effects of connecting resistors in series and parallel, in terms of circuit resistance.

9. Describe the correct method for using an ohmmeter.

10. State the relationship between resistance, current, and voltage.

11. Name three types of fixed resistors.

Basic Concepts

If a short length of copper is connected across a battery, a great deal of current will flow — so much, in fact, that the battery will quickly discharge. If the same length of rubber is connected across the same battery, no measurable current will flow. Obviously, then copper and rubber have very different characteristics in regard to current flow.

The difference in these two materials stems from their atomic structure. In copper, there are a great number of free electrons drifting aimlessly through the spaces between the atoms. When an EMF is applied, these electrons are free to move and current flow results. In rubber, the situation is different. Here, very few electrons drift freely between the molecules. Therefore, an EMF can cause very few electrons to move. The result is little or no current flow.

Copper offers little opposition to current flow while rubber offers a great deal of opposition. This opposition to current flow is called **resistance**. The resistance of copper is very low while the resistance of rubber is very high. The resistance of a material is determined largely by the number of free electrons in the material.

The Ohm

The unit of measurement for resistance is the **ohm**. This unit is named for Georg Simon Ohm, a German physicist who discovered the relationship between voltage, current, and resistance.

An ohm may be defined in several different ways. Originally, the ohm was defined as the resistance of a column of mercury that is 106.3 centimeters long and 1 square millimeter in cross sectional area. Once the ohm was defined in this way, it allowed anyone with the proper equipment to construct a 1 ohm standard. Unfortunately, this particular standard makes the resistance of an ohm hard to visualize.

It may be helpful to think in terms of something with which you are more familiar. A length of number 22 insulated copper wire that is 60 feet long has a resistance of about one ohm.

The most common way to define the ohm is in terms of voltage and current. One ohm is the amount of resistance that will allow one ampere of current to flow in a circuit to which one volt of EMF is applied. Stated another way, if one volt causes one ampere of current in a circuit then the resistance of the circuit is one ohm. Figure 3-1 illustrates these three ways of defining the ohm.

The Greek letter omega (Ω) is commonly used to represent the ohm. Thus, 1 ohm may be written 1 Ω. Also, one thousand ohms may be written as 1000 Ω, 1 kilohms, or as 1 kΩ. Finally, one million ohms may be written as 1,000,000 Ω, 1 megohms, or a 1 MΩ.

In electronics, the letter R is used to represent resistance. Therefore, in the shorthand of electronics the statement "the resistance is ten ohms" may be written as an equation:

$$\text{``}R = 10\ \Omega.\text{''}$$

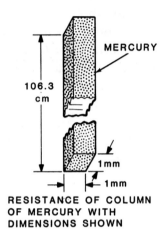

RESISTANCE OF COLUMN
OF MERCURY WITH
DIMENSIONS SHOWN

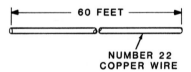

RESISTANCE OF 60 FEET
OF NUMBER 22 COPPER WIRE

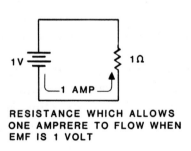

RESISTANCE WHICH ALLOWS
ONE AMPERE TO FLOW WHEN
EMF IS 1 VOLT

Figure 3-1 The ohm.

Resistivity

You cannot directly compare the resistances of two substances because their resistances will vary with their shape, size, and temperature. However, every substance has a property called **specific resistance** or **resistivity** that can be compared directly if all other characteristics are alike.

For wire, the resistivity is defined as the resistance of a one-foot length of wire. This one foot length must be exactly 0.001 inch (1 mil) in diameter and its temperature must be exactly 20 degrees centigrade. These requirements standardize the shape, size, and temperature of substances being compared so that any difference in resistance is caused solely by the material's atomic structure.

The resistivity of several substances is shown in Table 3-1. Notice that silver has the lowest resistivity while copper is a close second. At the bottom of the list are glass and rubber. Silver and copper are the best conductors while glass and rubber are two of the best insulators.

As you have seen, both conductors and insulators are important in electronics. Conductors have many free electrons so they conduct current very easily. Thus, they are used to carry current from one place to another. Most metals such as silver, copper, gold, aluminum, tungsten, zinc, brass, platinum, iron, nickel, tin, steel, and lead are good conductors.

SUBSTANCES	RESISTIVITY IN OHMS/MIL FOOT
Silver	9.9
Copper	10.4
Gold	15.3
Aluminum	17.0
Tungsten	33.8
Iron	58.0
Steel	100.0
Constawtan	295.0
Glass	10^{16}
Rubber	10^{20}

Table 3-1

Insulators, or nonconductors, are substances that have few free electrons. Therefore, they have very high values of resistivity. These substances are used to prevent electrical conduction. Most wires are coated with an insulator so that they do not accidentally short out when used to carry electricity. Some examples of insulators are glass, rubber, plastic, mica, and dry air.

To summarize, it is the resistivity of a material that determines if the material is a conductor or an insulator. Resistivity is the resistance of a specific size and shape of a material at a specific temperature.

Conductance

Sometimes it is more convenient to think in terms of how well a material conducts current rather than in terms of how well it opposes current. Because of this, a property called **conductance** is often used. Conductance is the opposite of resistance. It is de-

fined as the ease with which a substance allows current to flow. Mathematically, conductance is the reciprocal of resistance. This means that conductance is equal to the number 1 divided by the resistance. Or stated as an equation:

$$\text{Conductance} = \frac{1}{\text{Resistance}}$$

The letter G is used to represent conductance. Therefore, the equation can be written:

$$G = \frac{1}{R}$$

The unit of conductance is the **mho**, pronounced "moe." Notice that this is ohm spelled backwards. The mho is the reciprocal of the ohm. Therefore,

$$\text{mhos} = \frac{1}{\text{ohms}}$$

A substance with a resistance of 1 ohm has a conductance of 1 mho. However, a resistance of 2 ohms in a substance results in a conductance of 1/2 or 0.5 mhos and if the resistance is 1000 ohms or 1 kilohm, the conductance is 0.001 mhos or 1 millimho.

In most cases it is more convenient to think in terms of ohms (resistance) rather than in terms of mhos (conductance). Therefore, discussions in this course will be related to resistance. However, it is important to remember the mho because a key characteristic of the vacuum tube and the field-effect transistor is given in mhos.

Factors Determining Resistance

The most important factor in determining resistance is the resistivity of a material. However, three other factors also contribute to a substance's resistance. These are the length, cross-sectional area, and temperature of the material. This is why these three variables are carefully defined when determining resistivity. The following is a more detailed discussion of each of these factors.

Length.

A 60-foot length of number 22 (#22) insulated copper wire has a resistance of about 1 ohm. A 120-foot length of the same wire has a resistance of approximately 2 ohms. Thus, if you double the length of the wire, the resistance also doubles. In other words, the resistance of a conductor is directly proportional to its length. In fact, with any material, the greater the length, the higher will be the resistance. The reason for this is that the electrons must travel further through the resistant medium. Thus, if the length doubles, the resistance doubles; if the length triples, the resistance triples; and so forth.

Cross-Sectional Area.

The cross-sectional area of a conductor is determined by its thickness or diameter. As you know, good conductors have a large number of free electrons. In fact, the more free electrons available per unit of length, the better the conductor. Obviously then, a large diameter conductor has more free electrons per unit of length than a small diameter conductor of the same material simply because of its increased size. Therefore, large diameter conductors have less resistance than small diameter conductors.

All other things being equal, the resistance of a substance is inversely proportional to its cross-sectional area. If the cross-sectional area doubles, the resistance drops to one half its former value. Also, if the area triples, the resistance drops to one third of its previous value.

Temperature.

With most materials, the resistance changes when the temperature changes. With changes in length and cross-sectional area, you know exactly how the resistance will change because changes in these factors affect all materials in the same way. However, with changes in temperature, this is not the case. Not all materials change resistance in the same direction or by the same amount when temperature changes.

In most materials, an increase in temperature causes an increase in resistance. Materials that respond in this way are said to have a **positive temperature coefficient**. If a material has a positive temperature coefficient, its resistance increases as temperature increases and decreases as temperature decreases.

A few substances, such as carbon, have a **negative temperature coefficient**. This means that their resistance decreases as temperature increases. There are also materials whose resistance does not change at all with changes in temperature. These materials are said to have a **zero** or **constant temperature coefficient**.

In most elementary circuits, the temperature coefficients of the components are not critical and are simply ignored. However, in some circuits the temperature coefficients are important, and they must be considered in the design.

A device called a **thermistor** uses the effect of temperature on resistance to great advantage. A thermistor is a special type of resistor that changes resistance when its temperature changes. Such devices normally have a negative temperature coefficient. In many thermistors, the resistance value can drop to one half its former value for a temperature rise of 20 degrees centigrade. Thermistors are often used in temperature sensing circuits and as protective devices.

Resistance of Wire

You can determine the resistance of a length of copper wire from the information in Table 3-2. The first column of this table shows the gauge of the wire. This is the common reference used when speaking of wire. For example, wire can be referred to as 22 gauge or #22 wire. The diameter of

NUMBER	DIAMETER IN MILS	AREA IN CIRCULAR MILS	OHMS PER 1000 FT	
			COPPER * 68°F	COPPER * 167°F
0000	460	211,600	.049	.0596
000	410	167,800	.0618	.0752
00	365	133,100	.078	.0948
0	325	105,500	.0983	.1195
1	289	83,690	.1239	.151
2	258	66,370	.1563	.190
3	229	52,640	.1970	.240
4	204	41,740	.2485	.302
5	182	33,100	.3133	.381
6	162	26,250	.395	.481
7	144	20,820	.498	.606
8	128	16,510	.628	.764
9	114	13,090	.792	.963
10	102	10,380	.999	1.215
11	91	8,234	1.260	1.532
12	81	6,540	1.588	1.931
13	72	5,178	2.003	2.44
14	64	4,107	2.525	3.07
15	57	3,257	3.184	3.87
16	51	2,583	4.016	4.88
17	45.3	2,048	5.06	6.16
18	40.3	1,624	6.39	7.77
19	35.9	1,288	8.05	9.79
20	32.0	1,022	10.15	12.35
21	28.5	810	12.8	15.6
22	25.4	642	16.1	19.6
23	22.6	510	20.4	24.8
24	20.1	404	25.7	31.2
25	17.9	320	32.4	39.4
26	15.9	254	40.8	49.6
27	14.2	202	51.5	62.6
28	12.6	160	64.9	78.9
29	11.3	126.7	81.8	99.5
30	10.0	100.5	103.2	125.5
31	8.93	79.7	130.1	158.2
32	7.95	63.2	164.1	199.5
33	7.08	50.1	207	252
34	6.31	39.8	261	317
35	5.62	31.5	329	400
36	5.00	25.0	415	505
37	4.45	19.8	523	636
38	3.96	15.7	660	802
39	3.53	12.5	832	1012
40	3.15	9.9	1049	1276

Table 3-2 Wire gauge chart.

each wire in this chart is 1.123 times as large as the diameter of the succeeding wire. This is more obvious when you look at column two of the chart.

Column two lists the diameter of each gauge wire in mils. A mil is equal to .001 inches. If you look at #000 (pronounced "three aught") wire, you see that it has a diameter of 410 mils. Now if you multiply 410 mils times 1.123 you get the diameter of the next larger size wire—460 mils for #0000 wire.

Column three contains the cross sectional area of each wire in circular mils. A circular mil is the area of a circle with the diameter of 1 mil.

Columns four and five list the resistances of 1000 ft of a given gauge of wire. Column four contains the resistance of the wire at 68 degrees F, while in column five, the resistance values are given at 167 degrees F. For example, 1000 ft of #9 wire has a resistance of .792 ohms at 68 degrees F and .963 ohms at 167 degrees F.

If you want to determine the resistance of a specific length of copper wire, you use the formula:

$$\frac{\text{Length of wire}}{1000} \times \text{Resis. of 1000 ft of wire}$$

For example, the resistance of 150 ft of #15 copper wire at 67 degrees F is:

$$\frac{150 \text{ ft}}{1000} \times 3.184 \text{ ohms/1000 ft} = .48\Omega$$

Not all wire, however, is copper. Since each type of material has its own resistivity, you must adjust your resistance calculations according to the types of wire that you are using. You can do this by using the conversion factors given in Table 3-3.

If you look at this table, you see that the conversion factor for aluminum is 1.59. This means that resistance of aluminum wire is 1.59 times as great as the resistance of the same amount of copper wire. Therefore, if you use the calculations from the previous problem you see that the resistance of 150 ft of #15 aluminum wire is;

$$.48 \text{ ohms} \times 1.59 = .76 \text{ ohms}$$

In this way, you can determine the resistance of any of the types of wire shown in Table 3-3.

ALUMINUM	1.59
BRASS	4.40
GOLD	1.38
IRON	6.67
LEAD	12.76
NICHROME	60.00
NICKEL	7.73
PLATINUM	5.80
SILVER	0.92
STEEL	8.62
TIN	8.2
TUNGSTEN	3.2
ZINC	3.62

Table 3-3 Ratio of resistance of metals as compared to copper.

Self-Test Review

1. All substances oppose the flow of current to some extent, therefore, all substances have some _resistance_.

2. If an EMF of 1 volt causes a current of 1 ampere, then the resistance of the material through which the current is flowing is _1Ω_.

3. _1Ω_ is defined as the resistance of a one mil-foot section of a particular material at 20 degrees C.

4. Substances with very low resistivity values are good (Conductors/ Insulators).

5. Materials such as glass, rubber, mica, and dry air have (Low/High) resistivity values.

6. The ease with which a substance allows current to flow is called _mhos_.

7. The greater the length of a material, the _higher_ the resistance will be.

8. The greater the cross sectional area of a wire, the _lower_ the resistance of the wire will be.

9. If the resistance of a material increases when the temperature increases, the material is said to have a _positive_ temperature coefficient.

10. If the resistance of a material decreases as the temperature increases, the material is said to have a _negative_ temperature coefficient.

11. A special type of resistor which uses the temperature coefficient to good advantage is called a _thermistor_.

Resistors

A resistor is an electronic component that has a certain specified opposition to current flow or resistance. Of course, other types of components also have some resistance but the resistor is designed specifically to introduce a desired amount of resistance into a circuit.

Wire-Wound Resistors

You have seen that copper has a resistivity of about 10 ohms per mil-foot. You can wrap a one foot length of 1 mil diameter copper wire on an insulated form and attach leads as shown in Figure 3-2A. This gives you a 10 ohm wire-wound resistor. The process for producing practical wire-wound resistors is a little more involved but the idea is the same.

The resistance wire used is generally made from a nickel-chromium alloy, called nichrome, that is about 60 times as resistive as copper. The form on which the wire is wound is often a ceramic tube. After the leads are attached, the form and wire are covered with a hard protective coating. This type of resistor is often used in high current circuits where relatively high amounts of power must be dissipated. The resistance range can vary from less than an ohm to several thousand ohms. The wire-wound technique is also used to produce precise value resistors. Such precision values are often required in meter circuits.

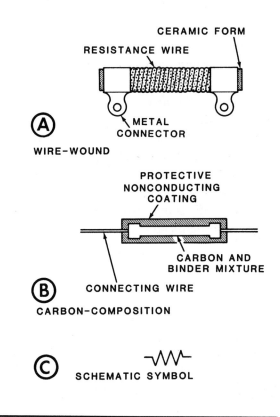

Figure 3-2 Types of resistors and their schematic symbols.

Carbon-Composition Resistors

The element carbon is neither a good conductor nor a good insulator. Instead, it falls in-between and is called a **semiconductor**. This makes carbon ideal as a material for resistors. By combining carbon granules and a powdered insulating material in various proportions production of a wide range of resistor values is possible.

Figure 3-2B shows the construction of this type of resistor. Granules of carbon and a binder material are mixed together and shaped into a rod. Wire leads are inserted and the package is sealed with a nonconductive coating.

Carbon-composition resistors are inexpensive and, at one time, were the most common type used in electronics. Generally, they are used in low current circuits where they are not subjected to great amounts of heat. Values can vary from 10 ohms or less to 20 megohms or more.

Incidentally, all resistors share the same schematic symbol. The schematic symbol for the resistor is shown in Figure 3-2C.

Deposited-Film Resistors

Another type of resistor that is presently the most popular type is the film-type resistor. The construction of a film-type resistor is shown in Figure 3-3. In these devices, a resistance film is deposited on a nonconductive rod. Then the value of resistance is set by cutting a spiral groove through the film. This changes the appearance of the film to that of a long, flat ribbon spiralled around the rod. The groove sets the length and width of the ribbon so that the desired resistance value is achieved. Several metal-film types are available. One uses a nickel-chromium (nichrome) film on an aluminum oxide rod while another uses a tin-oxide film on a glass rod. Carbon-film is used when precision resistors are required.

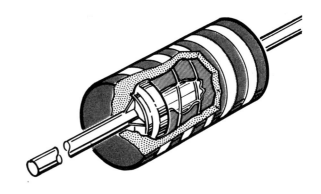

Figure 3-3 Deposited film resistor.

Resistor Ratings

Resistors have three very important ratings: resistance (in ohms), tolerance (in percent) and wattage (in watts). If you know what to look for, these ratings can usually be determined by examining the resistor. The following explains each of these ratings in more detail.

Resistance.

You have already learned about resistance in some detail. You know that resistance is determined by the length, the cross-sectional area, and the resistivity of a material.

It is possible to identify the resistance of any resistor. With wire wound resistors, the value is normally written somewhere on the resistor. However, with carbon-composition and film resistors the value is usually indicated by color bands.

Figure 3-4 shows the color code normally used on resistors. As you can see, there are four bands on the resistor. The code is read starting with the band closest to the end of the resistor; band 1. The color of band 1 corresponds with a number from 0 to 9 as indicated in column 1 of Figure 3-4. This is the first digit of the resistor's nominal value.

Band 2 also represents a number from 0 to 9 and is the second digit of the resistor's nominal value. Thus, if the colors of the first two bands are red-red, the first two numbers of the resistor's value are 22.

The third band on the resistor is the multiplier band. The number indicated in the first two bands is multiplied by the corresponding value given in column 3 of Figure 3-4. For example, a red-red-red color code is the number 22 multiplied by 100 or 2200. This means that the resistor has a nominal value of 2200 Ω.

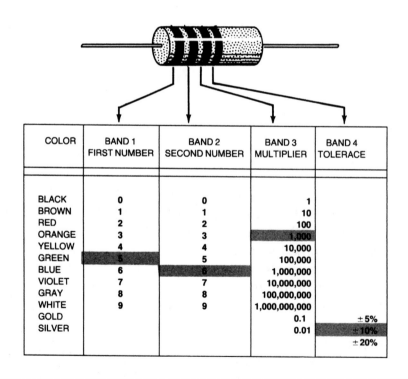

COLOR	BAND 1 FIRST NUMBER	BAND 2 SECOND NUMBER	BAND 3 MULTIPLIER	BAND 4 TOLERACE
BLACK	0	0	1	
BROWN	1	1	10	
RED	2	2	100	
ORANGE	3	3	1,000	
YELLOW	4	4	10,000	
GREEN	5	5	100,000	
BLUE	6	6	1,000,000	
VIOLET	7	7	10,000,000	
GRAY	8	8	100,000,000	
WHITE	9	9	1,000,000,000	
GOLD			0.1	±5%
SILVER			0.01	±10%
				±20%

Figure 3-4 Color code for resistors.

Some resistors have five color bands. If this is the case, the first three bands represent numbers and the fourth band is the multiplier band. In carbon resistors the fifth band is a failure rate specification.

The fourth band shown in Figure 3-4 is the tolerance band. It is discussed in the next section.

Tolerance.

The resistance of any resistor is rarely the exact value indicated on the resistor. It would be extremely difficult and expensive to produce resistors of exact values. For this reason, resistors have a tolerance rating. In the color code, different colors indicate various tolerance ratings. For example, a 1,000 ohm resistor may have the tolerance of ± 10 percent. Ten percent of 1000 is 100. Therefore, the actual value of the resistor can be anywhere from 900 ohms (1000 − 100) to 1100 Ohms (1000 + 100).

Tolerances of ± 5 percent, ± 10 percent, and ± 20 percent are common for carbon composition resistors. Precision resistors often have a tolerance of − 1 percent or less. Generally, the lower the tolerance, the more the resistor costs.

Wattage.

Wattage rating refers to the maximum amount of power or heat that the resistor can dissipate without burning up or significantly changing value. As shown in Figure 3-5, the larger the physical size of the resistor, the more power it can dissipate and the higher the wattage rating.

Carbon composition resistors generally have fairly low wattage ratings. Ratings of 2 watts, 1 watt, 1/2 watt, and 1/4 watt are the most common. Wire wound resistors can have much higher wattage ratings. A rating as high as 250 watts is not too uncommon for a wire wound resistor.

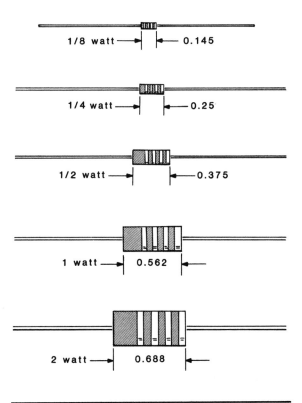

Figure 3-5 Dimension in inches of carbon composition resistors. (*Courtesy Allen-Bradley*)

Variable Resistors

The volume control on your TV receiver or radio is an example of a **variable resistor**. Variable resistors are resistors whose values can be changed in one way or another. As with fixed resistors, variable resistors can be constructed of many different materials.

Figure 3-6A illustrates the construction of a variable carbon resistor. Figure 3-6B shows the rear-view of the inside of this device. A flat, circular strip of carbon is mounted between the two end terminals. A contact that moves along the resistance element connects to the center terminal. This arm is attached to a moveable shaft. If the arm is moved in a clockwise direction as shown by the arrow, the resistance between terminals 1 and 2 increases because the amount of resistive material between these two terminals increases. Notice that, simultaneously, the resistance between terminals 2 and 3 decreases. This happens because the amount of resistive material between these two terminals decreases. This type of variable resistor is called a **potentiometer** or simply a **pot**. A potentiometer has **three** terminals.

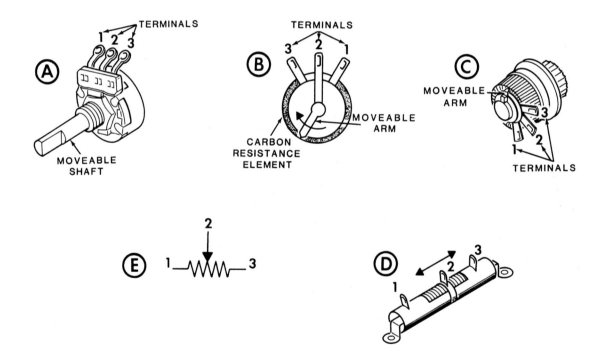

Figure 3-6 Variable resistors.

A slight variation of this arrangement is called a rheostat. A rheostat has only two terminals. Thus, this arrangement can be changed to a rheostat by removing or not using either terminal 1 or terminal 3. Notice that the resistance between terminals 1 and 2 can still be varied without terminal 3. However, without the third terminal the flexibility of the device is greatly reduced.

Wire-wound potentiometers are also common. Many have the same outward appearance as the potentiometer shown in Figure 3-6A. However, the internal construction is slightly different. As shown in Figure 3-6C, resistance wire is wound around an insulating core. A contact arm moves along the bare wire changing the resistance between the center and outside terminals.

Another type of variable resistor is shown in Figure 3-6D. This type is sometimes called a sliding contact resistor. It is used in high-power applications where the resistance value must be initially set or occasionally reset. The resistance value is changed by moving the sliding contact along the bare resistance wire. Figure 3-6E shows the schematic diagram of the variable resistor.

12. A resistor is an electronic component designed to introduce a specific and desired amount of _resistance_ into a circuit.

13. The schematic symbol for the resistor is _⋀⋀⋀_ .

14. One type of wire used in wire wound resistors is an alloy of nickel and chromium called _nichrome_ .

15. Wire-wound resistors generally have relatively low resistance values but can have high _wattage_ ratings.

16. Because it is extremely expensive to make resistors of exact values, resistors have a _tolerance_ rating.

17. Because of their relatively small physical size, carbon composition resistors are limited to relatively low _power_ applications.

18. With carbon-composition and deposited-film resistors, the resistance values are generally indicated by _color_ _bands_ around the resistor.

19. The _wattage_ rating is usually indicated by the physical size of the resistor.

20. Potentiometers, rheostats, and slide-wire resistors are examples of _variable_ resistors.

21. The _rheostat_ is a variable resistor that has only two terminals while the _pot_ has three terminals.

22. **The symbol for the variable resistor is?**
_____

Connecting Resistors

Resistors are often connected in series, in parallel, and in series-parallel combinations. In order to analyze and understand electronic circuits, you must be able to compute the total resistance of resistor networks.

Resistors In Series

As mentioned earlier, a series circuit is one in which the components are connected end to end as shown in Figure 3-7A. Notice that the same current flows through all components or, to state it another way, there is only one current path through the circuit. The current in the circuit must flow through all three resistors one after the other. Therefore, the total opposition to current flow is the total resistance of the three resistors.

An example is shown in Figure 3-7B. Here, three resistors are connected in series. The total resistance is called R_T and is the resistance across the entire series circuit. R_T is found by adding the individual resistor values together. That is:

$$R_T = R_1 + R_2 + R_3$$

$$R_T = 10\,\Omega + 20\,\Omega + 30\,\Omega$$

$$RT = 60\,\Omega$$

The three resistors in series present the same opposition to current flow as a single 60 ohm resistor.

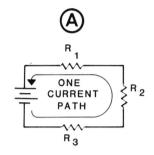

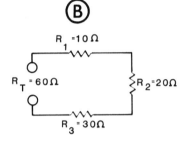

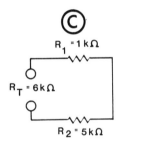

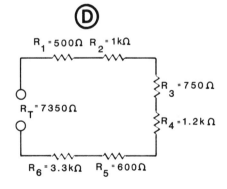

Figure 3-7 Resistors in series.

This example used three resistors. However, the same principle holds true for any number of series resistors. Thus, in Figure 3-7C a 1 kΩ resistor in series with a 5 kΩ resistor has a total resistance of 6 kΩ or 6000 Ω. The circuit shown in Figure 3-7D uses six resistors. Some of the values are given in kilohms while others are given in ohms. To avoid confusion, you can convert all values to ohms. R_1, R_3, and R_5 are already expressed in ohms. R_2 is equal to 1 kΩ or 1000 Ω. R_4 is 1.2 kΩ or 1,200 Ω. And R_6 is 3.3 kΩ or 3300 Ω. Thus, the total resistance R_T is found by adding:

$$R_T = R_1 + R_2 + R_3 + R_4 + R_5 + R_6$$

$$R_T = 500\ \Omega + 1000\ \Omega + 750\ \Omega + 1200\ \Omega + 600\ \Omega + 3300\ \Omega$$

$$R_T = 7350\ \Omega \text{ or } 7.35\ k\Omega$$

Resistors in Parallel

In parallel circuits, components are connected across each other so that there are two or more paths for current flow. Figure 3-8A is an example of a parallel circuit.

To see how resistors in parallel affect a circuit, you can add a switch, S_1, in series with R_2 so that you can switch R_2 in and out of the circuit. The resulting circuit is shown in Figure 3-8B. With S_1 open, a given amount of current flows through R_1. The amount of current is determined by the resistance of R_1 and the applied voltage. Because there is only one path for current flow, the current through R_1 is the total circuit current.

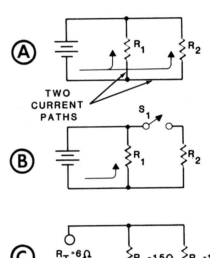
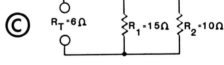
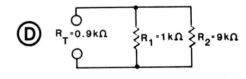

Figure 3-8 Resistors in parallel.

Now see what happens when the switch is closed. The current through R_1 remains unchanged since neither the resistance of R_1 nor the applied voltage has changed. However, an additional current path is now available through resistor R_2. As a result, current now flows through R_2. Thus, the total current provided by the battery increases. If R_2 has the same resistance as R_1, both resistors will offer the same amount of opposition to current flow. Thus, the current through R_1, will equal the current through R_2. In this case, the current provided by the battery doubles when R_2 is switched in parallel with R_1.

Regardless of the resistance of R_1 and R_2, the total current provided by the battery always increases when R_2 is placed in parallel with R_1 because a second current path is created. Obviously then, the total opposition to current flow, or total resistance, decreases since more current now flows. Thus, when one resistor is placed in parallel with another, the total resistance decreases. Assuming that R_1 and R_2 are equal, when the switch is closed the total current doubles. Thus, the total resistance has dropped to one half its former value.

There is a simple formula for finding the total resistance of two resistors in parallel. The formula is:

$$R_T = \frac{R_1 \times R_2}{R_1 + R_2}$$

Figure 3-8C shows an example of a parallel circuit where the value of the resistors is not equal. Here a 15 ohm resistor (R_1) is in parallel with a 10 ohm resistor (R_2). You can find the total resistance, R_T, in the following way.

$$R_T = \frac{R_1 \times R_2}{R_1 + R_2}$$

$$R_T = \frac{15\Omega \times 10\Omega}{15\Omega + 10\Omega}$$

$$R_T = \frac{150\Omega}{25\Omega}$$

$$R_T = 6\Omega$$

The two resistors in the circuit connected in parallel have the same effect on current flow as that of a single 6 Ω resistor. The total resistance calculated for a parallel circuit is also referred to as **equivalent resistance** or **effective resistance**.

Figure 3-8D shows another example. Here a 1 kΩ resistor is in parallel with a 9 kΩ resistor.

$$R_T = \frac{R_1 \times R_2}{R_1 + R_2}$$

$$R_T = \frac{1000\,\Omega \times 9000\,\Omega}{1000\,\Omega + 9000\,\Omega}$$

$$R_T = \frac{9,000,000\,\Omega}{10,000\,\Omega}$$

$$R_T = 900\,\Omega \text{ or } .9\,k\Omega$$

The product over sum formula is normally used when two resistors are in parallel. However, it can also be used with three or more resistors. For example, Figure 3-9A shows four resistors in parallel. Using the formula, an equivalent resistance for R_1 and R_2 can be found. Then, using the formula again, an equivalent resistance for R_3 and R_4 can be found. Finally, the formula can be applied to the two equivalent resistances so that the total resistance can be found. However, this method involves using the formula three different times to find the resistance of a single circuit.

There is a more efficient method for calculating total resistance when more than two resistors are connected in parallel. The formula is:

$$R_T = \cfrac{1}{\cfrac{1}{R_1} + \cfrac{1}{R_2} + \cfrac{1}{R_3} + \cfrac{1}{R_4} + \dots \cfrac{1}{R_N}}$$

Using this formula for the circuit shown in Figure 3-9A, you can find the total resistance (R_T):

$$R_T = \cfrac{1}{\cfrac{1}{100\ \Omega} + \cfrac{1}{100\ \Omega} + \cfrac{1}{400\ \Omega} + \cfrac{1}{400\ \Omega}}$$

$$R_T = \cfrac{1}{.01\ \Omega + .01\ \Omega + .0025\ \Omega + .0025\ \Omega}$$

$$R_T = \cfrac{1}{.025\ \Omega}$$

$$R_T = 40\ \Omega$$

Figure 3-9B shows an example using only three resistors. Again, to find R_T.

$$R_T = \cfrac{1}{\cfrac{1}{R_1} + \cfrac{1}{R_2} + \cfrac{1}{R_3}}$$

$$R_T = \cfrac{1}{\cfrac{1}{500\ \Omega} + \cfrac{1}{500\ \Omega} + \cfrac{1}{250\ \Omega}}$$

$$R_T = \cfrac{1}{.002\ \Omega + .002\ \Omega + .004\ \Omega}$$

$$R_T = \cfrac{1}{.008\ \Omega}$$

$$R_T = 125\ \Omega$$

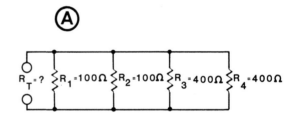

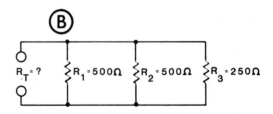

Figure 3-9 Compute the total resistance.

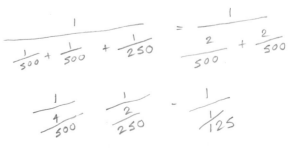

Equal Resistors In Parallel

Sometimes two or more resistors that have the same value are placed in parallel. There is a simple rule that covers this situation. When all the resistors in parallel have the same value, the total resistance can be found by dividing that value by the number of resistors in parallel. More simply, this rule states that:

$$R_T = \frac{\text{VALUE OF ONE RESISTOR}}{\text{NO. OF RESISTORS IN PARALLEL}}$$

$$R_T = \frac{20\ \Omega}{2}$$

$$R_T = 10\ \Omega$$

Likewise, when three resistors of the same size are connected in parallel, the total resistance is one third the value of one resistor. Thus, in Figure 3-10B:

$$R_T = \frac{330\ \Omega}{3}$$

$$R_T = 110\ \Omega$$

In Figure 3-10C:

$$R_T = \frac{16\ k\Omega}{4}$$

$$R_T = 4\ k\Omega$$

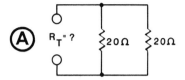

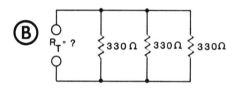

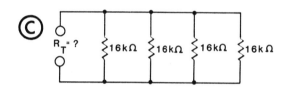

Figure 3-10 When all resistors have the same value, R_T equals a single resistor value divided by the number of resistors in parallel.

Series-Parallel Connections

In many circuits, a parallel branch is connected in series with one or more resistors as shown in Figure 3-11A. Even so, the total resistance is easy to calculate using the formulas shown earlier. The first step is to compute an equivalent resistance for the parallel branch. Then this equivalent resistance is added to the series resistance values.

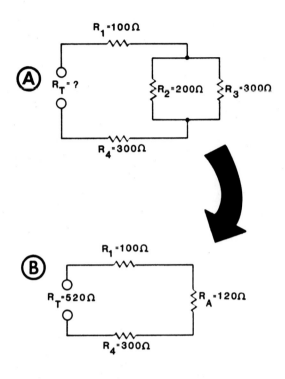

Figure 3-11 Simplifying the series parallel circuit.

Now you substitute R_A for the parallel network as shown in Figure 3-11B. You can do this because R_A has the same effect on the current flow through the circuit as the parallel branch that it replaces. Once you have the circuit in this simplified form, you use the formula for finding the total resistance in a series circuit.

$$R_T = R_1 + R_A + R_4$$

$$R_T = 100\ \Omega + 120\ \Omega + 300\ \Omega$$

$$R_T = 520\ \Omega$$

The circuit shown in Figure 3-12A is an example of a more complex series-parallel circuit. In order to determine the total resistance of this circuit, you must first simplify the circuit.

You may have difficulty determining where to begin the simplification process, especially when you first start doing these types of problems. An easy way to determine where to start is to trace the current flow through the circuit. When you reach the point where the current path divides for the last time, you've arrived at your starting point.

For example, you must first find the equivalent resistance for the parallel network made up of R_2 and R_3. Let's call this equivalent resistance R_A. Using the formula for a two resistor parallel branch, you find:

$$R_A = \frac{R_2 \times R_3}{R_2 + R_3}$$

$$R_A = \frac{200\ \Omega \times 300\ \Omega}{200\ \Omega + 300\ \Omega}$$

$$R_A = \frac{60,000\ \Omega}{500\ \Omega}$$

$$R_A = 120\ \Omega$$

In Figure 3-12A you can see that the current path splits for the last time at the branch made up of resistors R_2 and R_3.

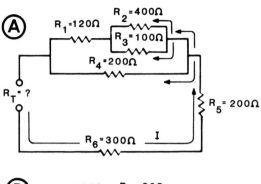

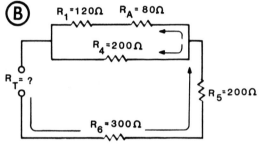

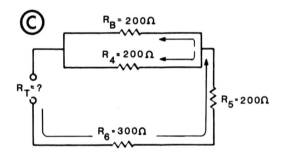

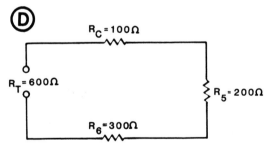

Figure 3-12 Complex series-parallel circuit.

The first step in determining the equivalent resistance of the circuit is to determine the resistance of the parallel network that is made up of R_2 and R_3. This is done using the two resistor parallel network formula. This resistance will be R_A.

$$R_A = \frac{R_2 \times R_3}{R_2 + R_3}$$

$$R_A = \frac{400 \ \Omega \times 100 \ \Omega}{400 \ \Omega + 100 \ \Omega}$$

$$R_A = \frac{40,000 \ \Omega}{500 \ \Omega}$$

$$R_A = 80 \ \Omega$$

Now look at Figure 3-12B. Here, you add the value of R_A to R_1 in order to find the resistance of the one leg of the branch formed by resistors R_1, R_2, and R_3. The resistance of this leg is called R_B, and you find:

$$R_B = R_A + R_1$$

$$R_B = 80 \ \Omega + 120 \ \Omega$$

$$R_B = 200 \ \Omega$$

Now, determine the equivalent resistance of the parallel network made up of R_B and R_4 as shown in Figure 3-12C. This time you use the equation for resistors having the same value in parallel. This resistance is called R_C. The resistance is:

$$R_C = \frac{\text{VALUE OF ONE RESISTOR}}{\text{NUMBER OF RESISTORS IN PARALLEL}}$$

$$R_C = \frac{200\ \Omega}{2}$$

$$R_C = 100\ \Omega$$

Finally, you have the circuit shown in Figure 3-12D. R_C is in series with resistors R_5 and R_6. In this simplified form, you use the formula for total resistance in a series circuit to determine total circuit resistance.

$$R_T = R_C + R_5 + R_6$$

$$R_T = 100\ \Omega + 200\ \Omega + 300\ \Omega$$

$$R_t = 600\ \Omega$$

Measuring Resistance

The device that is used to measure resistance is called an **ohmmeter**. If you are working with a meter movement type ohmmeter, the resistance value is read from a scale on the meter's face. A typical ohmmeter scale is shown in Figure 3-13A. Naturally, if you are using a digital ohmmeter, the resistance value is indicated with a numerical display. Most digital displays are similar to the one shown in 3-13B.

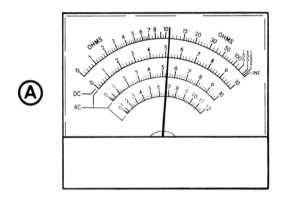

Figure 3-13 Ohmmeter displays.

When using an ohmmeter, resistance is measured simply by connecting the meter probes to either side of the component or components being tested. This is shown in

Figure 3-14. Unlike when using voltmeters and ammeters, the components under test should be removed from the circuit whenever possible. If it is not possible to remove the component from the circuit, you should ensure that power is not applied to the component or circuit under test.

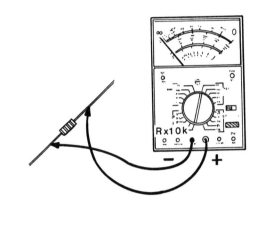

Figure 3-14 Using an ohmmeter.

It is possible to check components other than resistors with an ohmmeter. In fact, an ohmmeter can be used to test almost any component for resistance, as well as shorts or opens.

As you know, everything around you, including the air you breathe has a certain amount of resistance. Conductors pose very little opposition to current flow. Therefore, it is said that conductors have little resistance. Measuring the resistance of a conductor in a circuit, it is often times virtually impossible to obtain a resistance reading. Thus, if you get an extremely high resistance reading when checking the resistance of a conductor it is usually indicative of an electrical problem called an open. That is, at some point the conductor has separated and you are actually measuring the resistance of the air in the space between the conductor ends. For all practical purposes, the air presents an infinite opposition to current flow in this example.

At other times, you will discover an extremely low resistance where you expect to find a relatively high resistance. When this occurs, especially if the resistance is almost 0 ohms, you have probably encountered a short. The short offers almost no opposition to current flow. That is, a short bridges a component or components and provides an alternate current path for circuit current. At any rate, the ohmmeter can be very useful in finding shorts.

This is a brief description of the ohmmeter and its basic function. You will learn more about the ohmmeter when you perform the experiment "Using the Ohmmeter" in your Student Workbook.

Desk-Top Experiment 1
Resistive Circuits

Introduction

This experiment is intended to help you understand and implement the equations and rules governing the determination of total resistance in series, parallel, and series-parallel circuits. This experiment, also builds on the knowledge that you have gained in previous units, and you will be expected to tie together that material with the material presented in Unit 3. Remember this as you perform this experiment because you may find it necessary to reference material from previous units.

Objectives

1. To use specific equations and solve for total resistance in series, parallel, and series-parallel circuits.

2. To determine the effects of shorts and opens on various series and parallel circuits.

Procedure

1. In the space provided, draw a circuit consisting of a 5 V battery connected in series with two 1000 Ω resistors. Design the circuit so that the current flows in a counterclockwise direction through the circuit and use a switch as a control. Label the switch and resistors using appropriate designations.

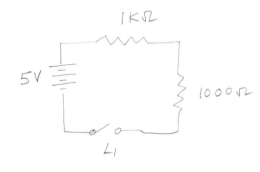

2. What is the total resistance of this circuit?

    _____2K_____ Ω

3. With the switch closed, the voltage drop across each resistor is:

    _____2.5_____ V.

4. What is the approximate resistance of the switch when it is closed?

    _____0_____ Ω

5. What is the approximate resistance of the switch when it is open?

    _____1 M_____ Ω

6. If a short occurs across one of the resistors, what is the measurable resistance of the circuit?

    _____1000_____ Ω

Discussion

In a series circuit, the total resistance of the circuit is determined by adding the value of the individual resistances in the circuit. Thus, the resistance of the circuit is 2 kΩ. As you know from Unit 2, all voltage applied to a circuit will be dropped at some point in the circuit. Since both resistors are of equal resistance, 2.5 V is dropped across each resistor.

When the switch is open it acts exactly like an open in the circuit. It prevents current from flowing in the circuit. Therefore, the resistance of an open switch is considered to be infinite. Conversely, when a switch is closed it acts as a short and does not interfere with current flow through a circuit. The resistance measurement across a closed switch is approximately 0 ohms. Finally, if a short develops across one of the resistors in the circuit, the resistor is effectively removed from the circuit. This means that the measured resistance of the circuit will be 1000Ω.

Procedure (Cont'd)

7. If an ohmmeter is connected to points A and B in Figure 3-15, what value will the ohmmeter indicate?

    _____0.5 K_____ Ω

8. If resistor R_1 opened, the resistance of the circuit (increase/decreases).

9. With R_1 open, what is the resistance of the circuit?

    _____1K_____ Ω

10. If R_2 shorted the resistance of the circuit (increases/decreases).

11. What is the resistance of the circuit with R_2 shorted?

    _____0_____ Ω

Discussion

You can use any of the parallel circuit equations to solve the circuit shown in Figure 3-15. No matter what method you use, the total resistance of the circuit is 500 Ω. Opening any resistor in the circuit is the same as removing that resistor from the circuit. Therefore, if resistor R_1 is open, the resistance of the circuit will increase. On the other hand, shorting across any resistor in a parallel circuit will, in effect, bypass the entire circuit. Thus, a short across R_2 removes the entire branch from the circuit. This results in a resistance measurement of 0 ohms across the branch.

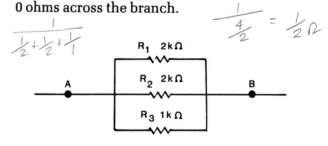

Figure 3-15 A typical parallel resistive circuit.

Procedure (Con't)

12. In the circuit shown in Figure 3-16, what is the resistance measured between points A and B?

    _____500_____ Ω

13. What is the total resistance of the circuit shown in Figure 3-16?

    _____1K_____ Ω

14. If a short develops across resistor R_1, what is the total resistance of the circuit?

    _____500_____ Ω

15. If R_1 is open, what is the total resistance of the circuit?

    _____1500_____ Ω

16. If resistor R_3 is open, what is the resistance measured between points A and C?

    _____Infinite_____ Ω

17. What is the resistance measured between points A and C if a short develops across resistor R_3?

    _____500_____ Ω

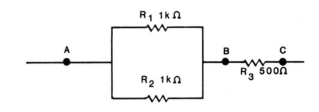

Figure 3-16 A series parallel circuit.

Discussion

The resistance of the circuit shown in Figure 3-16 is the sum of the resistance of the parallel branch made up of resistors R_1 and R_2 and the series resistor R_3. The resistance is 1 kΩ. In effect shorting across resistor R_1 removes the parallel branch from the circuit. This leaves the resistance of R_3 as the only measurable resistance between points A and C. On the other hand, opening R_1 removes it from the circuit. In this case, the resistance of the circuit increases because it is now made up of resistor R_2 in series with resistor R_3. If you open resistor R_3, the total resistance of the circuit becomes infinite.

Since all of the current through the circuit must travel through R_3, an open at this point is measured and results in an open of the entire circuit. Finally, if resistor R_3 is shorted, the resistance of the circuit is the resistance of the parallel branch consisting of resistors R_1 and R_2. Thus, there is a decrease in overall circuit resistance.

23. In order to determine the total resistance of the circuit shown in Figure 3-17, you must first calculate the effective resistance, R_A, of the branch made up of resistors _____$R4$_____, _____$R5$_____, and _____$R6$_____.

24. R_A equals _____5_____ Ω.

25. To further simplify the equation you next add the values of resistors _____$R7$_____, _____RA_____, and _____$R3$_____, to find R_B.

26. R_B is equal to _____50_____ Ω.

27. Substituting R_B into the circuit, you now solve for the parallel branch, R_C, using the equation _____'_____.

$$\frac{50}{2}$$

28. R_C is equal to _____25_____ Ω.

29. Finally, R_T is equal to _____75_____ Ω.

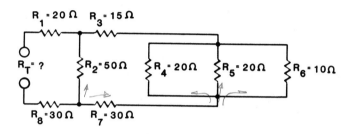

Figure 3-17 Circuit for problems 23-29.

$$\frac{1}{\frac{1}{20}+\frac{1}{20}+\frac{1}{10}}$$

$$\frac{2}{20}+\frac{2}{20}=\frac{4}{20}$$

$$=\frac{20}{4}=5$$

Summary

The following is a point to point summary of Unit 3.

Resistance is the opposition to current flow. All materials offer some opposition to current flow although some materials are more resistive than others.

The unit of measurement of resistance is the ohm. The ohm can be expressed in terms of voltage and current. It is equal to the amount of resistance which will allow one ampere of current to flow when an emf or 1 volt is applied. The Greek letter omega, Ω, is the symbol used to represent the ohm.

Resistivity is defined as the resistance of a one mil-foot length of a material at 20 degrees centigrade. A mil-foot is a one foot length of wire which is one thousandth of an inch in diameter. The resistivity determines if a material is an insulator or a conductor.

Most metals have a very low resistivity and are, therefore, good conductors. Some examples are silver, copper, aluminum, nickel, iron, lead, and gold. Other materials have values or resistivity billions of times higher than those of metals. These materials are good insulators. Examples are glass, rubber, mica, and plastics.

The resistance of a material is determined not only by its resistivity but also by its size and shape. The resistance of a conductor is directly proportional to the length of the conductor and inversely proportional to its cross sectional area.

Temperature also affects resistance to some extent. If the resistance of a material increases with temperature, the substance is said to have a positive temperature coefficient. If the resistance decreases with temperature the substance is said to have a negative temperature coefficient.

There are three popular types of fixed resistors. These are: carbon-composition, wire-wound, and deposited-film. Wire-wound resistors generally have relatively low resistance values but they can have high power ratings. Deposited-film resistors are the most common type of resistors in use today. They can be made more precise than composition resistors and they are cheaper than wire-wound resistors.

The resistance, tolerance, and wattage of most resistors can be determined by physical examination of the resistor. With many wire-wound resistors, this information is written on the body of the resistor. With the composition and film resistors, the resistance and tolerance are indicated by color bands. The wattage rating is indicated by the physical size of the resistor.

Not all resistors have a fixed value; some are variable. A resistor whose value can be changed is called a potentiometer if it has three terminals, or a rheostat if it has only two terminals.

Resistors can be connected in series, in parallel, or in series parallel combinations.

When connected in series their resistance values add. Thus, if two 1000 Ω resistors are connected in series, the total resistance is 2000 Ω.

When resistors are connected in parallel, the total resistance decreases. This occurs because the resistors connected in parallel offer additional current paths in the circuit. Since more current can flow through these paths, the effect on the circuit is a decrease in total resistance. Thus, if two 1000 Ω resistors are connected in parallel, the total resistance becomes 500 Ω.

The device used for measuring resistance is the ohmmeter. Most ohmmeters have a nonlinear scale with 0 at one end and infinity at the other. A range switch is provided so that a wide range of resistance values can be accurately measured. A zero adjust is also included on most meters. This control must be readjusted each time the range is changed.

All electronic components have some resistance value. The light bulb works only because of the resistance of its filament. It is the current forced through this resistance that produces the heat which causes the filament to glow. The fuse is another example. Here a fragile length of resistance wire is designed to burn in two when the current rating is exceeded.

The thermistor is a special type of resistor whose resistance value changes with temperature. The light dependent resistor, or photoconductive cell, is a resistor whose value changes when exposed to light. Both of these devices are used as control elements in electronic circuits.

Unit 4
OHM'S LAW

Contents

Introduction

Ohm's law is the most important and basic law of electricity and electronics. It defines the relationship between the three fundamental electrical quantities: current, voltage, and resistance. Fortunately, the relationship between these three quantities is quite simple. Several implications of this relationship have already been discussed in the previous units. Therefore, some of the information presented in this unit will not be entirely new to you.

When you have completed this unit, you will be able to:

1. Define the following terms: power, watt, dissipation, and horsepower.

2. State Ohm's law.

3. Depending on the unknown quantity, use one of the three power equations to determine the power dissipated in a circuit.

4. Select the proper equation and calculate the current in any simple circuit in which two of the following quantities are known: voltage, resistance, power.

5. Select the proper equation and calculate the voltage in any simple circuit in which two of the following quantities are known: current, resistance, power.

6. Select the proper equation and calculate the resistance of simple circuit in which two of the following quantities are known: voltage, current, power.

7. Select the proper equation and calculate the power dissipated in any simple circuit in which two of the following are known: voltage, current, resistance.

8. Describe how a voltmeter can be used to measure current.

9. State the three equation forms of Ohm's law.

Ohm's Law

Ohm's law defines the way in which current, voltage, and resistance are related. You examined this relationship to some extent in the previous units. Now, you will examine it more closely and in a systematic way.

Determining Current

Ohm's law states that **current is directly proportional to voltage and inversely proportional to resistance**. Figure 4-1A helps illustrate this point. The voltage source is the battery. As you know, voltage is the force that causes current to flow. Therefore, the higher the voltage applied to the circuit, the higher the current through the circuit. Conversely, a decrease in the applied voltage will result in a decrease in circuit current. This assumes that the circuit resistance, or opposition to current flow, remains constant.

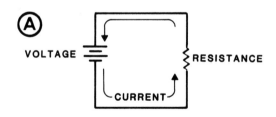

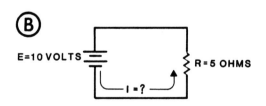

Figure 4-1 Current is determined by voltage and resistance.

However, the amount of current through a circuit is also determined by the resistance of the circuit. As you know, resistance is the opposition to current flow. Assuming that the voltage is constant, an increase in resistance results in a decrease in current flow. On the other hand, lowering the resistance brings an increase in current.

These facts can be summarized by a single formula:

$$current = \frac{voltage}{resistance}$$

Or, stated in terms of the units of current, voltage, and resistance:

$$amperes = \frac{volts}{ohms}$$

When used in formulas, letters of the alphabet can be used to represent current, voltage, and resistance. Resistance is represented by the letter R. Voltage may be represented either by the letter V (for voltage) or the letter E (for EMF). In this course, the letter E is used to represent EMF or voltage. Current is represented by the letter I. While this may seem a little illogical, this convention is used throughout electronics. If you substitute the letters I, E, and R for the quantities current, voltage, and resistance respectively, the formula for current becomes:

$$I = \frac{E}{R}$$

The formula may be used to find current in any circuit in which the voltage and resistance are known.

Figure 4-1B shows a circuit in which the values of voltage and resistance are given. To determine the current you substitute the known values into the formula:

$$I = \frac{E}{R}$$

$$I = \frac{10\ V}{5\ \Omega}$$

$$I = 2A$$

Notice that dividing 5 Ω into 10 V gives you the final answer of 2 A. Anytime you divide ohms into volts the answer is expressed in amperes. Thus, the current in the circuit shown in Figure 4-1B is 2 amperes.

Figure 4-2A shows another circuit in which the quantities E and R are given. Solving for I, you find that the current is:

$$I = \frac{E}{R}$$

$$I = \frac{200\ V}{50\ \Omega}$$

$$I = 4A$$

Look what happens to the current if you double the applied voltage as shown in Figure 4-2B.

$$I = \frac{E}{R}$$

$$I = \frac{400\ V}{50\ \Omega}$$

$$I = 8A$$

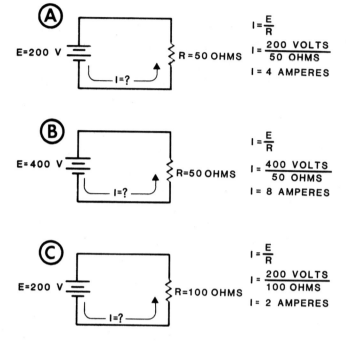

Figure 4-2 Current is directly proportional to voltage and inversely proportional to resistance.

Notice that when the voltage is doubled, the current also doubles. You should expect this because the change current is **directly proportional** to the change voltage.

Return to Figure 4-2A. What happens if you double the resistance and hold the voltage constant? This situation is shown in Figure 4-2C. The current becomes:

$$I = \frac{E}{R}$$

$$I = \frac{200\ V}{100\ \Omega}$$

$$I = 2A$$

Thus, when you double the resistance, the current is reduced to one-half its former value. Again, you should expect this since current is **inversely proportional** to resistance. That is, as the resistance increases, the current decreases.

Consider another example. How much current flows through a 3 kΩ resistor when it is connected across a 9 V battery?

The easiest way to solve this problem is to convert 3 kΩ to 3000 Ω. Thus:

$$I = \frac{E}{R}$$

$$I = \frac{9\,V}{3000\,\Omega}$$

$$I = .003\,A$$

You will recall that 0.003 amperes is another way of saying 3 milliamperes or 3 mA. Because resistance values are often given in kilohms, it is convenient to be able to work problems without converting kilohms to ohms. In current problems, when volts are divided by kilohms, the result is expressed in milliamperes.

For example, how much current flows when a lamp with a resistance of 2.4 kΩ is connected across a 120 V line? The current in milliamperes is:

$$I = \frac{E}{R}$$

$$I = \frac{120\,V}{2.4\,k\Omega}$$

$$I = 50\,mA$$

You can check this by converting 2.4 kΩ to 2400 ohms and solving as you did earlier:

$$I = \frac{E}{R}$$

$$I = \frac{120\,V}{2400\,\Omega}$$

$$I = .05\,A$$

Remember that 0.05 A is the same as 50 mA.

Resistance is often given in megohms or MΩ. For example, what is the current when a 5 MΩ resistor is connected across a 25 V battery? You can convert 5 MΩ to 5,000,000 Ω and solve for current in amperes:

$$I = \frac{E}{R}$$

$$I = \frac{25\,V}{5,000,000\,\Omega}$$

$$I = 0.000005\,A$$

This is 5 microamperes or 5 μA. Thus, when you divide volts by megohms the answer is in microamperes. That is:

$$I = \frac{E}{R}$$

$$I = \frac{25\,V}{5\,M\Omega}$$

$$I = 5\,\mu A$$

To summarize, the basic formula for current is:

$$I = \frac{E}{R}$$

If R is given in ohms, you can think of the equation as:

$$\text{amperes} = \frac{\text{volts}}{\text{ohms}}$$

However, if R is given in kilohms, you should think of the equation as:

$$\text{milliamperes} = \frac{\text{volts}}{\text{kilohms}}$$

Finally, if R is given in megohms, we can think of the equation as:

$$\text{microamperes} = \frac{\text{volts}}{\text{megohms}}$$

Finding Voltage

You have seen that the formula for current is:

$$I = \frac{E}{R}$$

By **transposing** this equation, you can develop a formula for voltage. Transposing simply means changing the equation from one form to another. Since you are interested in finding voltage, you must change the formula so that E is on one side of the equation by itself. This is easy to do if you remember a basic algebra rule for transposing equations. The rule states that you can multiply or divide both sides of the equation by any quantity without changing the equality. The current equation is:

$$I = \frac{E}{R}$$

Multiplying both sides by R you have:

$$I \times R = \frac{E \times R}{R}$$

Notice that R appears in both the numerator and the denominator of the fraction on the right side of the equation. You will recall from basic mathematics that the two R's in the fraction can be cancelled like this:

$$I \times R = \frac{E \times \cancel{R}}{\cancel{R}}$$

This leaves:

$$I \times R = E$$

You can reverse the position of the two sides of the equation without changing the equality. Reversing the position, you find the basic equation for voltage:

$$E = I \times R$$

In other words, voltage is equal to current times resistance. Generally, the times sign (×) is omitted so that the formula is written:

$$E = IR$$

Figure 4-3A shows a circuit in which the resistance and current are known. To find the voltage:

$$E = IR$$

$$E = 0.5 \text{ A} \times 125 \text{ }\Omega$$

$$E = 62.5 \text{ V}$$

$$R_T = 1.2 \text{ k}\Omega + 3.3 \text{ k}\Omega$$

$$R_T = 4.5 \text{ k}\Omega$$

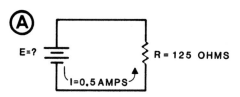

Notice that multiplying amperes times ohms results in an answer given in volts.

Figure 4-3B shows a slightly different problem. Here, you want to find the voltage drop across R_1. This voltage is represented as E_{R_1}. You know from the information given in the Figure that R_1 is 20 Ω and that the current through R_1 is 2 A. Consequently, the voltage drop across R_1 is:

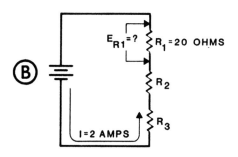

$$E_{R_1} = I \times R_1$$

$$E_{R_1} = 2 \text{ A} \times 20 \text{ }\Omega$$

$$E_{R_1} = 40 \text{ volts}$$

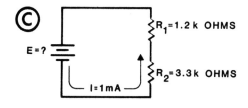

In Figure 4-3C, the values of the resistors in the circuit as well as the amount of circuit current are given. Here, you want to determine the battery, or source, voltage. To find the battery voltage you must multiply the total resistance (R_T) times the current. This is done because in a series circuit all of the current flows through each individual resistor. The total resistance is calculated by adding the two series resistances. Thus:

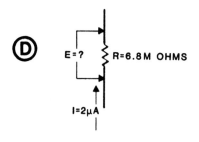

Figure 4-3 Finding voltage.

$$R_T = R_1 + R_2$$

Once you know the total resistance, it is easy to compute the voltage using the Ohm's Law formula. Thus:

$$E = I \times R_T$$

$$E = 1\,mA \times 4.5\,k\Omega$$

$$E = 4.5\,V$$

Figure 4-3D shows a partial schematic in which the resistance is given in megohms, the current is given in microamperes, and the voltage drop is unknown. In order to find the voltage drop across R, simply multiply:

$$E = I \times R$$

$$E = 2\,\mu A \times 6.8\,M\Omega$$

$$E = 13.6\,V$$

Finding Resistance

You can transpose the current formula or the voltage formula to get a resistance formula. For example, the voltage formula is:

$$E = IR$$

Dividing both sides by I, you get:

$$\frac{E}{I} = \frac{IR}{I}$$

The I's in the fraction on the right cancel:

$$\frac{E}{I} = \frac{\cancel{I}R}{\cancel{I}}$$

So the formula becomes:

$$\frac{E}{I} = R$$

By changing the position of the terms in the resistance formula you get:

$$R = \frac{E}{I}$$

This indicates that resistance is equal to voltage divided by current or:

$$ohms = \frac{volts}{amperes}$$

Using this formula, you can find the resistance in any circuit in which the voltage and current are known. Figure 4-4A shows such a circuit. Solving for R, you find that:

$$R = \frac{E}{I}$$

$$R = \frac{24\,V}{4.8\,A}$$

$$R = 5\,\Omega$$

Figure 4-4B shows another example. Here the current is given in milliamperes while the EMF is expressed in volts. When milliamperes are divided into volts the answer is given in kilohms. Thus:

$$R = \frac{E}{I}$$

$$R = \frac{15\ V}{5\ mA}$$

$$R = 3\ k\Omega$$

This can be easily proven by converting 5 mA to 0.005 A and solving for R:

$$R = \frac{E}{I}$$

$$R = \frac{15\ V}{0.005\ A}$$

$$R = 3000\ \Omega$$

Finally, in Figure 4-4C, you must find the value of the resistance that drops 6 V when the current is 2 μA. When microamps are divided into volts the result is given in megohms. Thus:

$$R = \frac{E}{I}$$

$$R = \frac{6V}{2\ \mu A}$$

$$R = 3\ M\Omega$$

Once again this can be proven by converting 2 μA to 0.000 002 A and dividing:

$$R = \frac{E}{I}$$

$$R = \frac{6V}{0.000\ 002A}$$

$$R = 3,000,000\ \Omega$$

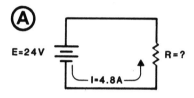

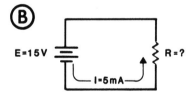

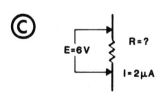

Figure 4-4 Finding resistance.

Summary (Ohm's Law)

Ohm's law may be expressed by three different formulas:

$$I = \frac{E}{R}$$

$$E = IR$$

$$R = \frac{E}{I}$$

In Figure 4-5A the three quantities are placed in a diagram in a way that may help you to remember these three equations. To use the diagram, cover the quantity for which you wish to find the equation. For example, in Figure 4-5B you cover the quantity I because you want to find current. The remaining two symbols represent the formula used to find the unknown. Notice that the remaining quantities are:

$$\frac{E}{R}$$

Hence:

$$I = \frac{E}{R}$$

Figures 4-5C and D show how to find the formulas for resistance and voltage.

A few other equally handy diagrams are shown in Figure 4-6. These diagrams are variations of the diagrams presented in Figure 4-5. They indicate how the quantities are grouped with and without metric prefixes. In Figure 4-6A no metric prefixes are used with any of the quantities. In any Ohm's law problem, if two of the quantities are given in the units shown in Figure 4-6A then the third quantity is given in the third unit. For example, if resistance is given in ohms while voltage is given in volts, then current will be in amperes.

In Figure 4-6B, EMF is still given in volts. However, current is given in milliamperes while resistance is given in kilohms. It is important to remember that these three quantities go together. This will help you to check problems as you solve them. Thus, if resistance is given in kilohms while EMF is given in volts, the current will be in milliamperes. Or, if current is in milliamperes while resistance is in kilohms, the resulting EMF is in volts.

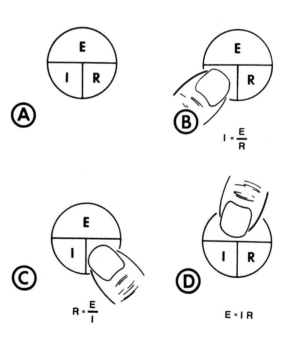

Figure 4-5 The three forms of Ohm's Law.

Figure 4-6C shows that a similar relationship exists between volts, microamps, and megohms. For example, if EMF is given in volts and current is given in microamperes, resistance is in megohms.

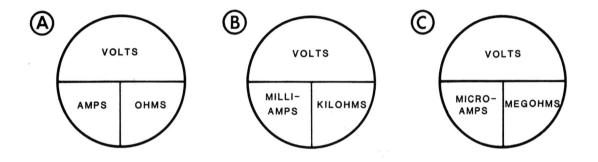

Figure 4-6 How the metric prefixes are related.

$$E = IR$$
$$I = \frac{E}{R}$$
$$R = \frac{E}{I}$$

Desk-Top Experiment 2
Ohm's Law

Introduction

The purpose of this experiment is to increase your understanding of Ohm's Law as it applies to series and parallel circuits. You will be presented with a number of circuits and, given two quantities, be expected to determine the third. You will use Ohm's Law in concert with the rules that you learned in the first three units to thoroughly analyze the circuits in this experiment.

Kirchhoff's

Objectives

1. To implement Ohm's Law and solve for the unknown quantities in a series circuit.

2. To determine the unknown quantities in a parallel circuit.

3. To analyze a series-parallel circuit.

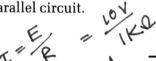

$$I = \frac{E}{R} = \frac{10V}{1K\Omega} = 10mA$$

Procedure

1. Determine the current through the series resistive circuit shown in Figure 4-7.

   $$I = \underline{\quad 10m \quad} \text{ A.}$$

2. Using the current value calculated in step 1, determine the voltage drop across resistors R_1, R_2, and R_3.

   $$E_{R_1} = \underline{\quad 1 \quad} \text{ V.}$$

$$10mA \times 100\Omega = 10^3 mV$$

$$E_{R_2} = \underline{\quad 4 \quad} \text{ V.}$$

$$E_{R_3} = \underline{\quad 5 \quad} \text{ V.}$$

3. Add the three voltages calculated in step 2 together. Does the sum of these three voltages equal the applied voltage?

   $$\underline{\quad Yes \quad}$$

4. What law does the results achieved in step 3 confirm?

   $$\underline{Kirchoff's \ Law}$$
   Ohm's

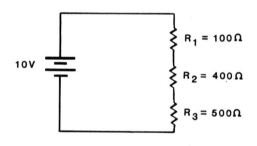

Figure 4-7 A series resistive circuit.

Discussion

When using the Ohm's Law formulas it is necessary to know two quantities in order to determine the third. In order to calculate the circuit current, you must first determine the total circuit resistance, R_T. Once you know this, substituting the correct values into the current formula you find that the circuit current is 10 mA.

In step 2 you once again use Ohm's Law. However, this time you used the voltage formula to calculate the voltage drop across the three resistors in the circuit. When this was done you added these voltages and found that their total equaled the applied voltage. This confirms Kirchhoff's Voltage Law. In any circuit, the sum of the voltage rises will equal the sum of the voltage drops.

Procedure (Cont.)

5. Look at the series circuit shown in Figure 4-8. Here you are given the value of R_2, the voltage drop across R_1, circuit current, and applied voltage. Determine the value of resistors R_1 and R_3.

$R_1 = \underline{\quad 100 \quad}$ Ω.

$R_3 = \underline{\quad 3K \quad}$ Ω. *[handwritten: 300, 3K crossed out]*

[handwritten: $E = IR$]

[handwritten: $\dfrac{6V}{20mA} = 3K\Omega$ $R = \dfrac{V}{I}$ $V_{R_2} = IR$ $= 20mA \cdot 100\Omega$ $2V$]

[circuit diagram labels: 10V, $E_{R_1} = 2V$, $R_1 = ?$, $R_2 = 100\Omega$, $R_3 = ?$, 20mA]

[handwritten near diagram: $2V$ 100Ω, 500Ω crossed out, $6V$, 300Ω]

[handwritten: $R_T = \dfrac{10V}{20mA}$]

[handwritten: $.5K\Omega$ 500Ω]

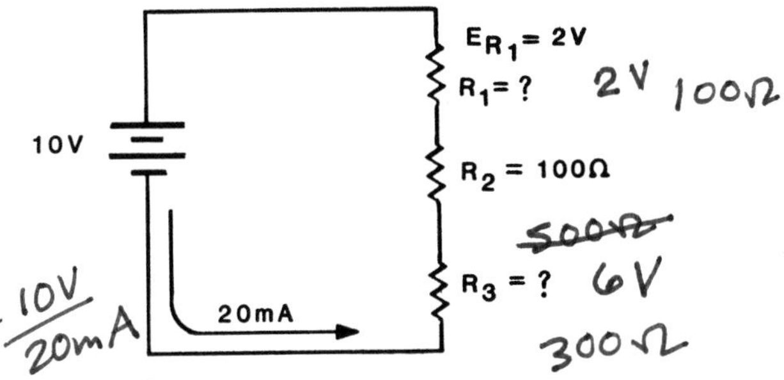

Figure 4-8 Determine the unknown resistance.

[handwritten: $\dfrac{6V}{20mA} = .3K\Omega$]

Discussion

You can begin to solve this problem either by determining the resistance of R_1 or R_3. It is a relatively easy matter to determine the resistance of R_1. Just substitute the known values into the Ohm's Law formula. With E_R at 2 V and I at 20 mA, the value of R_1 is 100 Ω.

Calculating the resistance of R_1 is relatively straight forward. However, finding the value of R_3 requires a bit of thought. You know from your study of resistance in Unit 3 that resistance in a series circuit is additive. That is, the total resistance of a series circuit is equal to the sum of the individual resistors in the circuit. It stands to reason, that if you know the total resistance and the values of two of the resistors in the circuit then you can determine the unknown resistance R_3 using the variation of the resistance formula:

$$R_3 = R_T - (R_1 + R_2)$$

To use this formula, however, you must know the value of R_T. Here again, you use the Ohm's Law formula for resistance with the known circuit current value, 20 mA, and the applied voltage, 10 V.

Once the total circuit resistance is determined, it is a matter of simple subtraction to determine the value of R_3.

Procedure (Cont.)

6. Figure 4-9 is an elementary parallel circuit. It is drawn somewhat different than you are accustomed to seeing. In this case, the positive side of the power supply is shown at the left-hand side of the schematic while the ground is shown on the right. Current flow in this instance is from right to left as indicated by the arrow under R_3. At any rate, the values of the three resistors in the circuit are given as well as the current through R_3. Using Ohm's Law, determine the applied voltage, total current, and the current through R_1 and R_2.

E = ___~~250m~~ 1~~ V.

I_T = ___4___ mA.

I_{R_1} = ___1___ mA.

I_{R_2} = ___2___ mA.

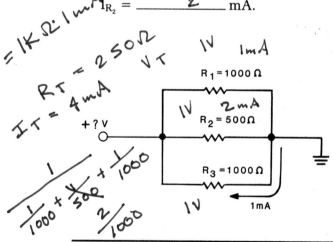

(handwritten annotations around figure:)
I_T
$\frac{1V}{250\Omega}$
4 mA
$V = 1K\Omega \cdot 1mA$
$R_T = 250\Omega$ V_T
$I_T = 4mA$
$+?V$
$\frac{1}{\frac{1}{1000}+\frac{1}{500}+\frac{1}{1000}}$
$\frac{2}{1000}$

(figure labels:)
1V 1mA
$R_1 = 1000\Omega$
1V 2mA $R_2 = 500\Omega$
$R_3 = 1000\Omega$
1V 1mA

Figure 4-9 Solve for total current and applied voltage.

(handwritten below:)
$\frac{1}{\frac{4}{1000}} = \frac{1000}{4} = 250\Omega$

(handwritten:)
$V = IR$
$= 1mA \cdot 250\Omega$
$= 250 mV$

Discussion

As you know, in a parallel circuit the voltage is constant. Therefore, if you can determine the voltage across any resistor in Figure 4-9, you can determine the voltage dropped across the parallel branch. Since both the value of R_3 and the current through R_3 is known, it is a simple matter to find the voltage drop across R_3. The voltage dropped across R_3 is also the applied voltage in the case of this basic parallel circuit.

I_T can be determined in two ways. From your study of current in Unit 1, you know that current in a parallel is additive. You can determine the total current by calculating the current through each resistor and then adding these values. Since I_{R_1} and I_{R_2} are also asked for, this way will save you a few steps.

However, you can also calculate the total current by dividing the applied voltage by R_T. In this case it is first necessary to use the equations you learned in Unit 3 to determine the total resistance. Now you can use Ohm's Law to calculate I_T. In both cases, I_T is 4 mA.

In the next section of this experiment, you will analyze a series-parallel circuit. It is somewhat more complex than the circuits with which you have already worked. The easiest, and most reliable, way to determine the unknown values in this or any other circuit is to pick a starting point and then determine everything that you can about the individual components. If you become stuck at any point, move on to another component.

Procedure (Cont.)

7. Determine all of the unknown voltage, current, and resistance values for the circuit shown in Figure 4-10. The following lists all of the known and unknown values. Fill in the appropriate blanks. *1.5*

E_A = ___~~1.5~~__ V. R_3 = 500 Ω.

I_T = __1 m__ A. E_{R_3} = __250 m__ V.

R_T = __1500__ Ω. I_{R_3} = __.5m__ ~~250~~ A.

R_1 = 1000 Ω. R_4 = __500__ Ω.

E_{R_1} = __1__ V. E_{R_4} = __250 m__ V.

I_{R_1} = 1 mA. I_{R_4} = __.5m__ A.

R_2 = 1000 Ω.

E_{R_2} = .5 V.

I_{R_2} = __.5 m__ A.

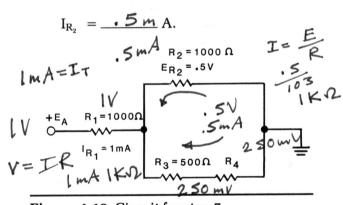

.5mA R_2 = 1000 Ω $I = \dfrac{E}{R}$
1mA = I_T E_{R_2} = .5V
$\dfrac{.5}{10^3}$
1V   *.5V*   *1KΩ*
1V +E_A R_1 = 1000Ω   *.5mA*
$V = IR$ I_{R_1} = 1mA   *250mV*
1mA 1KΩ R_3 = 500Ω R_4
250 mV

Figure 4-10 Circuit for step 7.

Discussion

$V = .5mA$ 500Ω
250 mV

I_T is actually given in the circuit diagram.

1KΩ

1KΩ

1KΩ

It is the same as I_{R_1} since R_1 is a resistor that is in series with the rest of the circuit.

In the circuit shown in Figure 4-10, there are two possible starting points, R_1 or R_2, since two quantities are given for each of these resistors. In either case, the unknown values E_{R_1} and I_{R_2} are determined by using the appropriate Ohm's Law formulas.

Once you have determined the current through R_2, you use your knowledge of current behavior in parallel circuits to determine the current through resistors R_3 and R_4. Once the current is known, simply apply Ohm's Law to R_3 and determine the voltage drop across this resistor.

The final resistor, R_4, poses no problem once all of the other values in the parallel branch are known. Since you already know E_{R_3}, your understanding of voltage in series and parallel circuits will enable you to determine E_{R_4}. From this point, it is simply apply Ohm's Law to find the resistance of R_4. $E = I \cdot R$

Once you have determined the unknown values for the individual components, you can apply the rules for resistive circuits to calculate R_T which is 1.5 kΩ and the rules for voltage in series and parallel circuits to find E_A, 1.5 V.

Incidentally, when you do a problem of this type always check your answers. To do this, take the unknown values that you have found and put them in the Ohm's Law formulas. If the answers that you get from this procedure match the given values, then your calculations are probably correct.

Summary

Although Ohm's Law is in itself a powerful tool to be used in analyzing circuits, it becomes much more valuable when combined with other rules governing the behavior of voltage, current, and resistance in the circuit. In each section of this experiment, you applied variations of the Ohm's Law formula to determine different circuit unknowns. However, in each instance it was demonstrated that an understanding of current, voltage, and resistance rules was also necessary to completely understand the circuits.

Remember that Ohm's Law can be applied either to entire circuits or individual components within the circuits. When combined with other rules, it becomes easy to analyze DC circuits.

$E = IR$

1. Ohm's law defines the relationship between the three fundamental electrical quantities:

    __V__ , __I__ , and __R__ .

2. The Ohm's Law formula for current is

    $$I = \frac{E}{R}$$.

3. Using this formula, determine how much current flows through a 10 Ω resistor when 5 V are applied?

    __.5 A__ .

4. When the EMF is given in volts and the resistance is given in kilohms, then the current is in:

    __mA__

5. If the EMF is given in volts and the resistance is given in megohms, then the current is in:

    __μA__

6. According to Ohm's Law:

    E = __IR__ .

7. Using Ohm's Law, calculate the voltage drop across a 120 Ω resistor when the current through the resistor is 0.5 A.

    __60 V__

    $V = IR$

    $0.5 A \cdot 120 \Omega$

8. When current is in microamperes, resistance is in:

    __MΩ__

9. Ohm's Law formula used to determine resistance is:

    $$R = \frac{E}{I}$$.

10. What value resistor develops a voltage drop of 12 volts when a current of 0.75 amperes flows through it?

    __16__ Ω.

    $$R = \frac{12 V}{0.75 A}$$

11. If resistance is given in megohms and the EMF is given in volts, the current will be in:

    __μA__

    $$V = \frac{R}{I}$$

$$\frac{1200}{75} \qquad 12 \times 75$$

$$\begin{array}{r} 750 \\ 150 \\ \hline 900 \end{array}$$

$$\frac{300}{75} \qquad 4 \times 75 \qquad \begin{array}{r} 280 \\ 20 \\ \hline 300 \end{array}$$

In addition to the three basic electrical quantities (current, voltage, and resistance), there is a fourth quantity. This quantity is called power. **Power** is defined as the rate at which work is done. In other words, power refers to the amount of work done in a specific length of time. The use or loss of power in a circuit is called **dissipation**.

Work and Power

In an earlier unit, you learned that a joule is equal to the amount of work done by one volt of EMF in moving one coulomb of charge. Notice that time does not enter into this definition. Thus, the same amount of work is done whether the charge is moved in one second or in one hour.

Unlike work, power is related to time. Therefore, power is the measure of joules of work per unit of time. The unit of power is the **watt**. It is named in honor of James Watt who pioneered the development of the steam engine. The watt is equal to one joule per second. When you think of the power used by a circuit, it is in terms of the number of watts dissipated by the circuit.

The English unit of work (the foot-pound) is easier to visualize than the joule. If one pound is lifted a vertical distance of one foot then one foot-pound of work is done. The joule is equal to 0.738 foot-pounds. Therefore, the watt is equal to 0.738 foot-pounds of work per second.

The unit of mechanical power in the English system is the horsepower. One horsepower is equal to 550 foot-pounds per second. In other words, if 550 pounds are raised one foot in one second then one horsepower is expended. In terms of watts, the horsepower is equal to 746 watts. Or, stated another way, the watt is equal to 1/746 or 0.00134 horsepower.

Power, Current, and Voltage

You have learned that the watt is equal to one joule per second. That is, the watt is the work done in one second by one volt of EMF in moving one coulomb of charge. If one coulomb of charge flows in one second then the current is one ampere. Thus, one watt is the amount of power used in a circuit when one ampere of current flows as the result of one volt of applied EMF.

Power is directly proportional to both current and voltage. The formula for power is:

$$power = current \times voltage$$

Or, stated in terms of the units of the three quantities:

$$watts = amperes \times volts$$

The symbol P is used to represent power in equations. Thus, the formula for power is:

$$P = IE$$

As with Ohm's law, there are two other useful forms of this equation. The first expresses voltage in terms of current and power. It is found by rearranging the equation:

$$P = IE$$

Dividing both sides by I:

$$\frac{P}{I} = \frac{IE}{I}$$

Cancelling the two I's on the right side:

$$\frac{P}{I} = \frac{\cancel{I}E}{\cancel{I}}$$

Changing the position of the terms on both sides of the equation:

$$E = \frac{P}{I}$$

This states that voltage (in volts) is equal to power (in watts) divided by current (in amperes).

Another useful form of the equation is:

$$I = \frac{P}{E}$$

See if you can derive this formula from the original power formula given above.

To summarize, power, voltage, and current are related by the following formulas:

$$P = IE$$
$$E = \frac{P}{I}$$

$$I = \frac{P}{E}$$

The following problems show you how to solve for power using the formulas just presented.

What is the power dissipated in a circuit in which an EMF of 50 V is applied and a current of 3.2 A flows?

$$P = IE$$

$$P = 3.2\,A \times 50\,V$$

$$P = 160\,W$$

How much current flows through a 75 W light bulb which is connected across a 120 V power line?

$$I = \frac{P}{E}$$

$$I = \frac{75\,W}{120\,V}$$

$$I = 0.625\,A$$

What is the voltage drop across a light bulb that dissipates 60 W when the current through the bulb is 0.5 A?

$$E = \frac{P}{I}$$

$$E = \frac{60\,W}{0.5\,A}$$

$$E = 120\,V$$

Power Dissipation

In resistors and most other electronic components, power is dissipated in the form of heat. In some cases, this heat is a desired result. For example, the purpose of the resistance element in a toaster, heating pad, and electric stove is to produce heat. However, in most electronic devices, the heat produced by resistors or other components represents wasted power. Remember, all power used in a circuit must be supplied by the power source. This includes the power lost in the heating of resistors or other components. Since power costs money, circuits are designed in such a way as to use the minimum amount of power to perform a task.

Since resistors dissipate power, there must be some formula for power that involves resistance. Actually, there are two such formulas. One expresses power in terms of voltage and resistance. The other expresses power in terms of current and resistance. These equations are derived in the following manner.

First, consider how P can be expressed in terms of E and R. The basic formula for power is:

$$P = I \times E$$

However, from Ohm's law you know that:

$$I = \frac{E}{R}$$

Thus, you can substitute:

$$\frac{E}{R}$$

for I in the basic power equation. When this is done, the equation becomes:

$$P = E \times \frac{E}{R}$$

Or:

$$P = \frac{E^2}{R}$$

This formula is used when you want to find the power but only the voltage and resistance are known. For example, how much power is dissipated by a 22 Ω resistor if the voltage drop across the resistor is 5 V?

$$P = \frac{E^2}{R}$$

$$P = \frac{(5V)^2}{22\,\Omega}$$

$$P = \frac{25\,V}{22\,\Omega}$$

$$P = 1.136\,W$$

How much power is delivered to a 16 Ω circuit by a 12 V battery?

$$P = \frac{E^2}{R}$$

$$P = \frac{(12\,V)^2}{16\,\Omega}$$

$$P = \frac{144\,V}{16\,\Omega}$$

$$P = 9\,W$$

In some cases, only the current and resistance are known. By combining the basic power formula with one of the Ohm's law formulas, you can derive an equation in which P is expressed in terms of I and R. Recall that the basic power formula is:

$$P = I \times E$$

From Ohm's law you know that E = IR. Thus, you can substitute IR for E in the power formula. The equation becomes:

$$P = I \times IR$$

$$P = I^2R$$

This is the formula that you use when you wish to find power and only current and resistance are known. For example, how much power is dissipated by the circuit shown in Figure 4-11A?

$$P = I^2R$$

$$P = (0.5 \text{ A})^2 \times 40 \text{ }\Omega$$

$$P = .25 \text{ A} \times 40 \text{ }\Omega$$

$$P = 10 \text{ W}$$

How much power is dissipated by R_1 in Figure 4-11B?

$$R_1 \quad 2^2 \, 10\Omega$$

$$40W$$

$$P = I^2R_1$$

$$P = (2 \text{ A})^2 \times 10 \text{ }\Omega$$

$$P = 4 \text{ A} \times 10 \text{ }\Omega$$

$$P = 40 \text{ W}$$

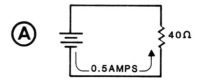

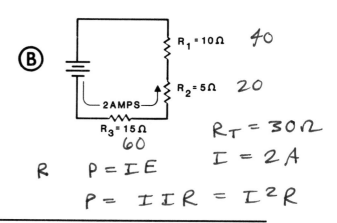

R₁ = 10Ω 40

R₂ = 5Ω 20

R₃ = 15Ω 60

$R_T = 30\Omega$

$I = 2A$

R   P = IE

$P = IIR = I^2R$

Figure 4-11 Finding power when R and I are known.

$$V = IR$$

$$2^2 \, 30 =$$

$$120W$$

Ohm's Law 4-23

You can verify that the above equations are correct by working a sample problem three different ways. For example, consider the circuit shown in Figure 4-12. The current and voltage are given so you can use the formula P = IE to calculate power. Thus:

$$P = IE$$

$$P = 0.5\,A \times 6\,V$$

$$P = 3\,W$$

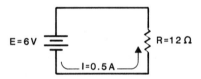

E=6V   R=12Ω
I=0.5A

Figure 4-12 Power can be found using either of the three power formulas.

Or, since voltage and resistance are given, you can use the formula:

$$P = \frac{E^2}{R}$$

$$P = \frac{(6\,V)^2}{12\,\Omega}$$

$$P = \frac{36\,V}{12\,\Omega}$$

$$P = 3W$$

Or, since current and resistance are given, you can use the formula:

$$P = I^2R$$

$$P = (0.5\,A)^2 \times 12\,\Omega$$

$$P = 0.25\,A \times 12\,\Omega$$

$$P = 3W$$

Notice that you get the same result regardless of the power equation that you use.

Deriving More Equations

Earlier you learned that the basic power equation (P = IE) can be rearranged to form current and voltage equations. These are:

$$E = \frac{P}{I}$$

$$I = \frac{P}{E}$$

In much the same way, the equation:

$$P = \frac{E^2}{R}$$

can be arranged to form an equation for voltage. That is:

$$P = \frac{E^2}{R}$$

Multiplying both sides of the equation by R, you find:

$$P \times R = \frac{E^2}{R} \times R$$

The two R's on the right cancel:

$$P \times R = \frac{E^2}{\cancel{R}} \times \cancel{R}$$

Thus:

$$P \times R = E^2$$

Now you can eliminate the exponent by taking the square root of both sides of the equation:

$$\sqrt{P \times R} = \sqrt{E^2}$$

Or:

$$\sqrt{P \times R} = E$$

Notice that this equation expresses voltage in terms of power and resistance.

This equation allows you to solve circuit problems like the one shown in Figure 4-13. Here, the resistance and power are given but the voltage is unknown. The voltage is calculated by:

$$E = \sqrt{PR}$$

$$E = \sqrt{3W \times 1200\,\Omega}$$

$$E = 60\text{ V}$$

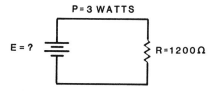

Figure 4-13 Finding voltage when resistance and power are known.

Note: If you are unfamiliar with the technique used to find the square root of a number, refer to Appendix B at the end of this text.

In the same way, the equation $P = I^2R$ can be converted to a current equation. That is:

$$P = I^2R$$

Dividing both terms by R and letting the R's on the right side cancel:

$$\frac{P}{R} = \frac{I^2\cancel{R}}{\cancel{R}}$$

This leaves:

$$\frac{P}{R} = I^2$$

Taking the square root of both terms:

$$\sqrt{\frac{P}{R}} = I$$

Thus, current can be expressed in terms of power and resistance.

By rearranging the equations:

$$P = I^2R$$

and:

$$P = \frac{E^2}{R}$$

equations for R can be obtained. The derivation is left to you but the final equations are:

$$R = \frac{P}{I^2}$$

$$R = \frac{E^2}{P}$$

Twelve very important formulas have been discussed in this unit. Figure 4-14 is a wheel diagram that may help you to remember these equations. The inner circle contains the four basic units: power, current, voltage, and resistance. The outer circle lists the three formulas for determining each quantity. For example, the three formulas for resistance are:

$$R = \frac{E}{I}$$

$$R = \frac{E^2}{P}$$

$$R = \frac{P}{I^2}$$

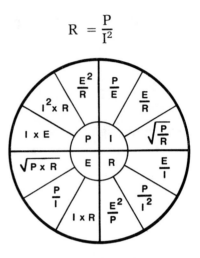

Figure 4-14 Wheel diagram for finding the proper equation for current, voltage, resistance, and power.

Using this diagram, you can quickly find the proper formula for any problem in which two of the quantities are known.

While it is not necessary to memorize these 12 equations, you should memorize the basic Ohm's law and power formulas as soon as possible. That is, you should memorize these two equations:

$$E = IR$$

$$P = IE$$

If you know these two formulas, you can derive any of the other formulas with some mathematical manipulations. Until you become more familiar with these equations, use the diagram shown in Figure 4-14 as an aid.

$$P = IE$$

12. In addition to current, voltage, and resistance, a fourth important electrical quantity is:

    $\underline{\quad Power \quad}$

13. Power is a measure of $\underline{\quad Joules \quad}$ per second.

14. The unit of power that is equal to work accomplished at a rate of 1 joule per second is called a:

    $\underline{\quad Watt \quad}$

15. One horsepower is equal to:

    $\underline{\quad 746 \quad}$ watts.

16. The formula that indicates that power is directly proportional to both current and voltage is:

    $\underline{\quad P = IE \quad}$

17. How much power is dissipated by a resistor which drops 3.2 V when a current of 0.75 A flows through it?

    $\underline{\quad 2.4 \quad}$ watts.

    $$P = IE$$
    $$E = IR$$

    $.03 \times 4$
    $= 1.2 \quad .12$

18. The basic power formula expressed in terms of power and voltage becomes:

    $$I = \frac{P}{E}.$$

19. Voltage can be expressed in terms of power and current as:

    $$E = \frac{P}{I}.$$

20. In a problem in which I and R are known but P is unknown, the proper equation for finding P is:

    $$P = \frac{I^2 R}{}$$
    $$P = IE \qquad E = IR$$

21. If power and voltage are known, the formula for finding resistance is:

    $R = E$ $\left(\frac{E}{P}\right)$
    $\frac{E}{P}$ $\left(\frac{E}{P}\right)$ $R = \frac{E}{I}$

    $$R = \frac{E^2}{P} \qquad I = \frac{E}{R} \quad \frac{P}{E}$$

22. Calculate the resistance of the heating element in a 1000 W, 120 V toaster?

    $$R = \frac{(120V)^2}{1000W}$$
    $\underline{14.4\,\Omega}$
    $12 \times 12 = 144$
    $\frac{14400}{1000}$

23. The current through the toaster in the previous problem is:

    $\underline{\quad 1.2 \quad}$ A. $.12A$ $120\,mA$

    $3.2V = E$ $\quad I = \frac{R}{E} = \frac{14.4\,\Omega}{120V}$
    $I = 0.75 A$

    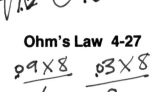

    $\frac{1.44}{12}$

    $\frac{.72}{6} \quad \frac{.09 \times 8}{6} \quad \frac{.03 \times 8}{2}$

Ohm's Law 4-27

Summary

The following is a point by point summary of this unit.

Ohm's law defines the relationship between the three fundamental electrical quantities. It describes how current, voltage, and resistance are related.

Formulas are used to define the relationships between the three fundamental electrical quantities. In these formulas, the letter I is used to represent current; E is used to represent voltage; and R is used to represent resistance.

The current formula states that current is equal to voltage divided by resistance. Stated as an equation:

$$I = \frac{E}{R}$$

The unit of current in the Ohm's Law equations depends on the units of voltage and resistance. Assuming that EMF is expressed in volts, the current will be in amperes if the resistance is in ohms. However, the current will be in milliamperes if the resistance is in kilohms. Finally, the current will be in microamperes if the resistance is in megohms.

The voltage formula states that voltage is equal to the current multiplied by the resistance. That is:

$$E = I \times R$$

E is expressed in volts when I is in amperes and R is in ohms. E is also in volts when I is in milliamperes and R is in kilohms. Finally, E is in volts when I is in microamperes and R is in megohms.

The resistance formula states that resistance is equal to voltage divided by current. That is:

$$R = \frac{E}{I}$$

Assuming that E is given in volts, R will be in ohms when I is in amperes. However, R will be in kilohms when I is in milliamperes. Finally, R will be in megohms when I is in microamperes.

While it is handy to remember which of the metric prefixes go together when solving Ohm's law problems, it is not absolutely essential. If you will convert all quantities to volts, ohms, and amperes, you can solve any Ohm's law problem without worrying about metric prefixes.

Power is defined as the rate at which work is done. The unit of work is the joule while the unit of power is the watt. The watt is equal to one joule per second.

Expressed in English units, the watt is approximately equal to three-fourths of a foot-pound of work per second. The horsepower is equal to 746 watts or about three-fourths of a kilowatt.

The watt can also be expressed in terms of current and voltage. The watt is the amount of power expended when one volt of EMF causes one ampere of current.

The letter P is used to represent power in equations. Power is equal to voltage multiplied by current or:

$$P = \dot{I} \times E$$

Power can also be expressed in terms of current and resistance or in terms of voltage and resistance.

$$V = IR$$
$$E = IR$$

$$J = work$$
$$P = watt = J/s$$

Unit 5
Magnetism

Contents

Introduction

Electricity and magnetism are inseparable. In any study of electricity or electronics, the effects of magnetism must be considered. Electric currents produce magnetic fields and magnetic fields can produce electric currents. Electricity and magnetism are often considered to be two different aspects of a more general effect called the **electromagnetic phenomenon**.

Unit Objectives

When you have completed this unit, you will be able to:

1. Define the following terms: Field, permanent magnet, temporary magnet, flux lines, ferromagnetic, paramagnetic, diamagnetic, permeance, permeability, artificial magnet, natural magnet, flux density, field intensity, reluctance, ampere turn, magnetic induction, residual magnetism, retentivity, alternator, and dc generator.

2. List the four basic characteristics of flux lines.

3. State the left-hand rule for conductors, coils, and generators.

4. Name the common factor that links electricity and magnetism.

5. List the four factors that determine the amount of EMF induced in a conductor and state how they relate to the induced EMF.

6. List the four basic parts of a simple DC generator.

7. State the right-hand motor rule.

8. List ten electrical or electronic devices that use magnetism in one form or another and explain how they work.

9. State Faraday's law of magnetic induction.

The Magnetic Field

In science, action-at-a-distance is explained in terms of fields. For example, you have seen that a charged particle can attract or repel another charged particle simply by coming close to it. This happens because a region of electrical influence extends outside each particle. This region of influence is called a **field**. An **electrical field** made up of lines of force is said to exist around every charged particle.

The field concept is also used to explain why certain metals can attract other metals. Everyone knows that a magnet attracts small pieces of iron or steel. A region of influence extends outside the magnet into the surrounding space. In this case, the region is called a **magnetic field** and is said to be made up of **magnetic lines of force**. Thus, a magnet is a piece of material that has a concentrated magnetic field surrounding it.

Magnets

Magnets may be classified in several different ways. First, they can be classified according to the method by which they obtain their magnetic field. The first known magnets were **natural** magnets, called magnetites or lodestones. These materials in their natural state are surrounded by a magnetic field.

Artificial magnets can be created from natural magnets. For example, if soft iron is rubbed repeatedly over a piece of lodestone, a magnetic field is transferred to the iron.

Another type of artificial magnet is the **electromagnet**. Its magnetic field is produced by an electric current. The electromagnet will be discussed in much greater detail later.

Magnets can also be classified by their shape. Thus, there are horseshoe magnets, bar magnets, and ring magnets.

Some materials readily retain their magnetic fields for long periods of time. These are called **permanent magnets**. Other materials quickly lose their magnetism and are called **temporary magnets**. Both of these types are widely use in electronics.

Finally, magnets are classified by the type of material used in their construction. Some examples of these are metallic magnets or ceramic magnets. Often this is carried even further and magnets are named according to the alloy from which they are made. Two popular classifications are Alnico (an alloy of aluminum, nickel, and cobalt) and Cunife (an alloy of copper, nickel, and iron).

The two ends of a magnet have different characteristics. One end is called a south (S) pole while the other is called a north (N) pole. One reason for choosing these names is that a bar magnet will align itself in a north-south direction if allowed freedom of movement as shown in Figure 5-1. The north (N) pole of the magnet is defined as that end which points toward the north pole of the Earth.

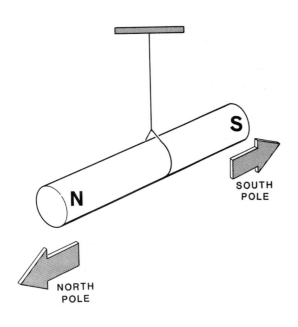

Figure 5-1 If allowed to swing freely, the magnet aligns itself in a north-south direction.

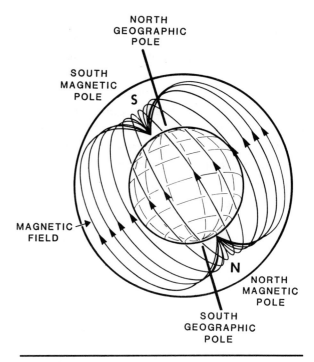

Figure 5-2 The Earth's magnetic field.

The magnet lines up in this way because the Earth itself is a huge magnet. As shown in Figure 5-2, it has its own magnetic field, which influences any magnet on Earth. This fact has been used for centuries by mariners and explorers who rely on the magnetic compass. The compass itself is nothing more than a tiny magnet balanced on a pin so that the needle rotates freely.

Magnets tend to align in a north-south direction because of a fundamental law of magnetism. This law states that like poles repel while unlike poles attract. Figure 5-3 illustrates this point. Thus, the north geographic pole in Figure 5-2 is labeled S while the

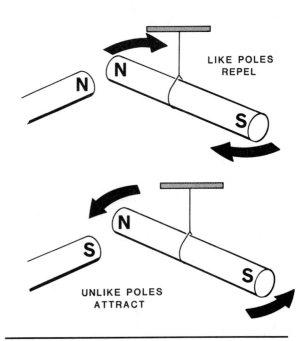

Figure 5-3 Action of like and unlike poles.

south geographic pole is labeled N. In this way, the north end of a magnet is attracted to the north geographic pole while the south end of the magnet points to the south geographic pole. To see why magnets behave in this way, you must consider the nature of the magnetic lines of force.

Lines of Force

To explain a magnetic field, scientists proved that lines of magnetic force called **flux lines** surround a magnet. Figure 5-4A shows the flux lines as they might appear around a bar magnet. While these lines are invisible, their effects can be demonstrated in several different ways. One of the most dramatic demonstrations is illustrated in Figure 5-4B. Iron filings are sprinkled evenly over a piece of paper. When the paper is placed over the magnet, the filings align so that the effects of the lines of force are clearly visible.

There are several basic rules and characteristics of flux lines that you should know. Four of the most important are:

1.   **Flux lines have direction or polarity**. The direction of the flux lines outside the magnet are arbitrarily assumed to be from the north pole to the south pole. This direction is often indicated by arrowheads as shown in Figure 5-4A.

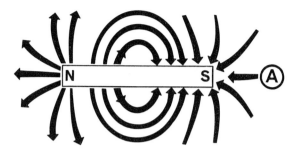

IRON FILINGS

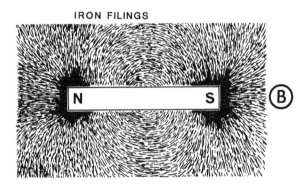

Figure 5-4 Line of force surround the magnet.

2.   **The lines of force always form complete loops**. This may not be obvious from Figure 5-4A, but each line curves back around the body of the magnet to form a complete loop.

3.   **Flux lines cannot cross each other**. This is the reason that like poles repel. Lines that have the same polarity can neither connect nor cross. When one field intrudes into another as shown in Figure 5-5A, the lines repel and the magnets tend to move apart.

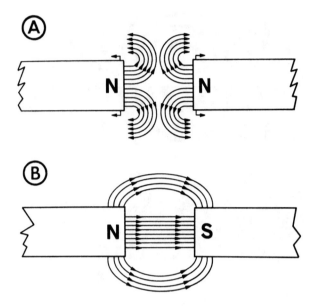

Figure 5-5 Similar direction flux lines repel; opposite direction flux lines attract and join.

4. **Flux lines tend to form the smallest possible loops.** This explains why unlike poles attract. Lines that have opposite polarity can link up as shown in Figure 5-5B. Then the loops attempt to shorten by pulling the two magnets together.

Magnetic Materials

Of the 92 natural elements, only three respond readily to magnetic fields. These are iron, cobalt, and nickel. All three are metals and they have atomic numbers of 26, 27, and 28 respectively. Each has two valence electrons so that their chemical and electrical characteristics are quite similar. In addition to these elements, there are dozens of alloys that have magnetic characteristics. Substances, like these that readily respond to magnetic fields, are called **ferromagnetic substances**. Ferromagnetic materials are strongly influenced by magnetic fields.

Most substances are classified as **paramagnetic**. These are substances that are attracted only slightly by a strong magnetic field. Generally, the force of attraction is so tiny, that these materials are considered to be non-magnetic. Substances such as air, aluminum, and wood are paramagnetic in nature.

Technically speaking, there is one other classification called **diamagnetic**. Diamagnetic materials are slightly repelled by magnetic fields. However, here again, the force of repulsion is so tiny that these materials are generally considered non-magnetic. Examples of diamagnetic materials are bismuth, quartz, water, and copper.

The characteristic that determines if a substance is ferromagnetic, paramagnetic, or diamagnetic is called **permeance** or **permeability**. Permeability refers to the ability of various materials to accept or allow magnetic lines of force to exist in them. Air is considered the standard with a permeability of 1. Other substances are given a permeability rating lower or higher than one depending on their magnetic characteristics. Iron is about 7000 times more effective in accepting flux lines than is air. Consequently, iron has a permeability of about 7000.

Table 5-1 lists the relative permeabilities of several different substances. Notice that those substances that have values of permeability less than 1 are diamagnetic and are slightly repelled by flux lines. Those having values slightly greater than 1 are paramagnetic and are slightly attracted by flux lines. Finally, those having permeabilities much higher than 1 are ferromagnetic and are strongly attracted by flux lines.

The permeability of materials can be compared to conductance in an electrical circuit. Recall that conductance indicates the ease with which a material or circuit allows current to flow. In much the same way, permeability is the ease with which a material accepts lines of flux.

MATERIAL	PERMEABILITY	CHARACTERISTIC	ACTION
BISMUTH	0.999833	DIAMAGNETIC	SLIGHTLY REPELLED
WATER	0.999991	DIAMAGNETIC	SLIGHTLY REPELLED
COPPER	0.999995	DIAMAGNETIC	SLIGHTLY REPELLED
AIR	1.000000	PARAMAGNETIC	NON-MAGNETIC
OXYGEN	1.000002	PARAMAGNETIC	SLIGHTLY ATTRACTED
ALUMINUM	1.000021	PARAMAGNETIC	SLIGHTLY ATTRACTED
COBALT	170.	FERROMAGNETIC	STRONGLY ATTRACTED
NICKEL	1000.	FERROMAGNETIC	STRONGLY ATTRACTED
IRON	7000.	FERROMAGNETIC	STRONGLY ATTRACTED
PERMALLOY*	100,000.	FERROMAGNETIC	STRONGLY ATTRACTED
SUPERMALLOY**	1,000,000.	FERROMAGNETIC	STRONGLY ATTRACTED

*PERMALLOY—AN ALLOY OF 17% IRON, 4% MOLYBDENUM, 79% NICKEL
**SUPERMALLOY—AN ALLOY OF 16% IRON, 5% MOLYBDENUM, 79% NICKEL

Table 5-1 Relative permeabilities of materials.

Figure 5-6A shows a permanent magnet surrounded by its lines of flux. Notice that these lines of flux form symmetrical loops around the magnet. Figure 5-6B shows how the flux lines are distorted when a piece of iron is brought near the magnet. Since iron has a high permeability, it can support lines of flux much more easily than the surrounding air. Consequently, a large number of the flux lines pass through the iron bar. At the same time, the lines attempt to contract to the smallest possible loops. This attracts the iron bar to the magnet.

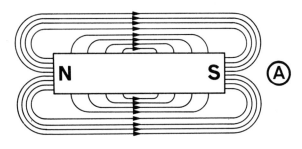

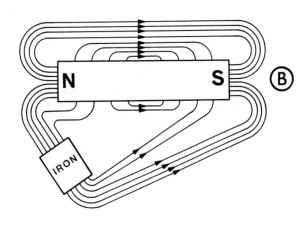

Figure 5-6 The flux lines pass through iron more easily than they do through air.

Theory of Magnetism

While it is difficult to explain exactly what magnetism is, a theory has been developed that explains the observed phenomenon. As with the basic theories of electricity, this one starts with the electron. You have seen that the electron orbits the nucleus of the atom in much the same way that the Earth orbits the sun. It also appears that the electron spins on its axis as shown in Figure 5-7A in much the same way that the Earth does.

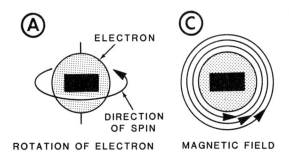

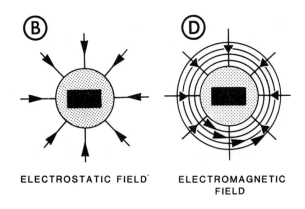

Figure 5-7 The electron's role in magnetism.

You have also seen that the electron has an electrostatic field as shown in Figure 5-7B. It appears to be a fact of nature that a moving electrical charge produces a magnetic field.

It is theorized that the electron is also surrounded by a magnetic field. The magnetic field is produced by the spinning charge and exists as a number of concentric circles around the electron as shown in Figure 5-7C. The direction of the magnetic field depends on the direction of spin of the electron.

At any given point, the electrostatic field is at right angles to the magnetic field. These combined fields at right angles are often called an electromagnetic field. Figure 5-7D shows the complete picture of the electron and its associated fields.

As you know, iron, nickel, and cobalt are the only natural magnetic elements. Each of these elements has two valence electrons. In other substances, the electrons that spin in a given direction tend to pair off with electrons of opposite spin. This means that the electrons have opposite magnetic characteristics that tend to cancel. However, in iron, nickel, and cobalt the two valence electrons have the same spin direction. Consequently, their magnetic fields do not cancel; they add. Thus, an atom of iron, nickel, or cobalt has a net magnetic field.

Small groups of these atoms tend to form tiny permanent magnets called **magnetic domains**. When not in the presence of a magnetic field, these domains are arranged

haphazardly as shown in Figure 5-8A. Because the domains are turned at odd angles, the net magnetic effect is zero. A piece of metal such as this can be magnetized by subjecting it to a strong magnetic field. As shown in Figure 5-8B, this causes all the domains to align in the same direction. With all the domains aligned in a common direction, the entire piece of metal becomes a magnet.

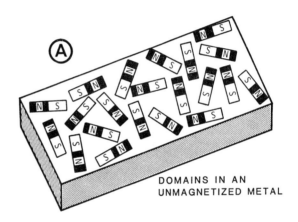

DOMAINS IN AN
UNMAGNETIZED METAL

DOMAINS IN A
MAGNETIZED METAL

Figure 5-8 Alignment of magnetic domains.

There are several experiments that seem to verify the **domain theory**. The first is shown in Figure 5-9A. If a bar magnet is cut into several pieces, each piece becomes a complete magnet having both a north and a south pole. Figure 5-9B shows another experiment. When the magnet is hit with a hammer, the domains are jarred back to a random pattern and the overall magnetic field is lost. Figure 5-9C shows that the same thing happens when the magnet is heated. The heat energy causes the domains to vibrate enough to rearrange themselves in a random pattern.

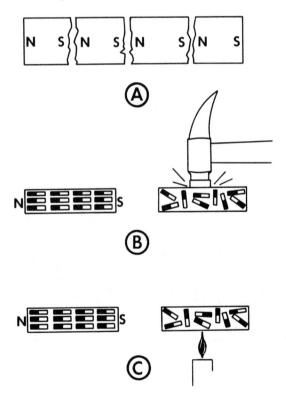

Figure 5-9 These experiments seem to verify the domain theory of magnetism.

1. The region of influence around a magnet is called a _magnetic field_.

2. The individual lines of force in a magnetic field are called _flux lines_.

3. A magnet is a device that is surrounded by a _magnetic field_.

4. A lodestone is an example of a _natural_ magnet.

5. Man-made magnets are referred to as _alloy_ magnets. _artificial_

6. A _temporary_ magnet is one that loses its magnetism very quickly.

7. If allowed to swing freely, a magnet will align itself so that its _North_ pole points toward the north pole of the Earth.

8. A common device that works on this principle and is used to indicate direction is called a _compass_.

9. A basic rule of magnetism is that like poles _repel_ while unlike poles _attract_.

10. A material that is readily magnetized is called _ferromagnetic_

11. A material that is only slightly attracted by a very strong magnetic field is classified as _paramagnetic_

12. A material that is slightly repelled by a strong magnetic field is classified as _diamagnetic_

13. The three elements in nature that are naturally magnetic are _cobalt_, _iron_, and _nickel_.

14. The property that determines a material's magnetic characteristic is called permeance or _permeability_

15. Permeability is defined as the ease with which a substance will accept _flux_ lines.

16. A commonly accepted theory of magnetism assumes that the magnetic field is initially caused by the _electron_ spinning on its axis.

17. In naturally magnetic elements, the two electrons in the valence shell spin in the (same/different) direction.

18. The result of the electron spin in iron, cobalt, and nickel is that these atoms have a net _magnetic_ field.

19. These magnetic atoms tend to bunch together in tiny groups called _magnetic domains_

20. When the domains in a piece of metal become aligned, the metal becomes a _magnetized_

Electricity and Magnetism

Electricity and magnetism are closely related. The electron has both an electrostatic field and a magnetic field. This may lead you to the conclusion that a charged object should have a magnetic field. However, this is not the case, since the magnetic field of about half the electrons will be opposite that of the other half. Nevertheless, the electron plays an important part in magnetism. It can be forced to produce a magnetic field in substances that are normally considered nonmagnetic such as copper and aluminum.

The key to creating a magnetic field electrically is motion. Motion is the catalyst that links electricity and magnetism. Anytime a charged particle moves, a magnetic field is produced. If a large number of charged particles are moved in a systematic way, a usable magnetic field is formed. You have learned that current flow is the systematic movement of large numbers of electrons. Thus, current flow, since it consists of a large number of charged particles moving in a systematic way, produces a magnetic field.

Current Flow and Magnetism

When current flows through a wire, a magnetic field is developed around the wire. The field exists as concentric flux lines as shown in Figure 5-10. While this field has no north or south pole, it does have direction. The direction of the field depends on the direction of current flow. The arrow heads on the flux lines indicate their direc-

tion. This does not mean that the flux lines are moving in this direction. It simply means that they are pointed in this direction.

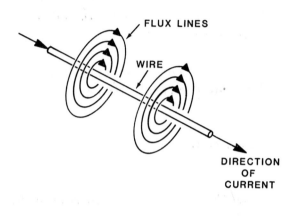

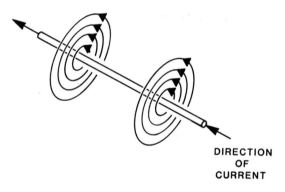

Figure 5-10 Flux lines exist as concentric circles around a current carrying conductor.

The direction of the flux lines can be determined if the direction of current flow is known. The rule for determining this is called the **left-hand magnetic-field rule** or the **left-hand rule for conductors**. It is illustrated in Figure 5-11.

Simply stated, if you grasp the conductor in your left hand with your thumb pointing in the direction of current flow through the conductor, your fingers now point in the direction of the flux lines.

Study Figure 5-11 until you understand this rule. Try this rule on the two conductors shown in Figure 5-10.

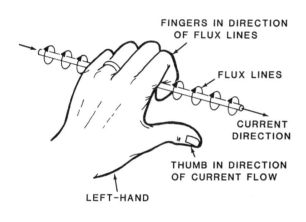

Figure 5-11 Left-hand magnetic field rule.

In explaining some aspects of electromagnetism, it is helpful to show current flow in a third dimension. To do this, two new symbols are necessary. Figure 5-12A shows current flowing into the page. If the wire is viewed from the end, the tail of the arrow appears as a cross as shown in Figure 5-12B. This cross is used to represent current flowing into the page. If the same wire is viewed from the other end, the head of the arrow appears as a round dot as shown in Figure 5-12D. The dot is used to represent current flowing out of the page.

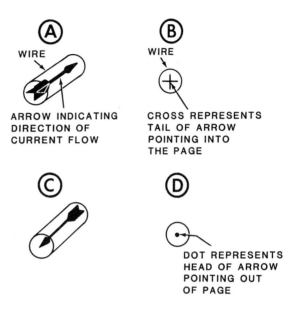

Figure 5-12 Developing two new symbols to represent current flow in a third dimension.

In Figure 5-13, these new symbols are used to show how opposite and similar currents establish magnetic fields. In Figure 5-13A, opposite currents are shown. Using the left-hand rule, you can verify the direction of the two magnetic fields. Since the fields point in opposite directions, they tend to repel each other. Figure 5-13B shows that the opposite situation exists when the two currents flow in the same direction. Here, the fields point in the same direction. This tends to draw the two fields together. Thus, they are free to connect and reinforce one another.

As long as the conductor is a straight piece of wire, the magnetic field produced is of little practical use. Although it has direction, it has no north or south pole. Also, unless the current is extremely high, the magnetic field has little strength. However, by changing the shape of a length of wire, you can greatly improve its magnetic characteristics.

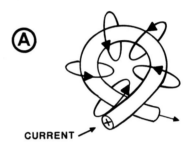

Figure 5-13 Opposite currents cause fields that repel; currents in the same direction cause fields that add and attract.

Figure 5-14 shows two views of a short piece of wire twisted into a loop. Simply forming the loop helps the magnetic characteristics in three ways. First, it brings the flux lines closer together. Second, it concentrates the majority of the flux lines in the center or core of the loop. Third, it creates north and south poles. The north pole is the side where the flux lines exit the loop; the south pole, the side where they enter the loop. Thus, this loop of wire has the characteristics of a magnet. In fact, this is an example of a simple electromagnet.

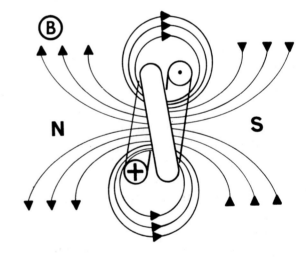

Figure 5-14 Flux lines around a loop of wire.

The Electromagnet

Electromagnetism is used in many different electronic devices. In its simplest form, the electromagnet is nothing more than a length of wire wrapped in coils as shown in Figure 5-15. When current passes through the wire, a magnetic field is established. Because the turns of wire are very close together, the flux lines of the individual turns reinforce one another to produce a strong magnetic field. The more turns in a coil, the more flux lines there will be to add together. Furthermore, as more current flows through the coil, more flux lines are created resulting in a strengthened magnetic field. Consequently, the strength of the magnetic field is directly proportional to both the number of turns in the coil and the amount of current through the coil.

The magnetic field around the coil has the same characteristics as the magnetic field around a permanent magnet. However, one difference is that the field around the coil exists only when current flows through the coil. Another important difference is that the strength of the magnetic field around the coil can be varied by changing the amount of current flowing through the coil.

You have learned about two ways to increase the strength of the magnetic field around an electromagnet. One way is to increase the current. Another is to increase the number of turns. However, a third method is the most dramatic of all. It involves the addition of a bar of ferromagnetic material, called a core, to the center of the coil.

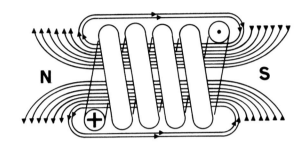

Figure 5-15 Magnetic field around a coil.

If you insert an iron core into the coil shown in Figure 5-15, the strength of the magnetic field increases dramatically. The reason for this is that the iron core is much more permeable than air. Consequently, the iron core can support many times more flux lines than air. Most electromagnets are made by winding many turns of wire around a bar of ferromagnetic material such as iron.

Often, it is helpful to know the polarity of an electromagnet. This can be determined if the direction of current through the coil is known. The rule used for doing this is called the **left-hand rule for coils** and is illustrated in Figure 5-16.

This rule states that if you grasp the coil with your left hand in such a way that your fingers are wrapped around it in the same direction that current is flowing, your thumb will then point toward the north pole of the magnet.

Remember that current flows from negative to positive. In Figure 5-16A, the current flows up the back side of the coil and down the front side. If the fingers are wrapped in this direction, the thumb points to the left. Thus, the left end of the electromagnet is the north pole. In Figure 5-16B, the coil is wrapped in the opposite direction and the north pole is on the right.

Using this same procedure, the direction of current flow can be determined if the north pole is known. Assume that you know the north pole is on the right but you do not know the direction of current. Simply grasp the coil in the left hand with the thumb pointing toward the north pole of the coil. Your fingers now point in the direction of current flow.

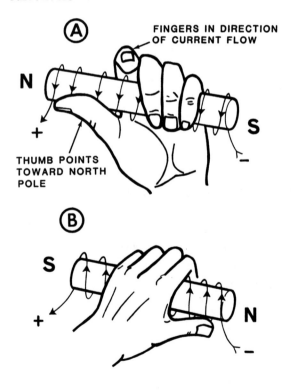

Figure 5-16 Left-hand rule for coils.

Magnetic Quantities

In your study of electricity, you use electrical quantities such as voltage, current, resistance, conductance, and power. In much the same way, the study of magnetism requires that you learn several magnetic quantities. Of particular importance are the magnetic quantities: flux, flux density, magnetomotive force, field intensity, reluctance, and permeability.

While the definitions of these quantities are straight forward, the units of measure for these quantities often become confusing. The reason for this is that three different systems of measurement have been used over the years. The first is the English system that uses the familiar inches, ounces, and pounds. The other two systems are based on metric units. One is called the cgs system. Cgs stands for centimeter, gram, and second. The other system based on metric units is the mks system. Mks stands for meter, kilogram, and second. In the following discussion, the English units are used because this is probably the system with which you are most familiar. At the end of this section, the English units are compared with the metric units.

Flux. The complete magnetic field of a coil or a magnet is known as its flux. Thus, the flux is the total number of lines of magnetic force. The Greek letter phi (Φ) is used to denote flux. In the English system, flux is measured in lines. A coil or magnet that produces 1000 lines of force has a flux of 1000 lines or 1 kiloline ($\Phi = 1$ k lines).

Flux Density. As the name implies, flux density refers to the number of flux lines per unit of area. In the English system the unit of area is the square inch. Thus, flux density is expressed as the number of lines per square inch. The letter β is used to represent flux density. If a coil with a cross sectional area of two square inches has a flux of 1000 lines then the flux density is 1000/2 or 500 lines per square inch (β = 500 lines/in/2).

Magnetomotive Force (MMF or mmf). Magnetomotive force is the force that produces the flux in an electromagnet or coil. As you have seen, this force is directly proportional to the number of turns in the coil and the amount of current flowing through the coil. For this reason, the unit of MMF is the ampere-turn or amp-turn. This is the amount of force developed by one turn of wire when the current flow is one ampere.

To determine the MMF, multiply the number of turns in a coil by the current through the coil. For example, a coil having 50 turns and a current of 2 amperes has a magnetomotive force of 50 × 2 = 100 ampere turns.

Field Intensity or Magnetizing Force. While MMF is a useful term, it is limited in application because it does not take into consideration the length of the coil. Thus, a coil with 50 turns may be 1 inch long or 10 inches long and still have the same MMF. However, it is obvious that the magnetic field in the 1 inch long coil is concentrated in a much smaller space than the field in the larger coil.

Field intensity takes into consideration not only the MMF but also the length of the coil. It is expressed as ampere-turns per inch and is represented by the letter H. To determine the field intensity of a coil, divide the MMF of the coil in ampere-turns by the length of the coil in inches. For example, if a 2-inch coil has an mmf of 100 ampere turns, then the field intensity is 100/2 or 50 ampere turns per inch (H = 50- amp-turns/in). Field intensity is sometimes called **magnetizing force**. You should be careful, however, not to confuse this term with magnetomotive force.

Permeability. You have already learned about this characteristic. You will recall that permeability is the ease with which a material can accept lines of force. It can also be thought of as the ability of a material to concentrate a large number of force lines in a small area. For example, a 1-inch column of soft iron can hold hundreds of times more flux lines than a comparable column of aluminum. The Greek letter mu (μ) is used to represent permeability.

Reluctance. The opposite or reciprocal of permeability is called reluctance and is represented by the letter R. Reluctance is generally defined as an opposition to flux. Thus, a material with high reluctance is reluctant to accept flux lines. Since reluctance is the reciprocal of permeability, it may be expressed by the equation:

$$R = \frac{1}{\mu}$$

For example, soft iron has a permeability of 2700. Thus, it has a reluctance of 1/2700. Since air has a permeability of 1, it has a reluctance of 1/1 or 1. Flux lines tend to follow the path of least reluctance.

Ohm's Law for Magnetic Quantities

Three of the above quantities are related by an equation that is very similar to the Ohm's law equation. In fact, these three magnetic quantities can be compared to the electrical units of current, voltage, and resistance. In this analogy, current corresponds to magnetic flux (Φ). You will recall that flux is produced by magnetomotive force (MMF). Consequently, MMF corresponds to voltage. Finally, the opposition to flux is called reluctance (R). Flux, MMF, and reluctance are related by the equation.

$$\Phi = \frac{MMF}{R}$$

This states that the magnetic flux developed in a core material is directly proportional to the magnetomotive force applied to the material and inversely proportional to the reluctance of the material. Because of the similarity of this equation to the Ohm's law

equation discussed earlier, this is often called the Ohm's law for magnetic circuits.

Comparison of Units

As previously stated, there are three systems of measurement in common use. The most familiar is the English system. However, the metric system is becoming increasingly popular. Unfortunately, the units for the various magnetic quantities are different in each system. A comparison of these units is given in Table 5-2.

In the English system, flux is measured in lines or kilolines; flux density is measured in kilolines per square inch; MMF is measured in ampere-turns; and field intensity is measured in ampere-turns per inch.

The cgs system introduces, four new terms: maxwell, gauss, gilbert, and oersted. The maxwell is equal to one line of force or flux. The gauss is equal to 1 maxwell per square centimeter. The gilbert is equivalent to 0.796 ampere-turns or, stated another way, the ampere-turn is equal to about 1.25 gilberts. Finally, the oersted is equal to 1 gilbert per centimeter.

In the mks system, the unit of flux is the weber. The weber is equivalent to 10^8 or 100,000,000 lines of force. Flux density is expressed as webers per square meter. As with the English system, the mks unit of MMF is the ampere-turn. Finally, field intensity is expressed as ampere-turns per meter.

This table ignores permeability and reluctance because neither has a unit of measurement assigned to it in any of the three systems.

TERM	DESCRIPTION	SYMBOL	ENGLISH UNITS	CGS UNITS	MKS UNITS
FLUX	TOTAL LINES OF FORCE	Φ	LINES OR KILOLINES	1 MAXWELL = 1 LINE	1 WEBER = 100,000,000 LINES
FLUX DENSITY	LINES PER UNIT AREA	β	$\dfrac{\text{KILOLINES}}{\text{IN}^2}$	$1\ \text{GAUSS} = \dfrac{1\ \text{MAXWELL}}{\text{CM}^2}$	$\dfrac{\text{WEBER}}{\text{M}^2}$
MAGNETOMOTIVE FORCE	TOTAL FORCE THAT PRODUCES FLUX	MMF	AMPERE-TURN	1 GILBERT = 0.796 AMP TURN 1 AMP-TURN = 1.25 GILBERT	AMPERE-TURN
FIELD INTENSITY, OR MAGNETIZING FORCE	FORCE PER UNIT LENGTH OF FLUX PATH	H	$\dfrac{\text{AMPERE-TURN}}{\text{IN}}$	$1\ \text{OERSTED} = \dfrac{1\ \text{GILBERT}}{\text{CM}}$	$\dfrac{\text{AMPERE-TURN}}{\text{M}}$

Table 5-2 Comparison of magnetic units.

21. When an electrical charge moves, a _____ field is produced.

22. The common factor that links magnetism and electricity is _____.

23. The direction of the magnetic field around a wire can be determined by the _____ magnetic field rule.

24. To apply the left-hand rule, you grasp the wire in your left hand with your _____ pointing in the direction of current flow.

25. Your _____ now point in the same direction as the flux lines.

26. The magnetic field produced around a conductor is relatively weak and although it has direction, it does not have north or south _____.

27. A strong magnetic field can be developed by winding a conductor in the form of _____.

28. To increase the strength of an electromagnet, a _____ _____ is added to the core of the magnet.

29. The coil with current flowing has many of the characteristics of a magnet, and is sometimes called an _____.

30. Using the left-hand rule for coils, when you grasp the coil in your left hand your fingers point in the direction of _____.

31. Again using the left-hand rule for coils, your thumb should point toward the _____ _____ of the coil.

32. Since iron is a ferromagnetic material, it has a much higher value of _____ than air.

33. The quantity that defines the total magnetic field or the total lines of force in kilolines is called _____.

34. In the English system, a quantity that refers to lines per square inch is called _____ _____.

35. In the English system, the unit of MMF is the _____-_____.

36. In the English system, field intensity is measured in _____-_____ per inch.

37. A material that is reluctant to accept flux lines is said to have a high _____.

38. The most common analogy used to compare electrical and magnetic quantities compares current, voltage, and resistance to _____, _____, and _____ respectively.

39. Match the following English units with their cgs counterparts.

    A. lines _____   1. oersted
    B. Kilo lines/in^2 _____   2. gilbert
    C. amp-turn _____   3. maxwell
    D. amp-turn/in _____   4. gauss

40. Match the following English units with their mks counterparts.

    A. lines _____   1. weber/m^2
    B. Kilo lines/in^2 _____   2. amp-turn
    C. amp-turn _____   3. amp-turn/m
    D. amp-turn/in _____   4. weber

41. Match the following magnetic quantities with their English units.

    A. flux _____   1. Kilo lines/in^2
    B. flux density _____   2. amp-turn
    C. field intensity _____   3. amp-turn/in
    D. magnetomotive   4. lines
       force _____

Induction may be defined as the effect that the magnet has on the iron bar without any physical contact between them. Earlier, you saw that a charged body can induce a charge in another body simply by coming close to it. This is possible because an electrostatic field surrounds every charged body. Thus, the field of a charged body can affect another body without the two bodies actually touching. This is an example of electrostatic induction.

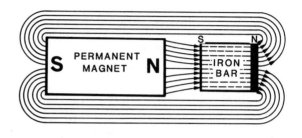

Figure 5-17 Magnetic induction.

Magnetic Induction

Another type of induction is called **magnetic induction**. Everyone knows that a magnet can affect objects from a distance. A strong magnet can cause a compass needle to deflect even at a distance of several feet. A magnet can also induce a magnetic field in a previously unmagnetized object. For example, a magnet placed near a piece of iron can cause the iron to become magnetized: in other words, to become a magnet.

Figure 5-17 shows a bar of soft iron close to a permanent magnet. Notice that part of the magnetic field passes through the iron bar. This happens because of the high permeability of the iron. Magnetic lines of force enter the left side of the iron and exit on the right. This magnetic field causes the magnetic domains in the iron to line up in one direction. Thus, the piece of iron itself becomes a magnet.

In the iron bar, the south pole must be on the left since this is the end where the flux lines enter the iron. The north pole is on the right since the flux lines exit at this point. Notice that the north pole of the permanent magnet is closest to the induced south pole of the iron bar. Because these opposite poles attract, the iron bar is attracted to the magnet. Therefore, the attraction of a piece of iron by a permanent magnet is a natural result of magnetic induction.

When the piece of iron is removed from the magnetic field, most of the magnetic domains return to random positions. However, a few of the domains will remain aligned in the north-south direction. Thus, the iron bar retains a weak magnetic field even after it is removed from the influence of the permanent magnet.

The magnetic field that remains in the iron bar is referred to as **residual magnetism**. The ability of material to retain a magnetic field even after the magnetizing force has been removed is called **retentivity**. Soft iron has a relatively low value of retentivity.

Thus, it retains little residual magnetism. Steel has a somewhat higher value of retentivity. Therefore, its residual magnetism is also higher. Some materials, such as alnico, have a very high value of retentivity. In these materials, the residual magnetic field is almost as strong as the original magnetizing field.

Electromagnetic Induction

Electromagnetic induction is the action that causes electrons to flow in a conductor when the conductor moves across a magnetic field. Figure 5-18 illustrates this action. When the conductor moves up through the magnetic field, the free electrons are pushed to the right end of the conductor. This causes an excess of electrons at the right end of the conductor and a deficiency of electrons at the other end. The result is a potential difference that develops between the two ends of the conductor.

The potential difference developed in the conductor exists only while the conductor is moving through, or cutting, the flux lines of the magnet. When the conductor moves out of the magnetic field, the electrons return to their original positions and the potential difference disappears. The potential difference also disappears if the conductor stops in the magnetic field. Thus, there must be relative movement between the conductor and the magnetic lines of flux before a potential difference develops in the conductor.

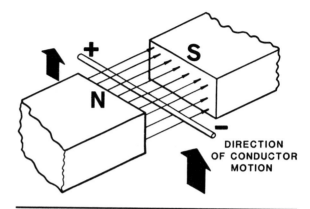

Figure 5-18 Electromagnetic induction.

Motion is essential to electromagnetic induction. Some outside force must be applied to the conductor in order to move it through the magnetic field. This mechanical force is converted to an electromotive force (EMF) by electromagnetic induction. In other words, an EMF is induced into the conductor. The potential difference across the conductor is called an **induced EMF** or an **induced voltage**.

The amount of EMF induced in a conductor is determined by four factors:

1. **The strength of the magnetic field.** The stronger the magnetic field, the greater the number of lines of flux in the field per unit area. If the magnetic field has a great number of lines of force, then the moving conductor can cut a great number of lines. The greater the number of lines cut for a given time period, the greater the induced EMF.

2. **The speed of the conductor with respect to the field**. As a conductor moves through a magnetic field, it cuts the magnetic lines of force. Increasing the conductor's speed through the field results in a greater number of lines of flux being cut for a given time period. This results in an increase in the EMF induced in the conductor.

3. **The angle at which the conductor cuts the field**. This might be a bit harder to visualize than the previous two statements. If one conductor moves perpendicular, or at right angles, to the magnetic lines of force, it will cut a maximum number lines of force per second and produce a maximum EMF. This movement is shown in Figure 5-18. An identical conductor moving at the same speed but at an angle other than perpendicular to the field will cut less lines of force in the same time and therefore produce a smaller EMF. Incidentally, a conductor moving parallel to the field crosses no lines of flux and therefore has no EMF induced in it. This is shown in Figure 5-19.

4. **The length of the conductor in the field**. A longer conductor must be coiled in order for it to fit into the magnetic field. Each loop in the coil cuts the field. Thus, the lines of flux are cut a greater number of times per second resulting in a greater induced voltage.

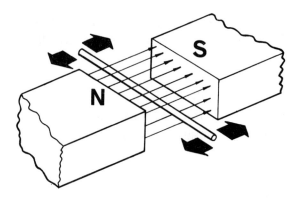

Figure 5-19 No voltage is induced when the conductor moves parallel to the flux lines.

All four of these factors are a natural consequence of a basic law of electromagnetic induction. This law is called Faraday's law and it states:

The voltage induced in the conductor is directly proportional to the rate at which the conductor cuts the magnetic lines of force.

In other words, the more flux lines cut per second, the higher the induced EMF.

The polarity of the induced EMF can be determined by another of the left-hand rules. This one is called the **left-hand rule for generators** and is illustrated in Figure 5-20. It involves the thumb and the first two fingers of the left hand. The thumb is pointed in the direction that the conductor is moving. The index or forefinger is pointed in the direction of the magnetic field: from north to south. Now, the middle finger is pointed straight out from the palm at a right angle to the index finger. The middle finger now points to the negative end of the conductor. This is the direction that current flows if an external circuit is connected across the two ends of the conductor.

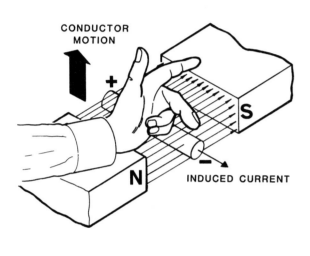

Figure 5-20 Left-hand rule for generators.

The AC Generator

Electromagnetic induction is important because it is this method used to produce the EMF that supplies virtually all of the electrical power used in the world today. It is the most efficient way known for producing electricity.

Figure 5-21 shows an elementary electric generator. This device converts mechanical energy into electrical energy through electromagnetic induction. Mechanical energy

is required to establish relative motion between the magnetic field and the conductor. Either the magnet or the conductor can be rotated. For this explanation, assume that the conductor rotates in a counterclockwise direction. Notice that the conductor is shaped like a loop and is called an **armature**. When the loop or armature rotates, one half moves up through the field near the south pole while the other half moves down through the field near the north pole.

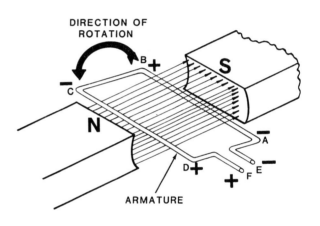

Figure 5-21 The AC generator.

If you apply the left hand generator rule to the side of the loop nearest the south pole, you find that the polarity of the induced voltage is negative at point A and positive at point B. Applying the same rule to the conductor near the north pole, you find that the induced voltage is negative at point C and positive at point D. Notice that these two induced voltages are connected series aiding. A voltmeter connected across points E and F will measure the sum of the two induced voltages.

Figure 5-22A shows the nature of the voltage that is induced into the armature. To see how this voltage is produced, you must follow the armature through one complete revolution. In each case, you must consider the voltage at point A with respect to the voltage at point B.

Figure 5-22B shows the armature at 90° increments. At 0°, the sides of the armature are moving parallel to the lines of flux. When this happens, no flux lines are cut, and there is no induced voltage at this time. However, as the armature rotates, the loop begins cutting the lines of flux and a voltage is induced. Point A becomes positive with respect to point B. You can prove this by implementing the left-hand generator rule.

The voltage continues to rise until it reaches its maximum value at 90° of rotation. The voltage is maximum at this point because the armature is cutting the flux at a right angle. Thus, it cuts the maximum number of lines per second at this time. Once past 90°, the voltage begins to decrease because fewer lines per second are being cut. At 180°, the induced voltage is again zero because the armature is moving parallel to the lines of force.

As the loop passes 180° and starts cutting the lines again, a voltage is induced once more. However, this time point A becomes negative with respect to point B. Again, you can prove this by applying the left-hand generator rule. The maximum negative voltage is produced at 270° when the armature is once again cutting the lines of force at

right angles. As the armature heads back toward its starting point, the voltage begins to decrease toward 0. At 360°, the armature is back where it started and the induced voltage is again zero.

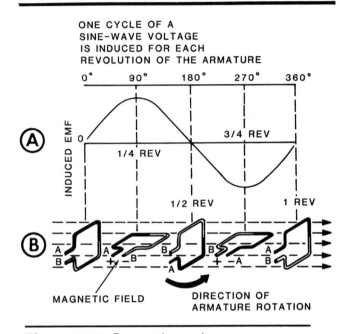

Figure 5-22 Generating a sine-wave.

The voltage waveform shown in Figure 5-22A is called a sine-wave. One cycle of the sine-wave, consisting of a positive and negative voltage swing, is produced for each revolution of the armature. If a load is connected across the armature between points A and B, current will flow through the load. For the first half cycle, current flows from point B through the load to point A. However, during the next half cycle, current flows in the opposite direction from point A through the load to point B. Thus, during each cycle, the current reverses direction — flowing in one direction half of the time and flowing in the opposite direction the other half of the time. This type of current flow is called alternating current and is abbreviated AC.

The voltage supplied to your home, office, or place where you work is an AC voltage. The armature of the generator at the plant that provides your power rotates 60 times each second. Thus, the voltage supplied by these power stations goes through 60 cycles like the one shown in Figure 5-22A each second. Most of the appliances in your home require 115 volts at 60 cycles.

The AC generator is often called an alternator because it produces alternating current. The simple machine shown here would not produce useful power because there is only a single turn of wire in the armature. In a practical alternator, hundreds of turns are wound into an armature that can produce considerable power.

The DC Generator

The AC generator or alternator can be converted to a DC generator. A device called a **commutator** is used to convert the AC voltage produced by the rotating loop into a DC voltage. The commutator is a cylinder shaped conductor. Two insulators are used to separate one half of the cylinder from the other half. Opposite sides of the armature are permanently connected to the opposite

sides of the commutator. Thus, the commutator rotates with the armature. Figure 5-23A shows how the commutator connects to the armature.

Brushes are used to make contact with the rotating commutator. They are stationary and rest against opposite sides of the commutator. The brushes are made of a conducting material so that the EMF produced by the armature is transferred to the brushes through the commutator. In turn, wires are connected to the brushes so that the EMF can be transferred to an external circuit.

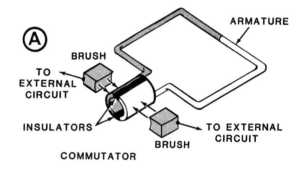

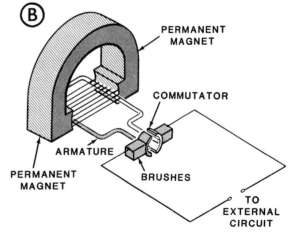

Figure 5-23 The DC generator.

The complete DC generator is shown in Figure 5-23B. Notice that it has four basic parts: a magnet to produce the magnetic field; an armature or loop that produces the EMF; a commutator that converts the induced EMF to a DC voltage; and the brushes that transfer the DC voltage to an external circuit.

Figure 5-24 illustrates the operation of the DC generator. At 0°, 180°, and 360°, the sides of the armature are moving parallel to the flux lines and 0 volts is produced. You will recall, that this same situation exists with the AC generator. At 90° and 270°, the sides of the loop are cutting the flux lines at right angles and maximum voltage is produced. However, unlike the alternator the voltage is positive at point A with respect to point B at both 90° and 270°. Here's why:

Since the brushes are stationary and the commutator is rotating, each brush is alternately connected to opposite sides of the ar-

mature. When the magnetic field is in the direction shown, the side of the loop that is moving up through the field produces a negative voltage at the commutator. At the same time, the side of the loop moving down through the field produces a positive voltage at the commutator. Notice that the brush on the right is always connected to the side of the armature that is moving up through the field. Consequently, this brush is always positive. Thus, if an external circuit is connected across A and B, current always flows in the same direction.

The nature of the induced EMF is shown in Figure 5-24B. This is called a pulsating DC voltage — DC because the current always flows in the same direction and pulsating because the level fluctuates. A pulsating DC voltage like this one is of little use in this form. However, as you will see in a future unit, this type of voltage can be smoothed out to form a constant DC voltage.

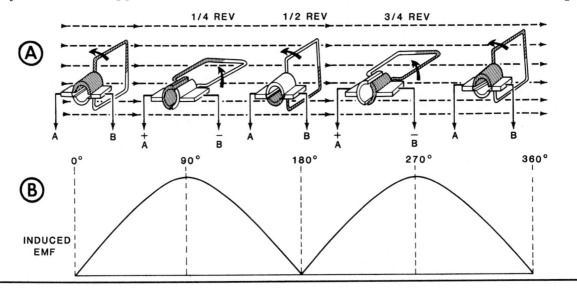

Figure 5-24 Operation of a DC generator.

42. The effect of one body on another body without physical contact between them is called:

_____.

43. When a charged object is brought close to a neutral object and the neutral object develops a charge of its own, this is called _____ _____.

44. In much the same way, when a permanent magnet induces a magnetic field in a previously unmagnetized object, this is called _____ _____.

45. The magnetic field that remains after the magnetizing force has been removed is called _____ magnetism.

46. The ability of a material to retain a magnetic field after the magnetizing force has been removed is called _____.

47. The action that causes electrons to move in a conductor when the conductor moves across a magnetic field is called _____ .

48. In a generator, the stronger the magnetic field, the (stronger/weaker) will be the induced EMF.

49. The faster the relative motion in a generator, the (stronger/weaker) the induced EMF will be.

50. The longer the conductor in the field, the (stronger/weaker) the induced EMF will be.

51. The induced EMF is maximum when the conductor cuts the magnetic field at a _____ angle.

52. The polarity of the induced EMF can be determined by the left-hand rule for

_____.

53. Using this rule the _____ of the left-hand is pointed in the same direction that the conductor is moving.

54. The _____ finger is pointed in the same direction as the flux lines.

55. If the middle finger is now pointed straight out from the palm at a right angle to the index finger, it will be pointing at the (negative/positive) end of the conductor.

56. A device that uses electromagnetic induction to convert mechanical energy to electrical energy is called a

_____.

57. An AC generator is called an alternator because it produces an _____ current EMF.

58. An AC generator produces a voltage waveform called a _____ wave.

59. In a DC generator, a _____ is used to convert the AC voltage to a pulsating DC voltage.

Magnetic and Electromagnetic Applications

You have already seen two important applications of electromagnetism – the alternator and the DC generator. It would be difficult to list all of the other applications of magnetic and electromagnetic devices. However, you can examine the operation of some of the more common applications.

Relay

The relay is one of the simplest, and most useful, electromagnetic devices. Figure 5-25 shows how the relay operates. When the switch is closed, current flows from the battery through the relay coil. The current develops a magnetic field in the core that attracts the armature (moving contact), pulling it down. This closes the contacts connecting the generator to the load.

When the switch is opened, the current through the relay coil stops. This allows the magnetic field to collapse. The spring pulls the armature up opening the contacts and disconnecting the generator from the load.

The relay is used when it is desirable to have one circuit control another. Notice that in Figure 5-25 there are two complete and separate circuits. Because the relay circuit is electrically isolated from the generator circuit, it can act as a protective device. The relay can be used to open and close high-voltage or high-current circuits and, at the same time, expose you to relatively little voltage and current in the coil circuit. It is also useful for remote control where the

switch is located at one point and the other circuit components are located at a distance. Also, a relay with several contact arms can open and close several circuits at once.

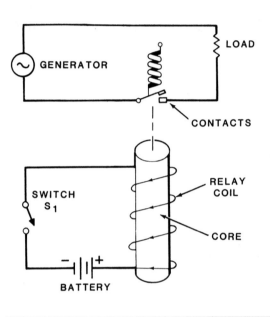

Figure 5-25 The relay.

An interesting variation of the relay is the door bell shown in Figure 5-26. When the switch is closed, current flows from the negative side of the battery through the switch, the breaker contacts, the two relay coils, and back to the positive side of the battery. The current flow through the relay sets up a magnetic field that attracts the soft-iron armature pulling it down. This pulls the hammer down causing it to strike the bell. The lower breaker contact is attached to the armature. Consequently, when the coils energize, the current path for the coil is broken. Thus, the relay de-energizes and releases the armature. The spring pulls the armature and the hammer upward. This closes the breaker contacts and once again completes the path for current flow through the relays. The operation repeats itself many times each second. Thus the bell rings as long as the circuit is energized.

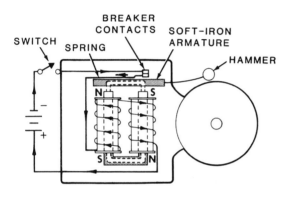

Figure 5-26 The door bell.

Reed Switch and Relay

Figure 5-27A shows a magnetic reed switch. It consists of two contacts in a sealed glass container. The contacts are made of a ferromagnetic material and are normally open. However, when a magnet is placed next to the reed switch as shown in Figure 5-27B, the contacts close. The reason for this is that a magnetic field is induced into each contact by the flux lines from the magnet. Thus, each contact becomes a tiny magnet having

the polarity shown. At the point where the two contacts are closest, opposite poles exist. These poles are attracted to each other closing the contacts. The reed switch allows you to control a circuit by changing the position of a permanent magnet. A practical application of this device will be shown later.

Figure 5-27C shows that the contacts can also be controlled with the field from an electromagnet. When the electromagnet is wound directly on the reed switch, the device is called a reed relay.

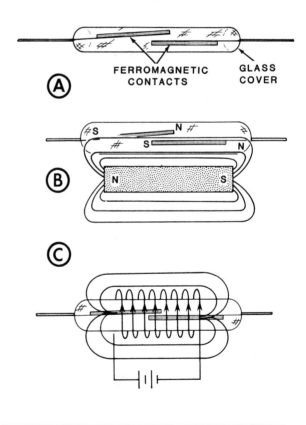

Figure 5-27 Reed switch and reed relay

Record Pickup

Electromagnetic principles are used in many types of recording and playback equipment. The pickup cartridge used in the tone arm of many record players is an electromagnetic device. Figure 5-28 shows the construction of a cartridge called a moving-coil or dynamic pickup. Here, a magnetic field is produced by the permanent magnet. A tiny coil is placed in this magnetic field. The core on which the coil is wound is attached to the stylus or needle. The coil is held in place by a flexible grommet.

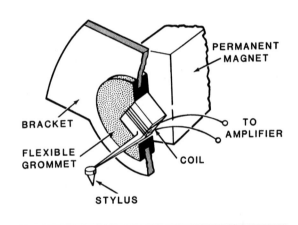

Figure 5-28 Simplified diagram of a magnetic pickup cartridge.

As the needle slips down the spiral groove on the record, it vibrates in response to the variations in the groove. These variations in the groove correspond to the audio tones recorded there. Thus, the needle vibrates at the same rate as the audio tones. Because the coil is connected to the needle, it also vibrates at this rate. The tiny movements of the coil in the magnetic field cause a minute EMF to be induced into the coil. The induced EMF also varies at the audio rate. This EMF can be amplified and used to drive a loudspeaker so that the original audio tone is reproduced.

Loudspeaker

Loudspeakers are used in all types of audio equipment. Most loudspeakers use a moving coil and a permanent magnet. A cutaway diagram of a loudspeaker is shown in Figure 5-29. A permanent magnet establishes a

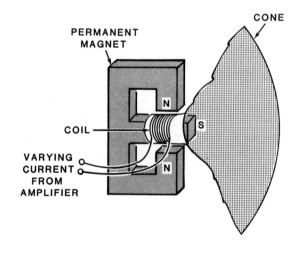

Figure 5-29 The loudspeaker.

strong stationary magnetic field. A coil that is free to move is placed in this magnetic field. A current that varies at an audio rate is then passed through the coil. The varying current establishes a varying magnetic field around the coil. The varying magnetic field of the coil is alternately attracted and repelled by the stationary field of the permanent magnet. Thus, the coil moves back and forth at the same rate as the varying current. The moving coil is attached to a large cone or diaphragm. As the coil vibrates, the cone also vibrates setting the air around the cone in motion at the same rate. This reproduces the original sound.

Magnetic Tape

The tape recorder uses electromagnetic principles to record electronic signals on magnetic tape. The device that actually "writes" the signal on the tape and later "reads" it back is called a record-playback head. It is nothing more than a coil with a ferromagnetic core. Figure 5-30A illustrates its operation in the record mode.

Notice that a tiny air gap exists between the two ends of the core. When current is applied to the coil, a magnetic field is concentrated in this gap. A length of plastic tape, covered with a ferromagnetic substance such as iron oxide, is pulled past the air gap. The magnetic field surrounding the air gap penetrates the tape magnetizing the ferromagnetic coating at this point. If the current applied to the coil varies at an audio

rate, then the magnetic field across the air gap varies at the same rate. The magnetic field alters the magnetic domains on the surface of the tape. Consequently, the magnetic pattern "written" on the tape corresponds to the original audio signal.

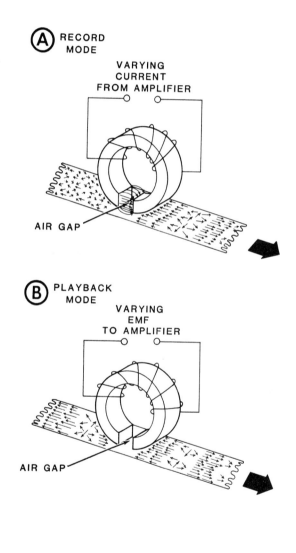

Figure 5-30 Tape record playback head.

To play back the tones recorded on the tape, the process is reversed as shown in Figure 5-30B. The tape is pulled past the air gap so that the core is subjected to the magnetic patterns on the tape. The changing magnetic field induces a tiny EMF into the coil windings. When this EMF is amplified and applied to a loudspeaker, the original audio tones are reproduced.

DC Motor

Earlier, you saw that a generator converts mechanical energy to electrical energy. A motor does just the opposite; it converts electrical energy to mechanical energy. Figure 5-31 illustrates the principle that makes this possible. Here a current carrying conductor is shown in a magnetic field. This is not an induced current; it flows because the conductor is connected across a battery. Because of the current, a magnetic field develops around the conductor in the direction shown. This can be verified by the left-hand rule for conductors that was discussed earlier.

The magnetic field around the conductor interacts with the field of the permanent magnet. Notice that on one side of the conductor the two magnetic fields have the same direction and they add thus producing a strong magnetic field. On the other side of the conductor, the two magnetic fields have opposite directions. Thus, they tend to cancel leaving a weak resultant field at this point. As you can see, the flux lines are more numerous on one side of the conductor than on the other. Thus, on one side, the lines

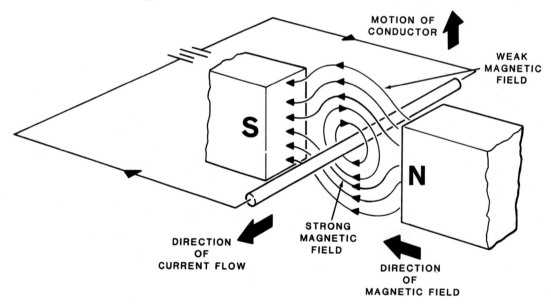

Figure 5-31 DC motor theory.

are bent and forced very close together. These lines have a natural tendency to straighten and move farther apart. However, the only way they can do this is to push the conductor out of the way. Thus, a force develops that pushes the conductor in the direction shown.

There is a rule used to determine the direction that the conductor will move in the magnetic field. It is called the right-hand motor rule, and is illustrated in Figure 5-32. Using the right-hand (not the left), point the index finger in the direction of the field of the permanent magnet. Point the middle finger in the direction of current flow through the conductor and at a right angle to the index finger. Point the thumb straight up and at a right angle to both the index and middle finger. The thumb now points in the direction that the conductor will move. Applying this rule you can see how a simple DC motor operates.

A simplified diagram of the DC motor is shown in Figure 5-33. Notice the similarity to the DC generator described earlier. However, there are two important differences. With the generator, the armature is turned by an outside mechanical force. Here the armature turns because of the motor action just discussed. In the generator, a DC voltage is produced at the brushes. Here, an external DC voltage from a battery is applied to the brushes.

Current flows through the armature as indicated by the arrows. Applying the right-hand motor rule to the side of the armature near the south pole of the magnet, you find that the conductor tends to move up. If you apply the same rule to the side near the north pole, you find that this side tends to move down. Thus, the armature rotates in a counterclockwise direction. After one half cycle of revolution, the two sides of the armature reverse positions. Nevertheless, cur-

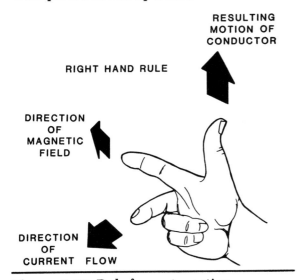

Figure 5-32 Rule for motor action.

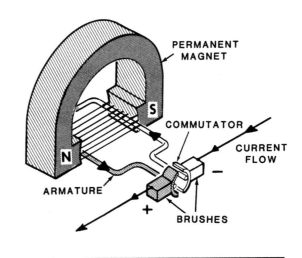

Figure 5-33 The DC motor.

rent still flows in the same direction through the side closest to the south pole. Whichever side of the armature appears at this point, the resulting motion is always up. The upward force at the south pole and the downward force at the north pole cause the armature to constantly rotate.

The simple motor shown here is not practical because a single loop of wire is used as an armature. Real motors use hundreds of turns of wire so that a very strong twisting motion, or torque, is developed.

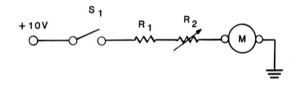

Figure 5-34 Elementary DC motor control.

DC Motor Control

It is possible to operate a DC motor using a switch to turn it on and off. However, there are time when you will want to vary the speed or direction of the motor's rotation. When this happens, it is possible to use resistors of variable resistors to accomplish this.

Figure 5-34 shows the simplest DC motor control circuit. The DC motor is shown as a circle with an M inside. This is the

schematic symbol for a DC motor. Switch S_1 controls the power to the circuit. Ultimately, this switch determines whether or not the motor is running. Resistor R_1 is a series limiting resistor. This resistor prevents excessive current through the circuit when the motor is operating without a load. It is good practice to have a current limiting resistor in the circuit when a motor is connected in series with a power source. The actual control in the circuit is variable resistor R_2.

When R_2 is adjusted to its maximum resistance, the voltage drop across the motor, and therefore the current through the motor, is severely restricted. This results in the motor turning at a low speed. As the resistor is adjusted for less resistance, the motor speeds up. In this way, you can control the speed of a DC motor.

You might assume that, even with R_2 adjusted to its maximum value, the motor would begin rotation the instant switch S_1 is closed. This, however, is not the case because one of the fundamental laws of physics states that **"Bodies in motion tend to stay in motion and bodies at rest tend to stay at rest"**. In order to start rotating and come to operating speed, the motor must overcome two quantities: inertia and friction.

Friction can be defined as the resistance to relative motion between two objects in contact. In other words, any time two objects come in contact, they tend to hold each other in place. In a DC motor, there are a number of points of contact: among them, the contact between the brushes and the commutator.

Inertia is the property of an object by which it remains at rest unless acted upon by some external force. Inertia is the result of the mass of an object. The greater the mass, the greater the force necessary to overcome the inertia. Anyone who has tried to push a stalled automobile will readily understand this concept.

It takes a certain amount of energy to overcome the properties of friction and inertia in a DC motor. For this reason, a given amount of voltage must be applied to the motor before it develops enough torque, or twisting motion, to begin turning. This voltage is called the **offset voltage**. In a well designed DC motor control circuit, torque and inertia are compensated for by using component values that ensure that the voltage applied to the motor always meets or exceeds the value of the offset voltage.

Incidentally, once the inertia and friction are overcome and the motor is running, you can decrease the voltage applied to the motor and still keep it operating.

There may be times when you must change a motor direction. Figure 5-35A shows a motor control circuit consisting of a potentiometer, switch, limiting resistor, and DC motor. In this figure, the wiper on the potentiometer is centered. That is, the resistance between point A and B equals the resistance between points B and C. At point B, the volt-

age is 10 volts positive with respect to one power supply and 10 volts negative with respect to the other. In this configuration, current flows from the +10 V supply to the −10 V supply. No current flows through the motor. This is the **null** position. The motor will move in neither direction.

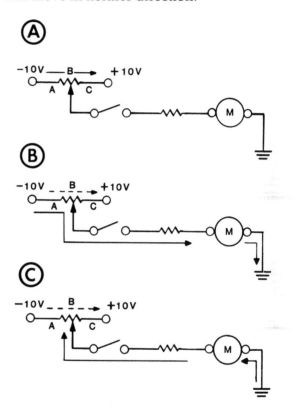

Figure 5-35 DC motor direction and speed control.

As the potentiometer is moved from its centered position, current begins to flow through the motor. This is shown in Figure 5-35B. Notice here that there is much less resistance between the −10 V supply and ground than there is between the -10 V and $+10$ V supplies. Therefore, the current flows from left to right in the illustration.

When the potentiometer is adjusted in the other direction, current begins to flow from right to left as shown in Figure 5-35C. In this instance, the motor direction has changed along with the direction of current flow through the motor.

Besides changing direction, the potentiometer can be used to vary the speed of the motor. The same problems with inertia and friction occur with this control as did with the elementary control shown in the preceding example.

Meter

The same motor action described in the section on DC motors is used in the moving-coil meter movement. Figure 5-36 shows a simplified diagram of this device. Like the motor, it has an armature that is free to move in the field of a permanent magnet. However, in the meter movement, the motion is restricted by one or more springs.

When current flows through the coil, it establishes a magnetic field the strength of which is directly proportional to the current. The motor action causes a torque to develop and the coil tries to rotate. However, the restraining springs prevent the coil from turning more than about 90°.

A pointer is attached to the coil. As the coil rotates, it moves the pointer in front of a graduated scale. The markings on the scale can indicate volts, amps, or ohms depending on the type of meter in which the movement is used. The more current that flows, the farther the coil rotates, and the farther the pointer moves across the scale. As the pointer moves, a reading is taken from the graduated scale. This reading is directly proportional to the amount of current that flows through the coil. This type of meter movement is commonly used in ammeters, voltmeters, and ohmmeters.

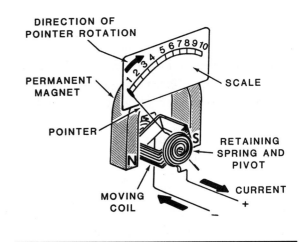

Figure 5-36 The moving-coil meter movement.

Computer Memories

Computers use a variety of electromagnetic devices to store information. One device that has been used to store information is the **core memory** where information is stored on small magnetic cores. These cores are tiny little doughnut-shaped pieces of ferrite material that can be magnetized in either of two directions.

As shown in Figure 5-37, wires are strung through the holes in the cores. By applying current to these wires in the appropriate direction, the cores can be magnetized in a certain pattern. A clockwise magnetic field can arbitrarily be called 1 while a counterclockwise field can be called 0. The circuitry inside the computer interprets patterns of 1's and 0's.

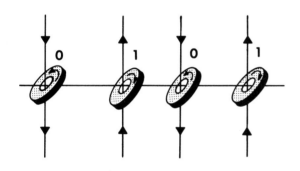

Figure 5-37 Four cores of a computer memory.

Because of the way in which they are magnetized, the cores in Figure 5-37 have the pattern 0101. Numbers, letters of the alphabet, and punctuation marks can be encoded using patterns of 1's and 0's. For example, one popular computer code uses seven digit patterns. The letter A is represented by 1000001; the number 6 by 0110110; and the question mark (?) by 01111111. Thus, if you are willing to use enough cores, the entire contents of this course can be stored in a core memory using seven digit patterns of 1's and 0's.

Magnetic Deflection of Electron Beams

You have learned that a current carrying conductor is deflected or moved by a magnetic field. However, it is not the conductor that is deflected but the electrons traveling through the conductor. Since the electrons are confined to the conductor, it also moves.

In some cases, streams of electrons are not confined to a wire but travel through space. Such a beam can be deflected in the same way as the electrons in a current carrying conductor. There are many practical applications of this principle. The most familiar of these is the TV picture tube shown in Figure 5-38.

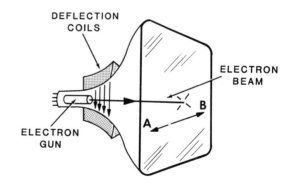

Figure 5-38 Magnetic deflection of the electron beam in a TV picture tube.

In the picture tube, a device called an electron gun produces a narrow beam of electrons that is fired at the TV screen. Wherever the beam hits the phosphor on the screen, light is given off. By moving the beam over the entire surface of the screen and varying the beam's intensity, a picture is produced.

To do this, two magnetic fields are used to deflect the beam. One moves the beam back and forth across the screen over 15,000 times each second. The other moves the beam up and down the screen 30 times each second. The result is that 30 complete pictures consisting of about 500 lines each are drawn each second.

The horizontal deflection coils are shown in Figure 5-38. When current flows in one direction through these coils, a magnetic field having the direction shown is produced. Using the right-hand motor rule, you can see that this field deflects the beam toward point A. If the direction of the field is reversed, the beam deflects toward point B. To deflect the beam in a vertical direction, vertical deflection coils are placed on the sides of the picture tube. This principle is used in radar sets and TV cameras as well as TV receivers.

60. The relay produces a _____ _____ that closes the contacts of a switch.

61. The relay circuit is electrically _____ from the circuit that it controls.

62. In the moving-coil record-player pickup, a voltage is developed by having a moving-coil vibrate in a stationary _____ _____.

63. In the loudspeaker, a speaker cone is made to vibrate by applying a varying current to a _____ _____.

64. The record-playback head used in tape recorder uses a varying current which establishes a varying magnetic field that aligns the _____ _____ on the tape.

65. The rule that is used to determine the direction that a current carrying conductor will move when the conductor is placed in a magnetic field is called the _____ _____ rule for motors.

66. Using this rule, the forefinger should point in the direction of the magnetic field, while the middle finger points in the direction of current flow through the conductor and _____ points in the direction that the conductor will move.

67. A _____ uses this technique to deflect a pointer in front of a scale.

68. The TV receiver uses this same technique to deflect an _____ _____ back and forth across the face of the picture tube.

69. In some computer memories, small magnetic doughnut shaped devices called _____ are used to store information.

Action-at-a-distance is explained in terms of a field. Because a magnet can affect objects at a distance, it is said to be surrounded by a magnetic field. The field is assumed to be made-up of lines of force called flux lines.

Magnets have north and south poles. Arbitrarily, the flux lines have been assigned a direction so that they leave the magnet at the north pole and enter the magnet at the south pole forming complete loops. The flux lines cannot cross each other and tend to form the smallest possible loops.

Like magnetic poles repel; unlike poles attract.

All materials are classified as either ferromagnetic, paramagnetic, or diamagnetic. Ferromagnetic materials are strongly attracted by magnetic fields; paramagnetic materials are only slightly attracted; and diamagnetic materials are slightly repelled. Generally, paramagnetic and diamagnetic materials are considered to be non-magnetic.

When an electrostatic charge moves, a magnetic field develops. The electron spins on its axis, producing a magnetic field. In most atoms, electrons with opposite spins pair off so that their magnetic fields cancel. However, in iron, nickel, and cobalt the two valence electrons spin in the same direction and thus their fields add.

In ferromagnetic materials the magnetic atoms bunch in groups called domains. The domains are arranged haphazardly and their fields cancel. However, when subjected to a magnetic field, the domains align in the same direction creating a magnet.

Magnetism and electricity are closely related. Current flow produces a magnetic field and a moving magnetic field can produce current flow.

The direction of the magnetic field caused by current flow can be determined by the left-hand rule for conductors. This rule states: Grasp the conductor in your left hand with the thumb pointing in the direction of current flow. Your fingers now point in the direction of the flux lines.

The magnetic field around the conductor can be strengthened and concentrated by winding the conductor as a coil. The result is called an electromagnet and it posesses many of the characteristics of a permanent magnet.

The north pole of the electromagnet can be determined by the left-hand rule for coils. It states: Grasp the coil in your left hand with your fingers wrapped around it in the direction of current flow. Your thumb now points toward the north pole of the coil.

Several magnetic quantities are important. Permeability is the ease with which a substance accepts lines of force. Its reciprocal is called reluctance. Flux is the total lines of force around a magnet. Flux density refers to the number of flux lines per unit of area. Magnetomotive force is the force that produces the flux in a coil. Field intensity is the amount of MMF per unit of length of the coil.

When one body has an electrostatic or magnetic field, it can induce a change in another body without actually touching the other body. This is called induction.

A magnet can induce a magnetic field into a ferromagnetic body without touching it. This is called magnetic induction. When the magnet is taken away, a magnetic field will remain in the ferromagnetic body. This is called residual magnetism. The ability of a substance to retain a magnetic field after the magnetizing force has been removed is called retentivity.

When a conductor moves across a magnetic field, an EMF is induced in the conductor. This is called electromagnetic induction.

The magnitude of the induced EMF is proportional to the rate at which the conductor cuts the magnetic lines of force. The more lines per second that are cut, the higher the induced EMF.

The polarity of the induced EMF can be determined by the left-hand rule for generators. Using this rule, the thumb is pointed in the direction that the conductor is moving. The index finger is pointed in the direction of the flux lines (from north to south). If the middle finger is now placed at right angles to the thumb and index finger, it points in the direction in which current will flow through the conductor.

A device that uses electromagnetic induction to convert mechanical energy to electrical energy is called a generator. A generator may produce AC or DC depending voltage on how it is constructed. An AC generator is called an alternator. The DC generator uses commutators and brushes to convert AC to DC.

There are many other devices that use magnetic or electromagnetic principles.

The relay uses an electromagnet to close switch contacts.

The record pickup uses a magnet and moving coil to convert stylus vibrations into voltage variations that can be amplified. The loudspeaker uses a similar arrangement to convert these amplified voltage variations back to sound.

The tape recorder uses an electromagnet as a record head. Current variations are applied to the electromagnet. This creates corresponding magnetic patterns on a length of tape. In the playback mode, the head converts to a tiny generator. The magnetic variations on the tape induce tiny voltage variations into the coil. These voltage variations are amplified, and applied to the loudspeaker where they are converted back to sound.

The motor converts electrical energy to mechanical energy. Current is passed through a coil, producing an electromagnetic field. This field interacts with a permanent magnet's field. As a result, the coil is forced to move. By proper design, a constant circular motion is achieved.

The meter works on the same principle as the motor. Here the movement of the coil is restricted by springs. A pointer attached to the coil moves in front of a scale indicating the current through the meter.

Electromagnetism is also used to deflect the electron beam in TV receivers, TV cameras, and radar indicators.

The direction of movement of the coil in the motor or meter, or the direction of deflection of the electron beam can be determined by the right-hand motor rule. Using this rule, the thumb, index finger, and middle finger of the right hand are held at right angles to each other. If the index finger is pointed in direction of the magnetic field and the middle finger is pointed in the direction of electron flow, the thumb will point in the direction in which the conductor (or electron beam) will move.

Electrical Measurements

Contents

Introduction

This unit deals with electrical measurements. In this unit you will learn about the construction and operation of the most commonly used electrical measuring instrument — the volt-ohm-milliammeter (VOM). As the name implies, this instrument is used to measure voltage, resistance, and current.

The heart of this instrument is a moving-coil meter movement like the one discussed in the previous unit on magnetism. In this unit, you will learn much more about this type of meter movement and see how it can be used to measure current, voltage, and resistance.

Unit Objectives

When you have completed this unit you will be able to do the following:

1. List six parts of the moving-coil meter movement and explain the purpose of each.

2. Demonstrate how the ammeter, voltmeter, and ohmmeter should be connected to a circuit under test.

3. Given the full scale deflection and the meter resistance, calculate the proper value of shunt required to increase the current capability to a given value.

4. Given the full scale deflection and the meter resistance, calculate the series dropping resistance required to increase the voltage capability to a given value.

5. Draw the schematic diagrams of a simple series ohmmeter and a simple shunt ohmmeter.

6. Define and calculate meter sensitivity for a given meter movement.

7. Explain how a single meter movement can be used in a VOM to indicate current, voltage, and resistance.

8. Define voltmeter loading and explain how its effects can be minimized.

9. Name the components used to increase the range of a voltmeter and an ammeter.

10. State at what point on a meter scale the most accurate readings are obtained.

11. State the purpose of the "ZERO OHMS" variable resistor in an ohmmeter.

12. Name the three components that make up the most basic ohmmeter.

13. State how an ammeter can introduce an error when it is used to measure current.

14. Define the term parallax.

The Meter Movement

The heart of the volt-ohm-milliammeter (VOM) is the meter movement. The most popular type of meter movement is the permanent-magnet, moving-coil movement discussed in the previous unit. This device is also called the d'Arsonval movement after its inventor Arsene d'Arsonval. The first version, introduced in 1882, is called a galvanometer. It is quite delicate and somewhat crude. In 1888, Edward Weston introduced an improved version of the device that is similar to the designs used today.

Construction

Figure 6-1 shows the construction of a meter movement. Several important parts are listed. In the following section, each of these is discussed in detail starting with the permanent magnet.

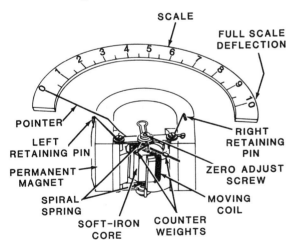

Figure 6-1 Permanent-magnet, moving-coil meter movement.

Figure 6-2 shows the permanent magnet system. A horse shoe magnet produces the stationary magnetic field. To concentrate the magnetic field in the area of the moving coil, pole pieces are added to the magnet. These are made of soft iron and have a very low reluctance. Consequently, the lines of flux tend to concentrate in the area shown. In addition, a stationary soft-iron core is placed between the pole pieces. Enough space is left between the pole pieces and the core so that the moving coil can rotate freely in this space. As you can see, the pole pieces and core restrict most of the flux to the area of the moving coil.

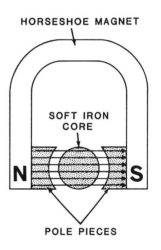

Figure 6-2 The permanent magnet.

Figure 6-3 shows how the moving coil fits around the soft-iron core. The coil consists of many turns of extremely fine wire on an aluminum frame. The aluminum frame is very light so that little torque is needed to move it. The two ends of the coil connect, through other circuitry, to the leads of the ammeter, voltmeter, or ohmmeter.

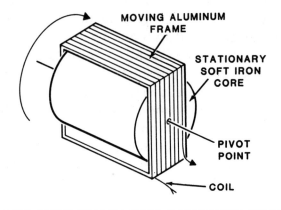

Figure 6-3 The moving coil.

Figure 6-4 shows the details of the pointer assembly. The pointer is attached to the moving coil so that it moves when the coil moves. Counter-weights are often attached to the pointer so that a perfect balance is achieved. This makes the pointer easier to move and helps the meter to attain the same accuracy in all positions. A well balanced meter will read the same whether held vertically or horizontally.

Retaining pins on either side of the movement limit the distance that the pointer and other rotating parts can move. Two spiral springs at opposite ends of the moving-coil force the pointer back to the zero position when no current is flowing through the coil. In most movements, the spiral springs are also used to apply current to the moving coil. The two ends of the coil connect to the inner ends of the spiral spring. The outer

end of the rear spring is fixed in place. However, the outer end of the front spring connects to a zero adjust screw. This allows you to set the pointer to exactly the zero point on the scale when no current is flowing through the coil.

The moving coil, pointer, and counterweight rotate around a pivot point. To hold the friction to an absolute minimum, jeweled bearings are used at this point just as they are in a fine watch.

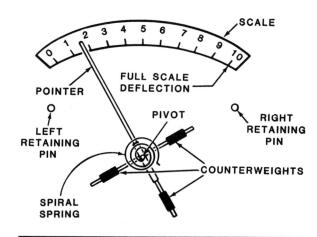

Figure 6-4 The pointer assembly.

Operation

Now that you have an idea of how the meter is constructed, look at the meter's operation. In the previous unit you learned that a conductor is deflected at a right angle to a stationary magnetic field if current flows through the conductor. This is the principle of operation of the DC motor. You also learned a rule, called the right-hand motor rule, that describes this action. Figure 6-5 illustrates this rule and the motor action that causes the meter to deflect. An end view of one turn of the moving-coil is shown. Current is forced to flow through the coil so that current flows "out of the page" on the left. Applying the right hand rule to the coil at this point, you find that the coil is forced up on the left and down on the right. This causes the pointer to move up scale or in the clockwise direction.

The amount of torque produced by this tiny "motor" is proportional to the magnitude of the current that flows through the moving coil. The more current, the greater the torque, and the farther the pointer is deflected.

Figure 6-5 can be used to illustrate an important characteristic of the d'Arsonval meter movement. You assume that the current is always flowing in the same direction through the moving coil. That is, a direct current, DC, is applied to the coil. This movement will work fine as long as the current is direct. However, the movement will not respond properly to an alternating current, AC. Each time the current reverses, the coil will attempt to reverse its direction of deflection. If the current changes direction more than a few times each second, the coil cannot follow the changes. Thus, AC must not be applied to this type of meter movement.

Notice also that if you allow current to pass through the coil in other than the direction shown in Figure 6-5, the pointer will deflect in the wrong direction. This indicates that this type of movement is **polarity sensitive**. This means that current must flow through the movement in one specific direction in

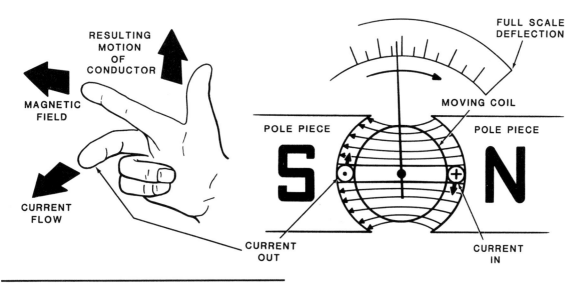

Figure 6-5 Motor action of the moving coil.

order to assure proper operation. If the meter movement is connected improperly, it deflects in the wrong direction and possibly damage the movement.

Meter movements are rated according to the amount of current needed to produce full-scale deflection. For example, a 50 microampere meter movement deflects full scale when 50 microamperes of current flows through it. The 50 μA meter movement is one of the most commonly used types of d'Arsonval movements. The 100 μA and 200 μA movements are also popular.

Taut-Band Movement

An important variation of the d'Arsonval movement is the taut-band meter movement. Figure 6-6 is a simplified diagram that shows the construction of this type of movement. The moving coil is suspended by two tiny stretched metal bands. One end of each band is connected to the moving coil while the other end is connected to a tension spring. The springs keep the bands pulled tight. The bands replace the pivots, bearing, and spiral springs used in the conventional d'Arsonval movement. This not only simplifies the construction of the meter, it also reduces the friction to practically zero. Consequently, the taut-band movement can be made somewhat more sensitive than the movement discussed earlier. Taut-band instruments with 10 μA movements are available.

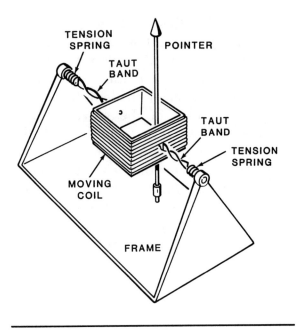

Figure 6-6 Taut-band meter movement.

The taut-bands serve several purposes. First, they suspend the coil in such a way that the friction is nearly zero. When current is applied, the coil rotates and the bands are twisted. When current is removed, the bands untwist returning the pointer to the zero position. The bands also serve as the current path to and from the coil.

The taut-band movement has several advantages over the original d'Arsonval movement. As you have seen, it is generally more sensitive. It is also more rugged and durable. Mechanical shocks simply deflect the tension springs which can then bounce back to their original positions. The instrument remains more accurate for the same reason. Because of these advantages, the taut-band movement is quite popular.

1. The permanent-magnet, moving-coil meter movement is often called the _____ movement after its inventor.

2. In this movement, a stationary magnetic field is provided by a _____ _____.

3. Pole pieces and a soft-iron core are used to concentrate the magnetic field in the air gap through which the _____ _____ rotates.

4. Attached to the coil is a _____, which rotates in front of a scale.

5. Two spiral springs are used to return the pointer to the _____ position when no current flows through the coil.

6. A rule that tells you which way the coil will rotate is called the _____-_____ motor rule.

7. This type of meter movement will indicate properly only when the applied current is:

   _____
   (DC/AC)

8. A meter that uses thin metal bands to replace the pivots, jeweled bearings, and spiral springs is called the _____-_____ type.

9. In the meter movement described in question 8, less _____ is required to cause full scale deflection.

The meter movements discussed in the previous section are basically current meters. That is, they deflect when current flows through them. In each case, the moving coil consists of many turns of extremely fine wire. Current is carried to the coil through the fragile spiral springs or the taut-bands of the movement. Because of the delicate nature of the coil and the springs or bands, care must be taken not to feed excessive current through the movement. The current necessary for full-scale deflection will not harm the movement, but a 100% overload might. The coil may burn out; the spring may be damaged; or the aluminum needle may be bent if driven too hard against the right retaining pin.

Care must also be taken to observe polarity when using the meter movement. A reverse current will cause the needle to deflect backwards. If the current is too great, the needle may be bent when it strikes the left retaining pin.

Measuring Current

The rules for using the ammeter were discussed in Unit 1. Here is a brief review of these rules.

First, the ammeter must be connected in series with the current that is to be measured. This means that the circuit under test must be broken so that the ammeter can be inserted. At times, this can be difficult to do and, for this reason, is considered the prime disadvantage of the ammeter.

Second, polarity must be observed when connecting the meter. This means that the ammeter should be connected so that it deflects up scale. The terminals of most meters are marked with − and +. Connect the meter so that current flows into the − terminal.

Third, you must not exceed the current ratings of the meter. Therefore, you should have some idea of the amount of current that you will be measuring before you connect the meter to the circuit. Too much current may damage the meter's pointer or burn out the moving coil.

Increasing the Range of the Ammeter

Each meter movement has its own current rating. This is the amount of current that will cause full-scale deflection. For example, an inexpensive meter movement may have a current rating of 1 mA. To obtain a usable reading, the current through the movement cannot be more than 1mA. By itself, the movement has a single usable range of 0 to 1mA.

Obviously, this meter movement would be much more useful if it could measure currents greater than 1mA as well as those less than 1mA. Fortunately, there is an easy way to convert a sensitive meter movement to a less sensitive current meter. This is done by connecting a small value resistor in parallel with the meter movement. The resistor is called a shunt. Its purpose is to act as a low resistance path around the movement so that most of the current flows through the shunt and only a small amount flows through the movement.

Figure 6-7A shows a 1 mA meter movement connected across a low resistance shunt to form a higher range ammeter. The range of the meter depends on how much current flows through the shunt. In Figure 6-7B, the current applied to the ammeter is 10 mA. However, only 1 mA of this flows through the meter movement. The other 9 mA flows through the shunt. Thus, to convert the 1 mA movement to a 0-10 mA meter, the shunt must be chosen so that 9/10 of the applied current flows through the shunt. Once this is done, the full scale position on the scale indicates 10 mA since this is the amount of current that must be applied before full scale deflection is reached.

If the value of the shunt is made smaller thus allowing a greater portion of the current to flow through the shunt, the meter can indicate even higher values of current. Figure 6-7C shows the requirements necessary to measure 100 mA. Here 99 mA or 99 percent of the current goes through the shunt. Thus, the resistance of the shunt must be much smaller than the resistance of the meter movement.

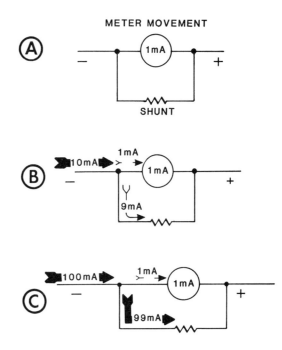

Figure 6-7 Increasing the current range of the ammeter.

Computing the Shunt Resistance

To determine the proper value of the shunt resistor, you must first know something of the characteristics of the meter movement. In an earlier example, you saw that full scale deflection required 1 mA. However, you must also know either the resistance of the meter movement or the voltage dropped by the movement when the current is 1 mA. Of course, if you know one, you can compute the other using Ohm's Law.

The resistance value of the meter movement is usually given in the manufacturer's literature, catalog, or operating instructions. Often it is printed right on the meter movement itself. If you assume that a 0-1 mA movement has a resistance of 1000 Ω or 1 kΩ, then 1 mA of current causes a voltage drop across the meter movement of:

$$E = IR$$

$$E = 1\,mA \times 1\,k\Omega$$

$$E = .001\,A \times 1000\,\Omega$$

$$E = 1\,V$$

If you refer to Figure 6-7, you will see that this is the voltage developed across the meter movement in each of the examples shown. Since the shunt resistance is connected in parallel with the meter movement, this same voltage must be developed across the shunt. This means that in the example shown in Figure 6-7B, the 9 mA current must develop 1 V across the shunt. Using Ohm's Law, you can now compute the value of the shunt since you now know the current through the shunt and the voltage dropped by the shunt. Thus, the value of the shunt should be:

$$R = \frac{E}{I}$$

$$R = \frac{1\,V}{9\,mA}$$

$$R = \frac{1\,V}{.009\,A}$$

$$R = 111\,\Omega$$

This is the resistance necessary to shunt 9 mA around the meter when a total current of 10 mA is flowing in the circuit. However, the shunt works equally well when the movement is indicating half-scale or 0.5 mA. Again, the voltage across the meter can be calculated by Ohm's Law:

$$E = IR$$

$$E = 0.5\,mA \times 1\,k\Omega$$

$$E = 0.0005\,A \times 1000\,\Omega$$

$$E = 0.5\,V$$

Since the voltage across the meter is the same as that across the 111 ohm resistor, the current through the shunt is:

$$I = \frac{E}{R}$$

$$I = \frac{0.5\,V}{111\,\Omega}$$

$$I = .0045\,A \text{ or } 4.5\,mA$$

As you can see, nine-tenths of the current still flows through the shunt while only one-tenth flows through the movement. Thus, the movement indicates 0.5 mA when 5 mA of current flows in the circuit. The meter scale is marked off 0 through 10 rather than 0 through 1, and a 111 ohm resistor is connected across the meter movement. This converts the circuit to a 0-10mA current meter.

Interestingly enough, you can find the value of shunt required in another way. Refer once again to Figure 6-7B. You know that 9 mA must flow through the shunt so that only 1mA flows through the meter movement. In order for the shunt to conduct 9 times as much current as the meter, its resistance must be only 1/9 that of the meter resistance. Now since the meter resistance is 1000 Ω the shunt resistance must be:

$$\frac{1000\ \Omega}{9} = 111\ \Omega$$

Try applying these two methods to the situation shown in Figure 6-7C. Once again the current through the meter movement is 1 mA. Thus, the voltage drop across the movement and across the shunt is still 1 V. This allows you to compute the value of the shunt:

$$R = \frac{E}{I}$$

$$R = \frac{1\ V}{99\ mA}$$

$$R = \frac{1\ V}{.099\ A}$$

$$R = 10.1\ \Omega$$

You arrive at this same answer by reasoning that the shunt resistance must be 1/99 that of the meter resistance since the shunt conducts 99 times as much current. Thus, the shunt resistance must be:

$$\frac{1000\ \Omega}{99} = 10.1\ \Omega$$

Here's another example. Figure 6-8A shows a 0-50 μA meter movement with a resistance of 1800 ohms. What value shunt is required to construct a 0-1 mA meter? Figure 6-8B shows the current distribution. Notice that 1 mA or 1000 μA of current flows through the circuit. However, only 50 μA can flow through the meter movement. The remaining 950 μA must flow through the shunt. Since you know the resistance of the meter movement (1800 Ω) and the current through it (50 μA), you can compute the voltage across it:

$$E = IR$$

$$E = 50\ \mu A \times 1800\ \Omega$$

$$E = 0.00005\ A \times 1800\ \Omega$$

$$E = 0.09\ V$$

Because the shunt is in parallel with the meter movement, this same voltage is developed across the shunt. Thus, you can compute the shunt value:

$$R_S = \frac{E}{I}$$

$$R_S = \frac{0.09\ V}{950\ \mu A}$$

$$R_S = \frac{0.09\ V}{0.00095\ A}$$

$$R_S = 94.7\ \Omega$$

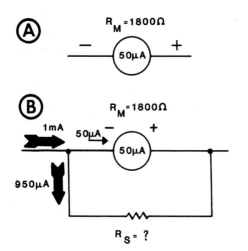

Figure 6-8 Find the value of R_S.

As before, you can arrive at this same answer by reasoning that 95% of the current flows through the shunt. This means that 95% or 19 times as much current flows through the shunt as through the meter movement. Because the shunt conducts 19 times as much current, the resistance of the shunt must be 1/19 that of the meter movement. Thus the shunt resistance must be:

$$\frac{1800\ \Omega}{19} = 94.7\ \Omega$$

Ammeter Accuracy

Every meter movement has a certain accuracy associated with it. The accuracy is specified as a percentage of error at full scale deflection. Accuracies of ±2% or ±3% of full-scale are common for good quality instruments. Figure 6-9 illustrates what is meant by ±3% of full scale. The scale shown is a 100 mA current scale. Remember, the meter accuracy refers to full scale deflection. At full scale, ±3% equals ±3 mA. For this meter, a current of exactly 100 mA would cause the meter to indicate anywhere from 97 mA to 103 mA. Another way to look at it is that a meter reading of exactly 100 mA might be caused by an actual current of from 97 mA to 103 mA.

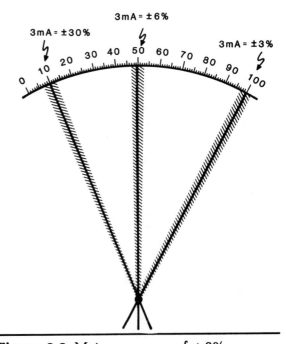

Figure 6-9 Meter accuracy of ±3%.

As you can see, ±3% accuracy means that the reading may be off by as much as ±3 mA at full scale. More importantly, it means that the reading may be off by as much as ±3 mA at any point on the scale. This may result in serious errors when readings are taken from the low end of the scale. For example, when the meter indicates 50 mA, the actual current may be anywhere from 47 mA to 53 mA. Thus, at half-scale the accuracy is no longer ±3%; it is now ±6%. By the same token, for an indicated current of 10 mA, the actual current may be anywhere from 7 mA to 13 mA. Here, the accuracy is only ±30%.

Because meter accuracy is specified in this manner, the accuracy gets progressively worse, as you move down the scale. For this reason, current measurements will be most accurate when a current range is selected that results in a near full scale deflection of the meter. The nearer full scale, the more accurate the reading will be.

10. The ammeter is a device for measuring _____.

11. Because many current meters measure currents less than 1 ampere, they are often called _____ ammeters or _____ ammeters.

12. The ammeter must always be connected in _____ with the circuit under test.

13. When inserting an ammeter into a circuit under test, _____ must be observed.

14. A resistor placed in parallel to the meter movement in order to increase the meter's range is called a _____ resistor.

15. Refer to Figure 6-8. The voltage drop across the meter movement is _____ V.

16. If you want to extend the range of the movement shown in Figure 6-8 to 10 mA, _____ mA of current must flow through the shunt resistor.

17. Because the meter's shunt parallels the meter movement, _____ V is dropped across the shunt.

18. The resistance of the shunt must be (more/less) than the resistance of the movement.

19. Using Ohm's Law, you find that the proper value of the shunt must be _____ ohms.

20. The accuracy of an ammeter refers to the percentage of error at _____-_____ deflection.

21. A 100 mA ammeter with an accuracy of ±2% of full scale will read with ±_____ mA of the actual current at any point on the scale.

22. A reading of 50 mA may be caused by a current of _____ mA to _____ mA.

23. Consequently, at 50 mA the accuracy of the meter is not ±2% but ±_____%.

The Voltmeter

The basic meter movement can be used to measure voltage as well as current. In fact every meter movement has a certain voltage rating as well as a current rating. This is the voltage that causes full scale deflection. Of course, the voltage rating is determined by the current rating and the meter resistance. For example, a 50 µA meter movement that has a resistance of 2000 Ω deflects full scale when connected across a voltage of:

$$E = IR$$

$$E = 50\,\mu A \times 2000\,\Omega$$

$$E = 0.1\,V$$

That is, the meter movement alone can be used to measure voltages up to 0.1 volt. Thus, the meter scale can be calibrated from 0 to 0.1 volt. However, if the meter movement is connected across a much higher voltage such as 10 volts, it may be damaged because the increase in voltage will cause a corresponding increase in current. Obviously, to be practical, there must be a way to extend the voltage range of the basic meter movement.

Extending the Range

You have seen that a 50 µA, 2000 Ω meter movement can withstand a voltage of 0.1 V without exceeding full scale. To extend the range, you must ensure that the voltage across the meter does not exceed 0.1 volt

when the meter movement is connected across a higher voltage. To do this, you connect a resistor in series with the meter movement as shown in Figure 6-10. The resistor is called a **multiplier** because it multiplies the range of the meter movement.

The purpose of the multiplier resistor is to limit the current that flows through the meter movement. For example, in the voltmeter shown in Figure 6-10, the current through the meter movement must be limited to 50 µA. Another way to look at it is that the multiplier must drop all the voltage applied to the voltmeter except the 0.1 V allowed across the meter movement. For example, if the range is to be extended to 10 V, then the multiplier must drop 10 V − 0.1 V = 9.9 V.

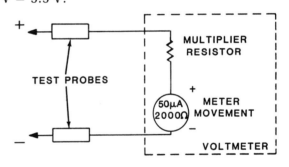

Figure 6-10 A voltmeter is formed by connecting a multiplier resistor in series with a microammeter.

Calculating the Multiplier

You have seen that the value of the multiplier must be high enough to limit the current to the full-scale current rating of the meter movement for any applied voltage. If you keep this in mind, you can easily calculate the required value of the multiplier for any voltage range.

Assume that you want to convert the 50 μA, 2000 Ω meter movement to a 10 V voltmeter by adding a multiplier resistor in series. Obviously, a current of only 50 μA must flow when the voltmeter is connected across 10 V. Thus, the total resistance of the voltmeter must be:

$$R_{total} = \frac{E_{full\text{-}scale}}{I_{full\text{-}scale}}$$

$$R_{total} = \frac{10 \text{ V}}{50 \text{ μA}}$$

$$R_{total} = 200,000 \text{ Ω}$$

However, the meter movement itself has a resistance of 2000 Ω. Thus, the multiplier must have a value of 200,000 Ω − 2000 Ω = 198,000 Ω or 198 kΩ.

This means that the basic 50 μA, 2000 Ω meter movement can now measure 0 to 10 volts because 10 volts must be applied to cause full-scale deflection. From a voltage standpoint, the multiplier resistor drops 99% of the applied voltage. That is, for an applied voltage of 10 volts, the multiplier drops:

$$E = IR$$

$$E = 50 \text{ μA} \times 198,000 \text{ Ω}$$

$$E = 9.9 \text{ V}$$

This leaves 0.1 volt to be dropped across the meter. Because the total voltmeter resistance is 100 times larger than the meter resistance, the range of the meter is multiplied by 100. Of course, the meter scale should now be calibrated from 0 to 10 V.

To be sure you have the idea, determine the value of multiplier required to convert the same meter movement to a 0-100 V voltmeter. This time, the multiplier must limit the current to 50 μA when 100 V is applied. Thus, the total resistance of the voltmeter must be:

$$R_{total} = \frac{E_{full\text{-}scale}}{I_{full\text{-}scale}}$$

$$R_{total} = \frac{100 \text{ V}}{50 \text{ μA}}$$

$$R_{total} = 2,000,000 \text{ Ω or 2 MΩ}$$

Here again, 2000 Ω are supplied by the meter movement. Thus, the value of the multiplier must be:

$$R_{multiplier} = R_{total} - R_{meter}$$

$$R_{multiplier} = 2,000,000 \text{ Ω} - 2000 \text{ Ω}$$

$$R_{total} = 1,998,000 \text{ Ω or 1.998 MΩ}$$

Notice that 1.998 MΩ is extremely close to 2 MΩ. The difference is so slight that you probably would not notice any difference in deflection regardless of which value was used. In this case, a standard value 2 MΩ resistor would probably be used instead of the 1.998 MΩ value which is not easily obtained.

Multiple-Range Voltmeters

A practical voltmeter has several ranges. One arrangement for achieving multiple ranges is shown in Figure 6-11. Here, the voltmeter has four ranges that can be selected by the range switch. Again, the 50 μA, 2000 Ω meter-movement is used. On the 0.1 V range, no multiplier is required since this is the voltage rating of the meter movement itself.

On the 1 V range, R_1 is switched in series with the meter movement. The value of R_1 is given as 18 kΩ . Using the procedure outlined earlier, verify that this is the proper value multiplier required.

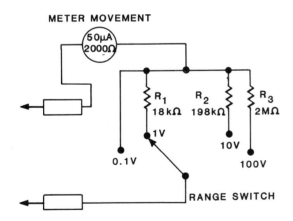

Figure 6-11 Multi-range voltmeter.

Notice that on the 10-volt and 100-volt ranges, the multiplier values computed earlier are switched in series with the meter movement.

Figure 6-12 shows another arrangement that is sometimes used when several ranges are required. On the 0.1 V range, no multiplier is required. On the 1 V range, an 18 kΩ multiplier is switched in series with the meter movement. Up to this point, the arrangement is similar to that shown in Figure 6-11. However, here the similarity ends. On the 10 V range, R_2 is switched in series with R_1. Thus, the total resistance in series with the meter movement is 18 kΩ + 180 kΩ = 198 kΩ. Notice that this is the same value of multiplier used on the 10 V range in Figure 6-11. The only difference is that in Figure 6-11 a single 198 kΩ resistor is used while in Figure 6-12 two resistors having a total resistance of 198 kΩ are used.

On the 100 V range, R_3 is switched in series with R_1 and R_2. Thus, the total multiplier resistance is 18 kΩ + 180 kΩ + 1.8 MΩ = 1.998 MΩ. You will recall that this is the exact multiplier value that was computed earlier for the 100 V range.

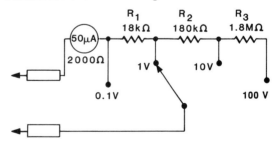

Figure 6-12 Here the multiplier resistors are connected in series.

Sensitivity (Ohms per Volt)

An important characteristic of any voltmeter is its sensitivity. Sensitivity can be thought of as the amount of current required to produce full scale deflection of the meter movement. For example, a 50 μA meter movement is more sensitive than a 1 mA meter movement because less current is required to produce full scale deflection.

However, sensitivity is more often defined in another way. Sensitivity is normally expressed in ohms per volt (also written ohms/volt). The more sensitive the meter is, the higher the ohms-per-volt rating will be. The sensitivity in ohms per volt of any voltmeter can be determined simply by dividing the full-scale current rating of the meter movement into 1 V. That is:

$$\text{Sensitivity} = \frac{1\text{ V}}{I_{\text{full scale}}}$$

Thus, the sensitivity of a voltmeter that uses a 50 μA meter movement is:

$$\text{Sensitivity} = \frac{1\text{ V}}{I_{\text{full scale}}}$$

$$\text{Sensitivity} = \frac{1\text{ V}}{50\text{ μA}}$$

$$\text{Sensitivity} = 20,000\text{ ohms per volt}$$

This means that on the 1 V range, the voltmeter has a total resistance of 20,000 ohms. You can prove this by referring back to Figures 6-11 or 6-12. On the 1 V range, the multiplier has a value of 18 kΩ and the meter movement has a resistance of 2 kΩ. Consequently, the total resistance is 20,000 Ω.

The sensitivity is determined solely by the full-scale current rating of the meter movement. Thus, it has the same sensitivity regardless of the range used. Consequently, on any range, the voltmeters shown in Figure 6-11 and 6-12 have a resistance of 20,000 Ω × V; where V is the selected full-scale voltage range. Thus, on the 10 V range, the total voltmeter resistance is 20,000 Ω × 10 = 200,000 Ω.

Here's another example. What is the sensitivity of a voltmeter that uses a 1 mA meter movement? Remember, sensitivity is determined by dividing the full-scale current into 1 V. That is:

$$\text{Sensitivity} = \frac{1\text{ V}}{I_{\text{full scale}}}$$

$$\text{Sensitivity} = \frac{1\text{ V}}{1\text{ mA}}$$

$$\text{Sensitivity} = 1000\text{ ohms per volt}$$

What is the total resistance of this voltmeter on the 5 V range? The resistance would be 1000 Ω × 5 = 5 kΩ.

Loading Effect of Voltmeters

An unfortunate aspect of test equipment is that in measuring an electrical quantity you change the quantity that you are attempting to measure. When measuring voltage, you must connect a voltmeter across the circuit under test. Since some current must flow through the voltmeter, the circuit behavior is modified somewhat. Often the effects of the voltmeter can be ignored, especially if the meter has a high ohms/volt rating. However, if the voltmeter has a low ohms/volt rating or the circuit or component under test has a high resistance, the effects of the meter cannot be ignored.

Consider the circuit shown in Figure 6-13. Here two 10 kΩ resistors are connected in series across a 6 V battery. Since the resistors are the same value, each drops one half of the applied voltage or 3 V. Thus, you would expect a voltmeter to indicate a reading of 3 volts if it were connnected across either resistor. However, if the voltmeter has a low ohms/volt rating, the actual reading may be very inaccurate.

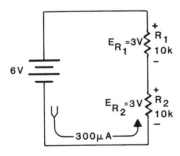

Figure 6-13 R_2 drops 3 volts.

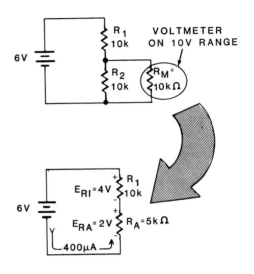

Figure 6-14 The 1000 ohms-per-volt meter loads down the circuit causing an inaccurate reading.

Figure 6-14A shows the same circuit with a low-sensitivity voltmeter connected across R_2. The voltmeter has a sensitivity of 1000 ohms/volt. Since you expect the voltage across R_2 to be about 3 volts, the voltmeter is on the 0-10 volt range. Thus, its resistance (R_M) is 1000 Ω × 10 = 10,000 Ω. Because R_M is in parallel with R_2, the total resistance is reduced. The parallel resistance (R_A) of the meter and R_2 can be computed as you learned earlier:

$$R_A = \frac{R_2 \times R_M}{R_2 + R_M}$$

$$R_A = \frac{10,000\ \Omega \times 10,000\ \Omega}{10,000\ \Omega + 10,000\ \Omega}$$

$$R_A = \frac{100,000,000\ \Omega}{20,000\ \Omega}$$

$$R_A = 5000\ \Omega \text{ or } 5\ k\Omega$$

Therefore, the circuit shown in Figure 6-14A reduces to the circuit in Figure 6-14B. Notice how this upsets the operation of the circuit. The total series resistance of R_1 and R_A is now only 15 kΩ instead of 20 kΩ. This allows more current to flow:

$$I = \frac{E}{R}$$

$$I = \frac{6\ V}{15,000\ \Omega}$$

$$I = 0.000400\ A\ or\ 400\ \mu A$$

Thus, the current increases from its previous value of 300 μA to a new value of 400 μA. The voltage distribution also changes since R_1 is now larger than R_A. The voltage dropped by R_A is:

$$E_{R_A} = I \times R_A$$

$$E_{R_A} = 0.0004\ A \times 5000\ \Omega$$

$$E_{R_A} = 2\ V$$

The voltage dropped by R_1 increases to:

$$E_{R_1} = I \times R_1$$

$$E_{R_1} = 0.0004\ A \times 10,000\ \Omega$$

$$E_{R_1} = 4\ V$$

Thus, instead of reading 3 V as you would expect, the meter measures only 2 V across R_2. This is an inaccuracy of 33%. This effect is called **loading**. The meter is loading down the circuit causing the voltage across R_2 to decrease. The loading effect becomes noticeable when the resistance of the meter approaches that of the resistor across which the meter is connected. For example, if the resistance of the meter is 10 times that of R_2, then the loading effect becomes barely noticeable.

Figure 6-15 shows the same circuit with a 20,000 ohms/volt meter connected across R_2. On the 10 V range, the resistance of the meter is 20,000 Ω × 10 Ω or 200,000 Ω or 200 kΩ. Here, the equivalent resistance of R_M and R_2 in parallel is:

$$R_A = \frac{R_M \times R_2}{R_M + R_2}$$

$$R_A = \frac{200\ k\Omega \times 10\ k\Omega}{200\ k\Omega + 10\ k\Omega}$$

$$R_A = \frac{2000\ M\Omega}{210\ k\Omega}$$

$$R_A = 9524\ \Omega\ or\ about\ 9.52\ k\Omega$$

Notice that R_A is very close to the value of R_2. Therefore, the circuit operation is only slightly upset. The current increases only slightly to about:

$$I = \frac{E}{R}$$

$$I = \frac{6\ V}{10\ k\Omega + 9.52\ k\Omega}$$

$$I = 0.000307\ A\ or\ 307\ \mu A$$

The voltage across R_1 rises to about:

$$E_{R_1} = I \times R_1$$

$$E_{R_1} = 0.000307 \text{ A} \times 10,000 \text{ }\Omega$$

$$E_{R_1} = 3.07 \text{ V}$$

Meanwhile, the voltage across R_2 decreases slightly to:

$$E_{R_A} = I \times R_A$$

$$E_{R_A} = 0.000307 \text{ A} \times 9250 \text{ }\Omega$$

$$E_{R_A} = 2.93 \text{ V}$$

Thus, instead of indicating 3 V, the meter indicates 2.93 V. The inaccuracy is so small that it probably would never be noticed. The loading effect is minimized by using a voltmeter whose resistance is much higher than the resistance across which the voltage is to be measured.

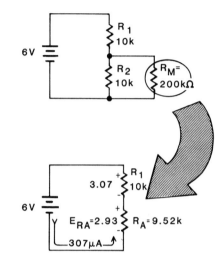

Figure 6-15 The 20,000 ohms-per-volt meter gives a much more accurate reading.

24. In the voltmeter, the range is extended by adding a resistor in (parallel/series) with the meter movement.

25. This resistor is called a _____ resistor.

26. The purpose of this resistor is to limit the current to the full-scale current rating of the _____ _____.

27. If you want to use a 100 µA, 1000 Ω meter movement in a 10 V voltmeter, a current of 100 µA should flow through the movement when the voltmeter is connected across _____ volts.

28. Thus, the total resistance of the voltmeter in question 27 must be _____.

29. Since the meter movement in the voltmeter from question 27 has a resistance of 1000 Ω, the value of the multiplier resistor should be _____ Ω.

30. The sensitivity of the voltmeter discussed in the previous questions is _____ ohms per volt.

31. The sensitivity or ohms-per-volt rating of a voltmeter is important since it determines the amount of _____ effect the meter will have on the circuit under test.

32. To minimize the loading effect, the ohms-per-volt rating should be as (high/low) as possible.

The Ohmmeter

The basic meter movement can be used to measure resistance. The resulting circuit is called an ohmmeter. In its most basic form, the ohmmeter is nothing more than a meter movement, a battery, and a series resistance.

Basic Circuit

Figure 6-16 shows the basic circuit of the ohmmeter. The idea behind the ohmmeter is to force a current to flow through an unknown resistance and then measure the current. For a given voltage, the current is be determined by the unknown resistance. That is, the amount of current measured by the meter is an indication of the unknown resistance.

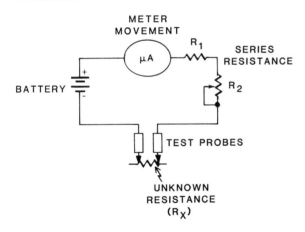

Figure 6-16 The basic ohmmeter.

The purpose of the battery is to supply an EMF to force current through the unknown resistance. The meter movement measures the resulting current. The test probes have long leads and they simplify the job of connecting the ohmmeter to the unknown resistance (R_X). Fixed resistor R_1 limits the current through the meter to a safe level. Variable resistor R_2 is called the ZERO OHMS adjustment. Its purpose is to compensate for the decrease in battery potential due to use or battery aging.

Scale Calibration

In ohmmeters of this type, the 0 Ω indication appears on the right side of the scale or at full scale deflection. The reason for this is shown in Figure 6-17A. Here, the two test probes are shorted together. Thus, the unknown resistance (R_X) between the probes is equal to 0 Ω. In this case, the meter should deflect full scale to the 0 Ω marking of the scale because the resistance between the probes is minimum allowing maximum current to flow through the meter circuit.

Full scale deflection for this meter is caused by a current of 50 µA. In order for the 1.5 V battery to force 50 µA of current through the circuit, the total circuit resistance must be:

$$R_T = \frac{E}{I}$$

$$R_T = \frac{1.5\,V}{.00005\,A}$$

$$R_T = 30,000\,\Omega$$

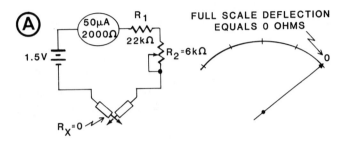

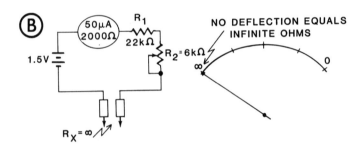

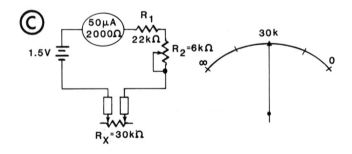

Figure 6-17 Calibrating the ends and center of the scale.

The meter's resistance is 2000 Ω while R_1 is 22,000 Ω. Thus, R_2, a variable resistor, must be set to exactly 6,000 Ω in order to insure a current of exactly 50 μA.

You may wonder why R_2 isn't a fixed 6,000 Ω resistor or better yet why R_1 isn't a fixed 28,000 Ω resistor. The reason is that the battery voltage will change as the battery discharges or ages. If the battery voltage drops to 1.45 volts then, to achieve full scale deflection, the circuit resistance must also decrease. The variable resistor must be reset be to:

$$R_T = \frac{E}{I}$$

$$R_T = \frac{1.45\ V}{.00005\ A}$$

$$R_T = 29,000\ \Omega$$

In this case R_2 must be reset to 5000 Ω to compensate for the lower voltage. R_2 is called the **ZERO OHMS adjust**. Changing this resistance to "zero the ohmmeter" is the first step in every resistance measurement.

You know that full scale deflection corresponds to an unknown resistance R_X of 0 Ω. Thus, the scale is marked 0 at this point. Now, what about the left side of the scale, no deflection?

Figure 6-17B illustrates this condition. Here an open circuit exists between the two test probes. This corresponds to an infinite resistance. No current flows through the meter movement and the pointer rests at the left side of the scale. Consequently, this point on the scale is marked with the infinity symbol (∞) Thus, you have a scale with 0 Ω on the right and infinite Ω on the left.

Now, look at what resistance is represented by 1/2 scale deflection. The pointer deflects to the center of the scale when the current is exactly 25 μA. This amount of current is caused by a total resistance of:

$$R_T = \frac{E}{I}$$

$$R_T = \frac{1.5\ V}{25\ \mu A}$$

$$R_T = \frac{1.5\ V}{.000025\ A}$$

$$R_T = 60,000\ \Omega$$

Since the meter, R_1, and R_2 have a combined resistance of only 30,000 Ω, the unknown resistance R_X supplies the other 30,000 Ω. That is, the meter deflects to half scale, 25 μA, when the unknown resistance has a value of 30 kΩ. Consequently, the 1/2 scale point is marked 30 k as shown in Figure 6-17C.

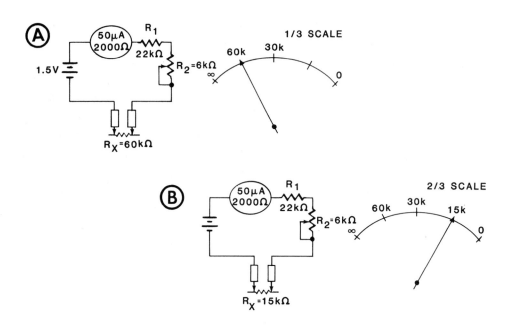

Figure 6-18 Calibrating for 1/3 and 2/3 scale deflection.

Using this same procedure, you can determine the amount of meter deflection for any value of R_X. Figure 6-18 illustrates that 1/3 full scale indicates an R_X of 60 kΩ while 2/3 full scale indicates an R_X of 15 kΩ. You can verify this by proving that 1/3 of 50 μA, or 16.66 μA, flows in the circuit shown in Figure 6-18A. Furthermore, you can verify that 2/3 of 50 μA or 33.33 μA flows in the circuit shown in Figure 6-18B.

If you determine the position of enough points on the scale, the scale will take the form shown in Figure 6-19. There are two

important differences between this scale and the ones used for current and voltage. First, on the ohm's scale, the zero indication is on the right side of the scale. Second, the scale is non-linear. For example, the entire lower end of the resistance scale is devoted to a range of only 30 kΩ; that is, from 0 to 30 kΩ. However, notice that the second 30 kΩ, from 30 kΩ to 60 kΩ, takes up less than 1/4 of the scale. Finally, the markings are squeezed closer together on the left side of the scale. On ammeters and voltmeters the scale is linear. That is, the scale is marked off in equal increments of current or voltage.

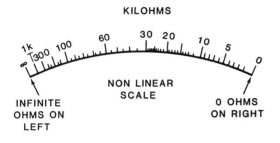

KILOHMS

NON LINEAR
SCALE

INFINITE
OHMS ON
LEFT

0 OHMS
ON RIGHT

Figure 6-19 The ohmmeter scale.

Creating Higher Ranges

A single range ohmmeter is of limited use. For this reason, multi-range ohmmeters have been developed. Two techniques have evolved for creating additional ranges. Both techniques are used in some ohmmeters.

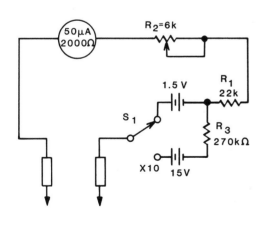

Figure 6-20 Creating higher resistance ranges.

Figure 6-20 shows how a higher resistance range can be implemented. First, a switch is added so that you can select either of the two ranges. Second, a higher voltage battery is added. Finally, a higher value series resistor is included in the circuit. To increase the range by a factor of 10, both the voltage and the total series resistance must increase by a factor of 10.

When the switch, S_1, is in the position shown, the meter operates exactly like the one shown earlier in Figures 6-17 and 6-18. However, when S_1 is switched to the × 10 position, the 15 volt battery is switched in series with R_3, R_1, R_2, and the meter. The higher voltage does not cause excessive current through the meter since the series resistance has been increased by the addition of R_3. Notice that the total resistance in the circuit is now 300 kΩ. Thus, when the leads are shorted together, the current is still:

$$I = \frac{E}{R}$$

$$I = \frac{15\,V}{300\,k\Omega}$$

$$I = 50\,\mu A$$

The right side of the scale still represents 0 Ω. However, half-scale deflection, that occurs when 25 μA moves through the circuit, now occurs when the total resistance is:

$$R_T = \frac{15\,V}{25\,\mu A}$$

$$R_T = 600\,k\Omega$$

Of this, the meter, R_1, R_2, and R_3 supply 300 kΩ. Therefore, the unknown resistance R_X must be 300 kΩ. This means that the center of the ohmmeter scale now represents 300 kΩ instead of 30 kΩ. The range has been increased by a factor of 10.

Of course, this technique cannot be carried much further because increasing the range by an additional factor of 10 would require a 150 volt battery. Fortunately, the range described above is sufficient for general purpose use. It can measure resistance values up to several megohms. Resistors larger than this are rarely used in most electronic applications.

Creating Lower Ranges

The basic ohmmeter can also be modified to measure lower values of resistance. This is done by switching a small value shunt resistor in parallel with the meter and its series resistance.

Refer to Figure 6-21. With switch S_1 in the position shown, the ohmmeter operates exactly like the one shown earlier in Figure 6-17. However, when the position of S_1 is changed, R_3 is connected in parallel with the series combination of the meter, R_1, and R_2. The value of R_3 is 300 Ω or 1 percent of the combined series resistance of R_1, R_2, and the meter (30,000 Ω). Therefore, 99 percent of the current flows through R_3 and only 1 percent flows through the meter circuit.

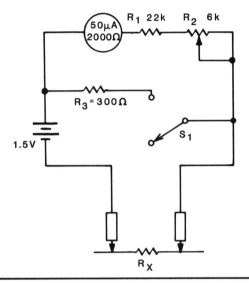

Figure 6-21 Creating lower resistance ranges.

Recall that 25 μA of current is required for half-scale deflection of the meter. Determine the value of R_X that will cause this amount of current to flow through the meter. The resistance of the meter circuit is now about 300 Ω. If an unknown resistance R_X of 300 Ω is now connected between the probes, the current from the battery becomes:

$$I = \frac{1.5 \text{ V}}{600 \text{ }\Omega}$$

$$I = 2.5 \text{ mA}$$

However, 99% of this current or 2.475 mA, flows through R_3. Only 1% or 25 μA flows through the meter movement. Thus, half-scale deflection now represents an unknown resistance of 300 Ω instead of 30 kΩ. Using this technique, lower ohmmeter ranges can be created.

Shunt Ohmmeter

The ohmmeters discussed up to this point are called series ohmmeters because the unknown resistance is always placed in series with the meter movement. A series ohmmeter can be recognized by its "backwards" scale. That is, 0 ohms is on the right while infinite ohms is on the left.

Another type of ohmmeter is called a shunt ohmmeter. Figure 6-22 illustrates the basic circuit of the shunt ohmmeter. This instrument gets its name from the fact that the unknown resistance is placed in parallel, or shunt, with the meter movement. This completely changes the characteristics of the ohmmeter. For example, notice that when an open (infinite ohms) exists between the probes, 50 μA of current flows through the meter movement. This produces full scale deflection. Consequently, infinite ohms are on the right side of the scale or at full scale deflection. This is just the opposite of the series ohmmeter.

When the probes on the shunt ohmmeter are shorted together, the meter movement is shorted out. This produces no deflection. Thus, 0 ohms is on the left.

Recall that with the series ohmmeter, the half-scale reading was 30,000 Ω for the 50 μA, 2000 Ω meter movement. However, with the shunt ohmmeter, this too is different. Here, 25 μA of current flows through the meter movement when R_X is the same resistance as the meter movement. Thus, half-scale deflection on the shunt ohmmeter is marked 2000 Ω.

The shunt ohmmeter has some disadvantages. For one thing, the battery discharges any time the ohmmeter is turned on. This is not the case with the series ohmmeter. It draws current from the battery only when measuring a resistance.

In addition, the meter movement in the shunt ohmmeter is more easily damaged if the meter is inadvertently connected across a voltage source. In the series meter, the 28,000 Ω in series with the meter movement limits the current. Even so, you should never connect either type of ohmmeter to a **live** circuit.

Finally, because the half-scale reading of the shunt ohmmeter is much less than that of the series ohmmeter, it is more difficult to accurately measure high resistance values on the shunt meter. However, it is easier to read low resistance values on the shunt meter for the same reason.

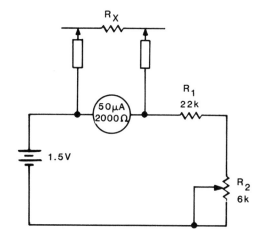

Figure 6-22 The shunt ohmmeter.

33. A device used to measure resistance is called an _____.

34. In its most basic form the ohmmeter consists of a _____ _____, a _____, and a resistance connected in series.

35. Generally, the series resistance in the ohmmeter consists of two parts: a fixed resistor that limits the current through the meter to a safe value and a variable resistor called the _____ _____ adjust.

36. The purpose of the variable resistor in the series ohmmeter is to compensate for different values of _____ voltage.

37. In the series ohmmeter, 0 appears on the _____ side of the scale.

38. If a 100 μA meter movement and a 9 V battery are used in a series ohmmeter circuit, when the leads are shorted together and the meter reads 0 ohms or full-scale deflection, the total resistance in the circuit is _____ ohms.

39. In the meter described in question 38, what value of unknown resistance R_X causes half-scale deflection? _____.

40. Thus, the half-scale point on the meter scale should be marked _____ ohms.

41. Using the type of ohmmeter described in question 38, it would be somewhat impractical to create a higher resistance range since this would require a _____ V battery.

42. You can convert your ohmmeter to a lower resistance range simply by connecting a small-value resistor in _____ with the meter and series resistance.

43. To obtain a half-scale reading of 900 Ω, a value of shunt is chosen that will conduct _____% of the current in the circuit.

44. In this meter, a value of approximately _____ ohms is required for the shunt.

45. An ohmmeter, no matter what type, should never be connected to a _____ _____.

Multimeters

Generally, the voltmeter, ammeter, and ohmmeter are combined into a single instrument called a multimeter. It is much easier to carry a single instrument than it is to carry 3 separate meters. Since many of the component parts are contained in most types of meters there are cost duplications. Therefore, a single meter movement, with range and function scales, to perform the various functions of the voltmeter, ammeter, and ohmmeter would be a considerable savings, when compared to the cost of 3 separate meter movements. There is also the ad-

ditional cost of other duplicated electronic components and 3 separate chassis. The most serious disadvantage of the single multimeter, when compared to 3 separate meters, is that only one measurement can be monitored at any given time.

Basic Circuit

A schematic diagram of a basic multimeter is shown in Figure 6-23. This meter has

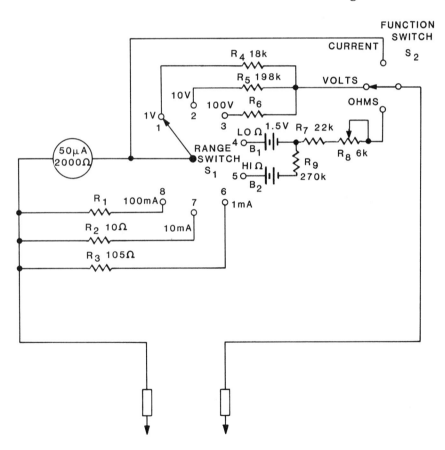

Figure 6-23 The multimeter.

three DC voltage ranges, two ohmmeter ranges, and three current ranges. Function switch S_2 determines if the multimeter is to act as an ammeter, a voltmeter, or an ohmmeter. Range switch S_1 determines the range of the meter.

When used as a voltmeter, S_2 must be placed in the **VOLTS** position and S_1 must be placed in one of the voltage range positions: 1 V, 10 V, or 100 V. As the circuit in Figure 6-23 is drawn, the multimeter is set up to measure DC voltages up to 1 V. Compare the voltmeter section of this meter with the multi-range voltmeter shown earlier in Figure 6-11. Notice that the two voltmeters are virtually identical.

The ohmmeter portion of the multimeter has only two ranges. On the LO Ω range, B_1 supplies the current that causes the meter to deflect when S_2 is the OHMS position and a resistance is connected between the two test probes. In the HI Ω position, a higher voltage battery and a larger value series resistor are used to increase the resistance range. The ohmmeter portion of the multimeter is exactly like the two range ohmmeter shown earlier in Figure 6-20.

When function switch S_2 is placed in the **CURRENT** position, the two test probes are connected directly to opposite ends of the meter movement. When the range switch S_1 is placed on one of the current ranges, a resistor is placed in parallel (shunt) with the meter movement. On the 1 mA range, 50 μA must flow through the meter movement when 1 mA flows through the circuit

under test. Thus, 950 μA must flow through the shunt R_3. Since 19 times as much current flows through R_3 as through the meter movement, R_3's resistance must be 1/19th that of the meter movement.

$$R_3 = \frac{2000\ \Omega}{19}$$

$$R_3 \approx 105\ \Omega$$

Using the same line of reasoning, the value of R_2 must be about 10 ohms.

Electronic Multimeter

All of the meters discussed up to this point are classified as electrical meters. They consist of a meter movement, precision resistors, and a battery for the ohmmeter. However, there is another family of meters called electronic meters. These contain electronic circuits that can amplify small voltages and currents. These instruments use devices such as transistors and integrated circuits that you have not learned about yet. For this reason, their circuitry will not be discussed in this course.

Generally, the electronic meter is used in the same way as the electrical meter. However, one important difference is that the electronic meter has a much higher resistance than the electrical meter. For example, a good electrical meter has a sensitivity of 20,000 ohms/volt. Thus, on the 10 volt range, its resistance is 20,000 Ω $\times$ 10 = 200 kΩ. By contrast, most electronic meters have a resistance of 10 or 11 MΩ on all DC ranges. Consequently, the electronic multimeter has very little loading effect on most circuits.

Measurement Inaccuracies

When using a multimeter, there are several ways in which inaccuracies can slip into your measurements. Some of the causes of inaccurate measurements have already been discussed. Voltmeter loading is a good example. This error is minimized by using a voltmeter that has a high resistance compared to the resistances under measurement.

In somewhat the same way, the ammeter introduces an error when it is used to measure current. Since the ammeter has a certain amount of resistance, it increases the overall circuit resistance when it is connected in series with the circuit. Of course, this reduces the current flowing in the circuit. As a result, the ammeter indicates a value of current lower than the actual current in the circuit without the meter connected. To minimize this error, an ammeter with a very low value of resistance must be used. The lower the ammeter resistance with respect to the circuit resistance, the smaller the error will be.

If the resistance value of the ammeter is known, its loading effect can be predicted and taken into consideration so that a more accurate interpretation of the reading can be made. Often the resistance of the ammeter is given in the manufacturer's literature. If this value is not given, the value can be determined using the procedure shown in Figure 6-24.

First, the ammeter is set to the desired range. Next, it is connected in series with a variable resistor and a voltage source as shown in Figure 6-24. R_1 is then adjusted for full scale deflection of the meter. Variable resistor R_2 is now added to the circuit as shown in Figure 6-24B. R_2 is adjusted until the meter reads exactly one-half scale deflection. At this time half the current flows through R_2 and half flows through the meter. Thus, the resistance of R_2 must be equal to the resistance of the meter. Therefore, you can determine the resistance of the meter by removing R_2 from the circuit and measuring its value with the ohmmeter section of the multimeter.

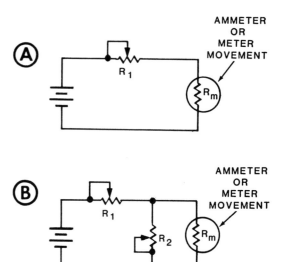

Figure 6-24 Finding the resistance of an ammeter or meter movement.

You may wonder why you do not simply measure the resistance of the ammeter directly with an ohmmeter. On high current ranges, this can be done if a separate ohmmeter is available. However, when the ammeter is set to a low current range, the ohmmeter may produce enough current to harm the ammeter. Earlier, you saw that the resistance of a meter movement is an important factor in designing meter circuits. The technique outlined above can be used to determine the resistance of any meter movement as well as that of an ammeter.

Aside from loading errors, the prime source of measurement inaccuracies is the tolerance of the components that make up the meter. The meter movement may have an inaccuracy of $\pm 2\%$ or $\pm 3\%$ of full scale. Furthermore, multiplier and shunt resistors may have a tolerance of 1%. Adding these inaccuracies, a typical multimeter may have an overall accuracy of $\pm 3\%$ to $\pm 4\%$ for DC voltage and current ranges.

Another error that can creep into measurements is caused by improperly reading the meter. The most common error is that caused by **parallax**. Figure 6-25 illustrates what is meant by parallax. In Figure 6-25A, the scale is viewed from directly in front of the meter. Viewing "straight on" like this, the meter indicates exactly 5 volts. If you move slightly to the right of the meter, the needle appears to point to the left of 5 volts as shown in Figure 6-25B. Also, if viewed from the left of center, the needle appears to point to the right of 5 volts as shown in Figure 6-25C. Obviously then, for a correct reading, you should always read the scale "straight on" from directly in front of the meter. However, because you have two eyes, one eye will be to the right of center while the other will be to the left of center. To prevent errors in reading the meter, you should close one eye, and read the scale "straight on" with the other eye. Some meters have a mirror on the scale to help eliminate parallax errors. With one eye closed, the needle you align with the reflection of the needle in the mirror. This ensures that your open eye is placed directly in front of the needle.

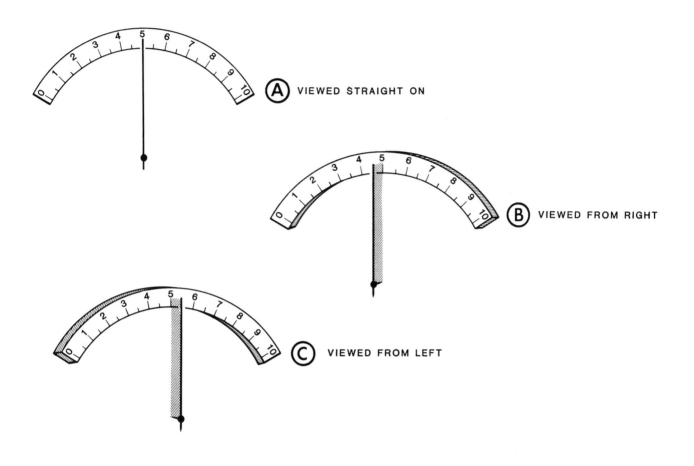

Figure 6-25 Errors can be caused by parallax.

Desk-Top Experiment 3
Designing a Multimeter

Introduction

In this unit you have learned about meters and their design. In this experiment, you will use what you have learned to design a multimeter of your own. This experiment will guide you step-by-step through the design procedure. Feel free to use the book as a reference if you must. However, it is better to do as much as you can without the aid of the text.

Objectives

1. To implement what you have learned about ammeters, voltmeters, and ohmmeters to design a multimeter.

2. To use what you have learned about Ohm's Law and DC circuits to determine the correct resistance values necessary to make an ammeter, ohmmeter, and voltmeter using a minimum amount of components.

Procedure

1. Figure 6-26 shows the schematic diagram for your multimeter. In this figure, label the terminals on the function switch according to their use; volts, current, or ohms.

2. Label the resistors in the ammeter section of the multimeter R_1, R_2, and R_3.

Use R_1 for the highest range and R_3 for the lowest range.

3. Now, label the resistors in the voltmeter section R_4, R_5, and R_6. R_4 should be in the lowest range while R_6 is in the highest range.

4. In the ohmmeter section, label the fixed resistor in the low range R_7 and the fixed resistor in the high range R_8. The zero adjust resistor should be labeled R_9.

Discussion

On switch S_2, you should have labeled terminal 1, current; terminal 2, volts; and terminal 3, ohms. The resistors should be labeled in the following manner:

Ammeter Range		Voltmeter Range		Ohmmeter Range	
100 mA	R_1	1 V	R_4	LO	R7
10 mA	R_2	10 V	R_5	HI	R_8
1 mA	R_3	100 V	R_6		

The zero adjust resistor, R_9, is the only variable resistor in the schematic and it is located in the ohmmeter section of the schematic.

If you had a problem identifying any section of this schematic or in labeling any of the resistors, return to the appropriate sections of the unit and review the material on these sections.

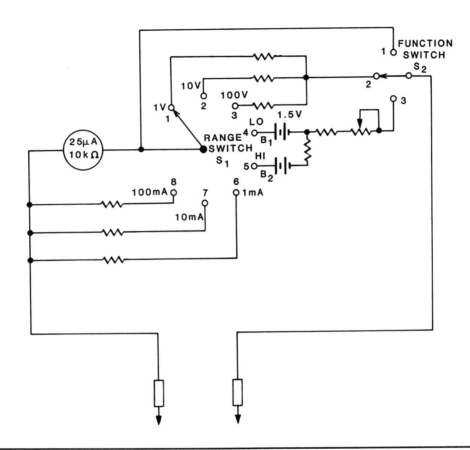

Figure 6-26 Multimeter for Desk Top Experiment 3.

Procedure (Cont.)

5. Using the appropriate procedure, determine the value of the shunt resistors used in the ammeter section of the multimeter. The values are:

    $R_1 = $ _____ Ω.

    $R_2 = $ _____ Ω.

    $R_3 = $ _____ Ω.

6. Once again, using the appropriate procedures, calculate the values of the resistors used in the voltmeter section of the multimeter. The values are:

    $R_4 = $ _____ Ω.

    $R_5 = $ _____ Ω.

    $R_6 = $ _____ Ω.

7. In the ohmmeter section, fixed resistor R_7 is 30 kΩ. What is the value of R_9 assuming that the 1.5 V battery is actually supplying 1.5 V?

$$R_9 = \text{_____} Ω.$$

8. In order to increase the range of the ohmmeter by a factor of 10, what value resistor must be used for R_8 and how large a battery must be used for B_2?

$$R_8 = \text{_____} Ω.$$

$$B_2 = \text{_____} V.$$

Discussion

The shunt resistors for the ammeter are connected in parallel with the meter movement. The meter will indicate maximum deflection when 25 μA of current flows through the movement. All other current must flow through the shunt resistor. Therefore, the highest current range should have the smallest of the three shunt resistors. In this case, the resistance of R_1 is 2.5 Ω. The other shunt resistors have substantially more resistance with R3 having the greatest resistance.

Incidentally, although it is possible to find a 2.5 Ω resistor suitable for use in the meter, short sections of high resistance wire such as nichrome can be substituted for an extremely low value resistor.

In the voltmeter section of the multimeter, the multiplier resistors are connected in series with the meter movement. These resistors drop most of the voltage applied to the circuit and also limit current through the circuit. R_4 in the 1 V range is a 30 kΩ resistor. The other multiplier resistors must be proportionately larger since they are used in higher voltage ranges and must, therefore, drop a larger portion of the voltage under test.

Using a 30 kΩ fixed resistor for R_7, it is necessary that the value of R_9 be 20 kΩ. Of course, R_9 is only 20 kΩ when battery B_1 is supplying 1.5 V. As B_1 ages or is used and its voltage decreases, R_9 is adjusted to compensate for this. Because of component tolerances, it is good practice to select a potentiometer whose midrange value is 20 kΩ.

In order to increase the resistance range by a factor of 10, it is necessary to increase both the resistance of the entire ohmmeter circuit as well as the voltage applied to the circuit by a factor of 10. When calculating R_8, however, you must remember that R_7 is in series with this resistor when the ohmmeter is switched to the high range.

Procedure (Cont.)

9. What is the ohms per volt rating of the voltmeter used in your multimeter?

$$\text{_____} \text{ ohms/volt.}$$

10. Why is it necessary to ensure that the function switch and the range select switch are both set for measuring the same quantity before using your multimeter?

_____

_____

_____ .

11. What is the minimum voltage required from battery B1 to ensure proper operation of the ohmmeter on the LO range?

_____ V.

12. Assuming that you have properly constructed the multimeter, what is the probable cause if after adjusting the zero ohms control you cannot get the pointer to travel the zero position?

_____ .

Discussion

As with any other meter, the ohms per volt rating is calculated by dividing 1 V by the current rating of the meter movement. In this case, the meter is rated at 40 kΩ/volt.

If both switches in the meter are not set to measure the same quantity, serious damage may occur to the meter movement or other components. For instance, if the range switch is left on anything other than current and the function switch is set to measure current, all the meter circuitry is bypassed and the meter is connected directly to the two probes.

The ohmmeter will operate properly as long as you can adjust R_9 to compensate for changes in the battery voltage. Assuming that the lowest resistance to which R_9 is adjustable is zero ohms, the circuit will operate as long as the battery can maintain 25 μA of current through R_7 and the meter movement when the probes are shorted together. With R_9 removed from the circuit, the total resistance of the circuit is 40 kΩ. It is necessary to apply 1 V to 40 kΩ to maintain 25 μA of current flow. If the battery voltage drops below 1 V, the meter will not operate properly.

The answer to the question in step 12 is derived from the information given about step 11. If battery voltage drops below 1 V, it is not possible to maintain the necessary current through the meter movement to assure full-scale deflection when zeroing the meter. Therefore, the probable cause of the problem described is a weak battery.

46. Generally, the voltmeter, ohmmeter, and ammeter are combined in a single unit called a _____.

47. In the multimeter shown in Figure 6-23, R_4, R_5, and R_6 are used in the _____ meter portion of the multimeter.

48. R_4, R_5, and R_6 are called _____ resistors.

49. Again in Figure 6-23, R_7, R_8, R_9, and the two batteries are used in the _____ meter portion of the multimeter.

50. R_8 is called the _____ _____ adjustment.

51. In Figure 6-23, R_1, R_2, and R_3 are used in the _____ section of the multimeter.

52. These are called _____ resistors.

53. Multimeters that have transistors or integrated circuits in addition to the meter movement circuits are called _____ meters.

54. The advantage of the electronic meter is that it has a very (high/low) resistance.

55. This means that it generally has less _____ effect than electrical meters.

Summary

The most popular type of meter movement is the d'Arsonval meter movement. It consists of a permanent magnet and a moving-coil. When current flows through the coil, a magnetic field develops that interacts with the permanent magnet's field. The coil rotates as described by the right-hand motor rule. The amount of rotation is proportional to the current.

The main parts of the d'Arsonval meter movement are the moving-coil, the permanent magnet, the scale, pivots, bearings, springs, retaining pins, counter weights, and a zero adjust mechanism.

A variation of the d'Arsonval movement is the taut-band movement. In this device, thin metal bands replace the pivots, jeweled bearings, and spiral springs. This makes a more sensitive and more rugged movement.

A 50 μA movement can be used to measure a much higher current value by connecting a small value resistor, called a shunt, in parallel with the movement. To determine the proper value of shunt, you must know the resistance of the meter movement. If the resistance of the meter movement is 1000 Ω, the current range can be doubled by connecting a 1000 Ω resistor in parallel with the meter movement. In the same way, if the shunt is to carry 9 times as much current as the meter movement, then the shunt resistance must be one-ninth that of the meter movement.

The accuracy of a meter movement is specified as a percentage of error at full scale deflection. If a 100 mA meter has an accuracy of ±3%, then the reading may be off by as much as ±3mA at any point on the scale.

A current operated meter movement can be used to measure voltage. A 1 mA, 1000 Ω meter movement indicates full scale when the applied voltage is:

$$E = I \times R$$

$$E = 1\,mA \times 1\,k\Omega$$

$$E = 1\,V$$

To extend the voltage range, a voltage dropping resistor, called a multiplier, is connected in series with the meter movement. To extend the range of the above meter to 10 V, the multiplier must drop 9 V when the current is 1 mA. Thus, its value must be:

$$R = \frac{E}{I}$$

$$R = \frac{9\,V}{1\,mA}$$

$$R = 9\,k\Omega$$

The sensitivity of a meter movement is given in ohms per volt. It is determined by dividing the full-scale current reading into 1 V. Thus, a 1 mA meter has a sensitivity of:

$$\frac{1\,V}{1\,mA} = 1000\,ohms/volt.$$

The ohms per volt rating is important because it indicates the loading effect of a voltmeter. The higher the sensitivity, the less the loading effect will be.

The series ohmmeter consists of a battery, a meter movement, and a resistance all connected in series. Zero ohms is indicated by full scale deflection while infinite ohms are indicated by no deflection. The internal series resistance of the ohmmeter circuit must be such that it allows full scale current to flow when the test leads are shorted together. Thus, a 50 μA meter movement and a 4.5 volt battery require an internal resistance of:

$$R = \frac{E}{I}$$

$$R = \frac{4.5\text{ V}}{50\text{ μA}}$$

$$R = 90\text{ k}\Omega$$

A multimeter is a combination voltmeter, ohmmeter, and ammeter built into a single case. A single meter movement is used. To measure voltage, multiplying resistors are switched in series.

To measure current, shunt resistors are switched in parallel. To measure ohms, in some instances a battery and zero ohms adjust are switched in series with the meter movement. The ohmmeter may also have a resistor in shunt with the meter movement.

Unit 7
DC Circuits

Contents

Introduction

The purpose of this unit is to expand your knowledge of basic DC circuits. After a brief review of series and parallel circuits, you will be introduced to some new applications of these circuits. Next you will study an entirely new circuit called a bridge. Finally, you will learn about several new analytical tools for evaluating circuits.

Unit Objectives

When you have completed this unit, you will be able to:

1. Define the following terms: Bleeder current, series dropping resistor, voltage divider, bridge network, linear circuit, and bilateral circuit.

2. Given the current and voltage requirements for the separate loads, calculate the values of the resistors in a voltage divider.

3. Given the values of the resistors in a bridge network, determine whether or not the bridge is balanced.

4. Name three applications for a bridge circuit.

5. Analyze a simple network by using the superposition theorem.

6. Analyze a simple network by using Thevenin's theorem.

7. Analyze a simple network by using Norton's theorem.

8. Calculate unknown currents and voltages in a simple network by using Kirchhoff's law.

9. Convert a Thevenin equivalent circuit to a Norton equivalent circuit.

Simple Circuits

Throughout your study of electronics, you will see certain circuits repeated over and over again. Some of the most used circuits are the easiest to understand. You have already studied the characteristics of several types of simple circuits. These include the series circuit, the parallel circuit, and the series-parallel circuit. The next section reviews the characteristics of these circuits. Later, you will learn about some more advanced concepts.

Series Circuit

In a series circuit, the current flows through the components consecutively. That is, the current flows along a single path and the components are located one after another along this path as shown in Figure 7-1. In such a circuit, you may wish to find the current, the voltage dropped by a resistor, or the power dissipated by any resistor.

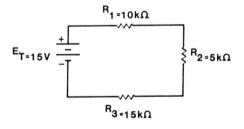

Figure 7-1 The series circuit.

Since there is only one current path in a series circuit, the current is the same through all of the resistors in the circuit.

This current is determined by dividing the total resistance into the applied voltage. The total resistance, R_T, in a series circuit is equal to the sum of the individual resistances. Thus, in Figure 7-1:

$$R_T = R_1 + R_2 + R_3$$

$$R_T = 10\,k\Omega + 5\,k\Omega + 15\,k\Omega$$

$$R_T = 30\,k\Omega$$

Once the total resistance is known, the current can be determined:

$$I = \frac{E}{R_T}$$

$$I = \frac{15\,V}{30\,k\Omega}$$

$$I = \frac{15\,V}{30,000\,\Omega}$$

$$I = 0.0005\,A \text{ or } 0.5\,mA$$

Since the current is the same through all resistors, the voltage drop across any one resistor can be determined by multiplying the total current times the value of that resistor. For example, the voltage across R_1 is:

$$E_{R_1} = I \times R_1$$

$$E_{R_1} = 0.0005\,A \times 10,000\,\Omega$$

$$E_{R_1} = 5\,V$$

In the same way E_{R_2} is:

$$E_{R_2} = I \times R_2$$

$$E_{R_2} = 0.0005\ A \times 5000\ \Omega$$

$$E_{R_2} = 2.5\ V$$

Also, E_{R_3} is:

$$E_{R_3} = I \times R_3$$

$$E_{R_3} = 0.0005\ A \times 15{,}000\ \Omega$$

$$E_{R_3} = 7.5\ V$$

The voltage drops across the three resistors have been calculated out so that another important characteristic of the series circuit can be illustrated. The applied voltage E_T is equal to the sum of the voltage drops. That is:

$$E_T = E_{R_1} + E_{R_2} + E_{R_3}$$

$$E_T = 5\ V + 2.5\ V + 7.5\ V$$

$$E_T = 15\ V$$

Finally, the power dissipated by any resistor is equal to the current times the voltage drop across the resistor. Thus, the power dissipated by R_1 is:

$$P_{R_1} = I \times E_{R_1}$$

$$P_{R_1} = 0.0005\ A \times 5\ V$$

$$P_{R_1} = 0.0025\ W\ or\ 2.5\ mW$$

Review the above equations until you can compute any of the electrical quantities in the circuit.

Parallel Circuit

A simple parallel circuit is shown in Figure 7-2. In a parallel circuit, the voltage applied to each branch is the same. That is, the voltage measured across any resistor in the parallel branch equals the voltage applied to the branch. Thus, in Figure 7-2 the voltage is the same across each resistor:

$$E_T = E_{R_1} = E_{R_2} = E_{R_3} = 15\ V$$

That is, 15 V is dropped across each resistor.

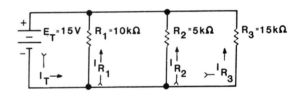

Figure 7-2 The parallel circuit.

To find the current through any resistor in the parallel branch according to Ohm's Law, you must divide the voltage by the resistance value of that resistor. For example, the current through R_1 is:

$$I_{R_1} = \frac{E}{R_1}$$

$$I_{R_1} = \frac{15\ V}{10\ k\Omega}$$

$$I_{R_1} = \frac{15\text{ V}}{10,000\ \Omega}$$

$$I_{R_1} = 0.0015\text{ A or }1.5\text{ mA}$$

Also, I_{R_2} is:

$$I_{R_2} = \frac{E}{R_2}$$

$$I_{R_2} = \frac{15\text{ V}}{5000\ \Omega}$$

$$I_{R_2} = 3\text{ mA}$$

And I_{R_3} is:

$$I_{R_3} = \frac{E}{R_3}$$

$$I_{R_3} = \frac{15\text{ V}}{15,000\ \Omega}$$

$$I_{R_3} = 1\text{ mA}$$

Since different current flows through each resistor in the parallel branch, the total current is the sum of the branch currents:

$$I_T = I_{R_1} + I_{R_2} + I_{R_3}$$

$$I_T = 1.5\text{ mA} + 3\text{ mA} + 1\text{ mA}$$

$$I_T = 5.5\text{ mA}$$

You can also determine the total current by dividing the total resistance (R_T) into the applied voltage. To find the total resistance, you must use the equation for parallel circuits:

$$R_T = \frac{1}{\dfrac{1}{R_1} + \dfrac{1}{R_2} + \dfrac{1}{R_3}}$$

$$R_T = \frac{1}{\dfrac{1}{10,000\ \Omega} + \dfrac{1}{5,000\ \Omega} + \dfrac{1}{15,000\ \Omega}}$$

$$R_T = \frac{1}{.0001\ \Omega + .0002\ \Omega + .00006667\ \Omega}$$

$$R_T = 2727\ \Omega$$

Using this value of R_T, you can determine that the total current is:

$$I_T = \frac{E}{R_T}$$

$$I_T = \frac{15\text{ V}}{2727\ \Omega}$$

$$I_T = 0.0055\text{ A or }5.5\text{ mA}$$

Notice that this agrees with the value computed by adding the individual branch current.

The power dissipated in any resistor can be found by multiplying the current through the resistor by the voltage dropped by the resistor. For example, the power dissipated by R_1 is:

$$P_{R_1} = I_{R_1} \times E_{R_1}$$

$$P_{R_1} = 0.0015\text{ A} \times 15\text{ V}$$

$$P_{R_1} = 0.0225\text{ W or }22.5\text{ mW}$$

Series-Parallel Circuit

Often a circuit has both series and parallel current paths as shown in Figure 7-3A. To compute electrical quantities in this type of circuit, you must first simplify the circuit by redrawing it as shown in Figure 7-3B.

Notice that the two parallel resistors, R_2 and R_3, are replaced with an equivalent resistance, R_A. The value of R_A is determined using the equation:

$$R_A = \frac{R_2 \times R_3}{R_2 + R_3}$$

$$R_A = \frac{2000\ \Omega \times 2000\ \Omega}{2000\ \Omega + 2000\ \Omega}$$

$$R_A = \frac{4{,}000{,}000\ \Omega}{4{,}000\ \Omega}$$

$$R_A = 1000\ \Omega \text{ or } 1\ k\Omega$$

The resulting circuit shown in Figure 7-3B can now be handled like any other series circuit.

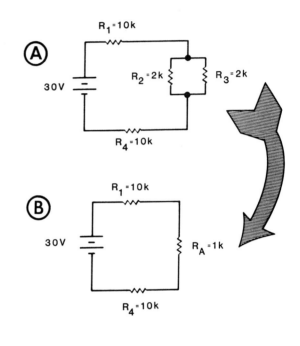

Figure 7-3 The series parallel circuit.

Self-Test Review

Refer to Figure 7-4A for questions 1 — 5.

1. In a series circuit, the _____ is the same at all points in the circuit.

2. In the series circuit shown in Figure 7-4A, the total resistance is _____.

3. The current in the circuit is _____.

4. The voltage drop across R_1 is _____.

5. The power dissipated by R_5 is _____.

Refer to Figure 7-4B for questions 6 — 9.

6. In a parallel circuit, the _____ is the same across all branches.

7. In the parallel circuit shown in Figure 7-4B, the current through R_1 is _____.

8. The total current, I_T, in the circuit shown in Figure 7-4B is _____.

9. The power dissipated by R_3 is _____.

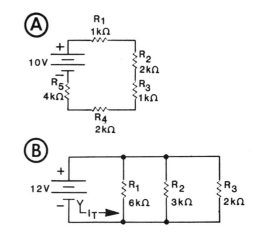

Figure 7-4 Review problems.

One of the most useful series-parallel circuits is the voltage divider. It is frequently used at the output of a power supply to provide a number of output voltages that are distributed to different circuits.

The design of a voltage divider is complicated by the current drawn by the load. If you could ignore the load current, the design of the voltage divider would be extremely simple. For example, let's suppose you have a 30 V power supply and that you want to obtain output voltages of +15 volts and +30 volts. Figure 7-5A shows a circuit that appears to perform this function. Since R_1 and R_2 are the same size, each drops one-half of the applied voltage. When a voltmeter is placed across R_1, it will indicate +15 volts. Thus, the top of R_1 is at +15 volts with respect to ground. Naturally, the top of R_2 is at +30 volts with respect to ground. Thus, the circuit appears to meet the requirements set above. However, if you examine the circuit more closely, you find that the above conditions exist only under the **no load** condition.

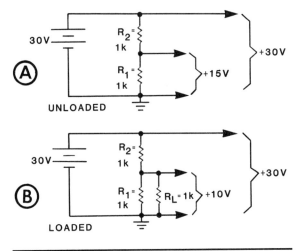

Figure 7-5 Simple voltage divider.

When you attempt to use the +15 volts at the top of R_1 to drive a load, an interesting thing happens as shown in Figure 7-5B. Here a 1 kΩ load, R_L, is connected across the +15 volt supply. Notice that R_L is in parallel with R_1. Thus the equivalent resistance of R_1 and R_L in parallel is:

$$R_T = \frac{R_1 \times R_L}{R_1 + R_L}$$

$$R_T = \frac{1,000\ \Omega \times 1,000\ \Omega}{1,000\ \Omega + 1,000\ \Omega}$$

$$R_T = \frac{1,000,000\ \Omega}{2,000\ \Omega}$$

$$R_T = 500\ \Omega$$

The resistance from the top of R_1 to ground decreases from 1 kΩ to 500 Ω. R_2 is now twice as large as this equivalent resistance. Consequently, R_2 drops 2/3 of the applied voltage while the equivalent resistance of R_1 and R_L drops only 1/3. That is, R_2 drops 20 V while R_1 and R_L in parallel drop only 10 V. Thus, the voltage from the top of R_1 to ground decreases from +15 V to +10 V. When a load is connected across the divider, the divider no longer fulfills the requirements that were originally specified.

The point of all of this is that in order to design a workable voltage divider, you must consider the current that flows through the load. To illustrate this point, assume you have three loads that must be driven from a single 12 V power supply. Again, assume that the first load requires +12 V at 1 A, the second load requires 8 V at 0.6 A while the third load requires 4 V at 0.2 A. Figure 7-6 shows what the circuit looks like.

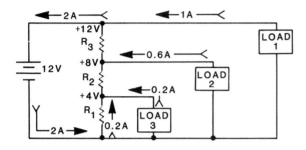

Figure 7-6 Designing the voltage divider.

Three resistors are used to develop the three desired voltages. The values of the three resistors, however, are not given. In order to design the circuit, you must determine the values required for these resistors. As you have learned, the value of any resistor can be determined by Ohm's Law if you know the current through the resistor and the voltage developed across it. If you analyze Figure 7-6 closely, you will see that enough information is given to allow you to find the resistor values.

Look at R_1. The current through R_1 is given as 0.2 A. This is the only current in the circuit that is not flowing through one of the loads. This current is called the **bleeder** current and R_1 is called the **bleeder resistor**. Because the bleeder current does not flow through any of the loads, its value is not critical. A circuit of this type is generally designed so that 10 percent of the total circuit current is bleeder current. For example, in Figure 7-6 the total current drawn from the supply is 2 A. Therefore, a bleeder current of 0.2 A is selected.

Once you determine what the bleeder current will be, you can determine the value of R_1. The current through R_1 is 0.2 A and the voltage across R_1 is 4 V. Therefore:

$$R_1 = \frac{4\text{ V}}{0.2\text{ A}}$$

$$R_1 = 20\ \Omega$$

The required value of R_2 can be determined by using a similar procedure. The current through R_2 is the sum of the 0.2 A bleeder current through R_1 and the 0.2 A through load 3. Therefore, the current through R_2 is 0.4 A. The voltage at the bottom of R_2 is +4 V while that at the top of R_2 is +8 V. Consequently, the voltage across R_2 is 4 V. Therefore:

$$R_2 = \frac{4\text{ V}}{0.4\text{ A}}$$

$$R_2 = 10\ \Omega$$

Finally, look at R_3. The current through R_3 is the sum of the 0.6 A through load 2 and the 0.4 A through R_2. Thus, the total current through R_3 is 1 A. The bottom end of R_3 is at +8 V while the top of R_3 is at +12 V. Therefore, the voltage across R_3 is 4 V. Using Ohm's Law, you find that the value of R_3 is:

$$R_3 = \frac{4\text{ V}}{1\text{ A}}$$

$$R_3 = 4\ \Omega$$

Using this procedure, you can design a voltage divider for one or more loads. All you need to know is the source voltage and the voltage and current requirements of each load.

To summarize, the step by step procedure is as follows:

1. Arbitrarily select a bleeder current that is about 10 percent of the total current in the circuit.

2. Using the bleeder current and the lowest voltage required by a load, compute the value of the bleeder resistor.

3. Using the total current through each resistor, and the voltage dropped by the resistor, determine the resistance values required.

    A special form of voltage divider that is frequently used in electronics consists of a resistor in series with a load of some type. The resistor is called a **series dropping resistor**. Its purpose is to ensure that the load is operated at its proper voltage and current rating. For example, consider the problem of using a 5 V relay in a system that has a 12 V power source.

Assume that the relay is designed to operate at 100 mA. The solution is to connect a resistor in series with the relay coil so that the current is limited to 100 mA. Also, since the relay must operate at 5 V, the series resistor must drop: 12 V − 5 V = 7 V. Thus, the size of the resistor must be:

$$R = \frac{E}{I}$$

$$R = \frac{7\ V}{100\ mA}$$

$$R = 70\ \Omega$$

Dropping resistors are often found in series with relays, light bulbs, motors, or other electronic devices. The series dropping resistor and its load form a very simple voltage divider.

10. The total current demanded by the three loads shown in Figure 7-7 is _____ mA.

11. In Figure 7-7, R_1 is called the _____ resistor.

12. If you want a 50 mA current through R_1, what is the proper resistance value of R_1? _____ Ω.

13. In the circuit described thus far, the current through R_2 is _____ mA.

14. The voltage drop across R_2 is _____ V.

15. What is the proper resistance value of R_2? _____ Ω.

16. The current through R_3 is _____ mA.

17. The voltage drop across R_3 is _____ volts.

18. What is the proper resistance value of R_3? _____ Ω.

19. If a relay coil has a resistance of 1 kΩ and is designed to operate with a current of 10 mA, what is the voltage at which the relay is designed to operate? _____ V.

20. If this relay is to be used in a system where the only voltage available is 24 volts, the series dropping resistor used with the relay must drop _____ V.

21. Since the current through the resistor must be 10 mA, the resistor value required is _____ Ω.

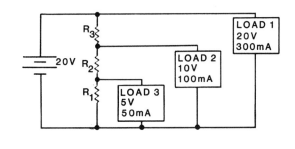

Figure 7-7 Find the values of R_1, R_2, and R_3.

Desk-Top Experiment 4
Voltage Dividers

Introduction

You have just learned about a couple of voltage dividers that are commonly used DC circuits. Designing these circuits requires a little thought and a thorough knowledge of series and parallel circuits and Ohm's Law. When necessary, use the following guide to help you design your circuit.

1. Select a bleeder current that is about 10% of the total circuit current.

2. Using the bleeder current and the lowest voltage required by a load, compute the value of the bleeder resistor.

3. Using the total current through each resistor, and the voltage dropped across each resistor, determine the resistance values required for the divider's resistors.

Take your time and try not to use the text unless absolutely necessary.

Objectives

1. To design voltage divider circuits with both single and multiple loads.

2. To use Ohm's Law and the rules governing series and parallel circuits to design voltage dividers.

3. Apply some of what you have learned about motor control circuits.

Procedure

1. Design a voltage divider so that you can operate a 12 V DC motor from a 24 V power supply. The motor draws 10 mA of current. Draw the circuit in the space provided below and label all voltage, current, and resistance values.

2. Is it possible to add a control to this circuit so that you can vary the motor's speed?

    _____

    If so, redraw the circuit below showing the control.

Discussion

It is possible to design a voltage divider for use with the motor simply by adding a series dropping resistor in the circuit with the motor. This circuit is shown in Figure 7-8A. To determine the value of the series dropping resistor, use the current that the motor draws, since this is the total current in a series circuit, and the voltage not dropped by the motor. The resistance value is:

$$R_1 = \frac{12\,V}{10\,mA}$$

$$R_1 = 1.2\,k\Omega$$

An elementary motor control circuit can be designed simply by adding a variable resistor in series with the rest of the circuit as shown in Figure 7-8B. When this is done, the motor will operate at its maximum speed when the variable resistor is adjusted to zero ohms. As the resistance of the variable resistor increases, the speed of the motor decreases.

Procedure (Cont.)

3. You have available a 24 V DC power supply. Design a voltage divider circuit that will operate with two 6 V lamps that draw 3 mA and a 12 V motor that draws 10 mA of current. Draw the circuit in the space provided below and include the appropriate voltage, current, and resistance values.

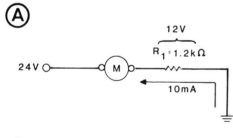

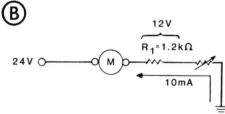

Figure 7-8 Voltage dividers using a series dropping resistor.

Discussion

This voltage divider was a bit more difficult to design than the divider given in the example in the text. In fact, there are a number of different ways that this divider can be designed. Two of these are shown in Figure 7-9.

Since each of the lamps requires 6 V, they can be connected in series resulting in a 12 V requirement for the two lamps. This works out well since the motor also requires 12 V. In this case, all of the loads can be connected in parallel across the bleeder resistor as shown in Figure 7-9.

Using a bleeder current of 1.3 mA and a voltage drop of 12 V, the appropriate resistance calculated for R_2 is 9230 Ω. R_1 must also drop 12 V, but the current through R_1 consists of the combined currents through the loads plus the current through the bleeder resistor. Therefore the resistance of R_1 is significantly lower than the resistance of R_2. The resistance of R_1 is 839 Ω. Since the loads require only 12 V, R_1 is a series dropping resistor for the parallel branches of the circuit.

Figure 7-9B shows another possible configuration for the given components. Here, the two lamps are in parallel and connected across the bleeder resistor. Meanwhile, a second resistor is added which ensures that the voltage drop across the motor is 12 V. The remaining 6 V delivered by the supply is dropped across R_1. You may have noticed that the total current for this configuration is somewhat greater than the total current needed by the circuit in Figure 7-9A.

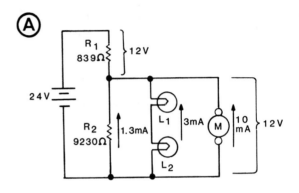

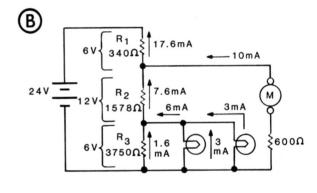

Figure 7-9 Voltage divider for Desk-Top Experiment 4.

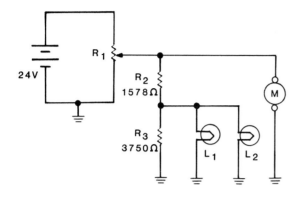

Figure 7-10 Voltage divider with a variable power supply.

Figure 7-10 is a variation of Figure 7-9B. Notice that the resistor values for R_2 and R_3 remain the same but that resistor R_1 has been replaced with a variable resistor. This circuit has one big advantage over the two circuits previously discussed. In this circuit, components can be added or removed. The variable resistor can be adjusted to compensate for any component changes.

Another type of series-parallel circuit that is widely used is the bridge circuit. In its simplest form, the bridge circuit is made up of four resistors connected as shown in Figure 7-11A. The circuit has two input terminals and two output terminals. In DC applications, the input terminals are connected to a DC voltage source such as a battery. Often a meter is connected across the output terminals as shown in Figure 7-11B.

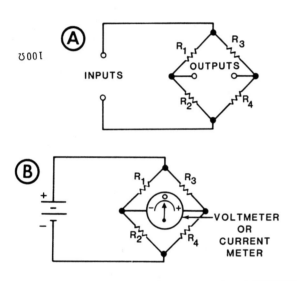

Figure 7-11 The bridge circuit.

Balanced Bridge

Before looking at some of the ways that bridge circuits can be used, you should first investigate the characteristics of a bridge circuit. A bridge circuit may be either balanced or unbalanced. A balanced bridge circuit is one in which the voltage measured between the two output terminals is 0 V. If the circuit shown in Figure 7-11B is balanced, a voltmeter or current meter connected across the output terminals, as shown, will indicate zero.

An example of a balanced bridge is shown in Figure 7-12A. Notice that R_1 is the same value as R_2. Thus, the voltage at point A with respect to ground must be one half the applied voltage or $+10$ volts. The voltage at point B is also $+10$ volts for the same reason. Therefore, point A is at the same potential as point B. No potential difference exists between the two points and a voltmeter connected from point A to point B will read 0 V. Furthermore, an ammeter would also read 0 μA since no current can flow unless there is a difference in potential. Notice that the bridge is balanced when all four resistors have the same value.

Figure 7-12B shows that a balanced condition can exist even when all the resistors have different values. Here you can determine the voltage at point A if you know the current through R_2 (I_A).

$$I_A = \frac{E}{R_1 + R_2}$$

$$I_A = \frac{30\,V}{1\,k\Omega + 2\,k\Omega}$$

$$I_A = \frac{30\,V}{3\,k\Omega}$$

$$I_A = 0.01\,A \text{ or } 10\,mA$$

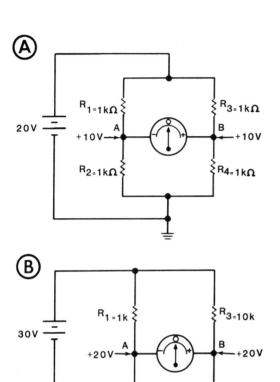

Figure 7-12 The balanced bridge.

Now the voltage across R_2 can be determined:

$$E_{R_2} = I_A \times R_2$$

$$E_{R_2} = 0.01\,A \times 2000\,\Omega$$

$$E_{R_2} = 20\,V$$

Thus, the voltage at point A with respect to ground is +20 volts.

Using a similar procedure, the voltage at point B can be determined. You will find that it is also +20 V. Thus, there is no difference of potential between points A and B. Consequently, the bridge is balanced.

If you examine Figure 7-12B carefully, you will see that R_2 is twice the value of R_1 and that R_4 is twice the value of R_3. R_1 and R_2 form a voltage divider that determines the voltage at point A. R_3 and R_4 form a divider that determines the voltage at point B. As long as the ratio between R_1 and R_2 is the same as the ratio between R_3 and R_4, the bridge is balanced. Expressed as an equation, the bridge is balanced when:

$$\frac{R_1}{R_2} = \frac{R_3}{R_4}$$

Notice that this equation describes both of the examples shown in Figure 7-12.

Unbalanced Bridge

Figure 7-13A shows a variation of the basic bridge circuit. Here R_4 is replaced with a potentiometer. If R_4 is set to the same value as the other three resistors, 200 Ω, the bridge is balanced. Both point A and point B are +15 V with respect to ground.

The balanced condition can be upset by changing the resistance of R_4. For example, in Figure 7-13B, R_4 is reset to 400 Ω. The voltage at point A remains at +15 volts since the values of R_1 and R_2 are unchanged. However, the voltage at point B changes. Because R_4 is now twice as large as R_3, it drops twice as much voltage as R_3. Thus, R_4 now drops 20 V while R_3 drops only 10 V. Consequently, the voltage at point B is +20 V with respect to ground. The bridge is no longer balanced because a difference of potential exists between points A and B. Because point B is more positive than point A, current flows through the voltmeter from point A to point B as shown. A voltmeter connected in this way indicates a 5 V difference of potential.

Figure 7-13C shows that the bridge can also be unbalanced by making the value of R_4 smaller than the value of R_3. Here R_3 develops only 10 V. Hence, the voltage at point B is only +10 V. Thus, current will flow in the opposite direction through the meter.

Wheatstone Bridge

Now that you have an understanding of how the bridge circuit operates, its time to examine some typical applications. The first practical application of the bridge circuit was the **wheatstone bridge**. The wheatstone bridge is a device for measuring resistance.

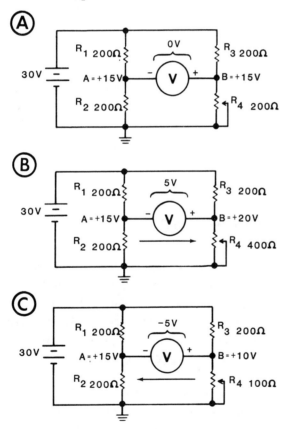

Figure 7-13 Unbalancing the bridge.

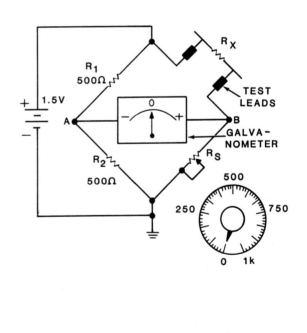

Figure 7-14 Wheatstone bridge.

A simple wheatstone bridge is shown in Figure 7-14. R_1 and R_2 are fixed matched precision resistors. R_S is a 1 kΩ potentiometer whose resistance is varied using a calibrated dial. At any setting, its value can be read directly from the dial. R_X is the unknown resistance that you want to measure. It is connected between the two test leads that form a part of the bridge. The meter is a very sensitive current meter called a galvanometer. Unlike the ammeters discussed earlier, the galvanometer can measure current flow in either direction. The center of the galvanometer scale is zero. Current flow in one direction is indicated by deflection to the left of center while current flow in the opposite direction is indicated by deflection to the right of center.

To see how the bridge can be used to measure resistance, assume that a 210 Ω resistor is connected between the test leads. Remember R_1 and R_2 form a voltage divider that determines the voltage at point A. Since R_1 and R_2 are equal, the bridge will be balanced only if values R_X and R_S are also equal. Thus, R_S is set so that the galvanometer reads exactly zero. At this point the bridge is balanced so R_S must equal R_X. The value of the unknown resistance can be read directly from the calibrated dial of R_S. This gives you a simple method for finding the value of the unknown resistor.

This simplified bridge can measure resistances up to 1 kΩ. In actual bridges, R_S is replaced with a device called a decade resistor box. By setting rotary switches, any value of resistance from a fraction of an ohm to several megohms can be placed in the circuit. Thus, the bridge can be used to measure a wide range of resistances.

Self-Balancing Bridge

Another interesting application of a bridge circuit is shown in Figure 7-15. Here, the four resistors are replaced by two potentiometers. The voltage is measured from the center taps of these two variable resistors. Also, the meter is replaced by a small DC motor (M). The motor turns on whenever the bridge is unbalanced.

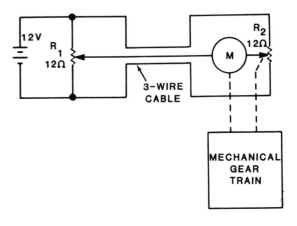

Figuer 7-15 Self-balancing bridge.

This circuit is called a self-balancing bridge and can be used for controlling motion at a distance. For example, if you have an antenna on a roof and you want to turn the antenna from ground level, this can be done with a self-balancing bridge. The motor and

R_2 are located on the roof with the antenna. R_1 and the power supply are located at ground level. The two circuits are connected by the 3-wire cable.

If you assume that the circuit is initially balanced with the arms of both potentiometers set at the center position and you wish to change the position of the antenna, you simply unbalance the bridge circuit by moving the arm of R_1. This allows current to flow through the motor causing the motor to turn. The motor is connected through a gear train to the antenna. Thus, as the motor turns, the antenna also turns. The motor is also connected to the arm of the potentiometer R_2. The motor turns until the arm of R_2 is at the same relative position as the arm of R_1. This rebalances the circuit and the motor stops turning. This circuit allows you to control the position of a remote antenna simply by setting the arm of a potentiometer.

Temperature Sensing Bridge

If one of the resistors in a bridge circuit is replaced with a thermistor, the bridge can be used as a temperature sensor. Figure 7-16 shows a temperature sensing bridge.

R_1 and R_5 are 1 kΩ resistors. At 0 degrees, the thermistor also has a resistance of 1 kΩ. If R_2 is set to 200 Ω, the fourth arm of the bridge also has a resistance of 1 kΩ. Consequently, the bridge is balanced and no

current flows through the 50 μA meter movement. Thus, the 0 μA point on the meter scale can be labeled 0 degrees.

As the temperature increases, the resistance of the thermistor decreases. This upsets the balanced condition and causes current to flow through the meter. The more the temperature increases, the more current flows through the meter. Thus, the current is an indication of the temperature. The meter scale is marked off in in degrees rather than microamperes. Therefore, the temperature can be read from the face of the meter.

R_4 is included to provide a means of calibrating the high end of the scale. For example, you may want the upper limit of your "thermometer" to be 100 degrees. In this case, the thermistor is exposed to a temperature of 100 degrees and R_4 is adjusted so that 50μA of current flows through the meter movement. This causes full scale deflection. Thus, the point of full-scale deflection can be labeled 100 degrees.

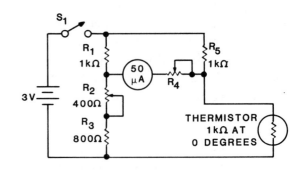

Figure 7-16 Temperature sensing bridge.

22. A bridge circuit has two input terminals and two _____ terminals.

23. A bridge circuit is said to be balanced when the voltage across the two output terminals is _____.

24. When the voltage across the output terminals is anything other than zero, the bridge is said to be _____.

25. The bridge circuit shown in Figure 7-11A will be _____ if all four resistors have the same value.

26. Actually, the circuit will be balanced any time the following equation is satisfied.

Many series-parallel circuits can be analyzed using the techniques described earlier. However, more complex circuits cannot always be analyzed by such simple methods. Often a circuit will have several interconnected series-parallel branches and two or more voltage sources. Several techniques have been developed to help analyze circuits of this type. These techniques are generally grouped together under the name "network theorems."

A network is simply a circuit made up of several components such as resistors. Thus, the series-parallel circuits discussed earlier can be called networks. A network theorem is a logical method for analyzing a network. One of the most useful tools for analyzing a network is Kirchhoff's Law.

One form of Kirchhoff's law was discussed earlier. It states the relationship between the voltage rises and the voltage drops around the closed loop in a circuit. Recall that the sum of the voltage drops is equal to the sum of the voltage rises. This fact is referred to as Kirchhoff's Voltage Law.

The voltage law is deceptively simple. At this point it is almost self-evident. Nevertheless, this law is a powerful tool when used properly. Look at the following discussion.

Kirchhoff's Voltage Law

The voltage law can be stated in several different ways. Up to now, it has been stated: **around a closed loop, the sum of the voltage drops is equal to the sum of the voltage rises**. Figure 7-17A illustrates this law.

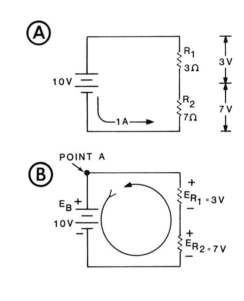

Figure 7-17 Kirchhoff's voltage law.

Another way of saying the same thing is: **around a closed loop, the algebraic sum of all the voltages is zero**. It becomes apparent that this statement is true when you trace around the loop shown in Figure 7-17B. Notice that this is the same circuit shown in Figure 7-17A. To keep the polarity of the voltages correct, it is helpful to establish a rule for adding the voltages. A convenient 3-part rule is:

1. Choose which direction you prefer to trace the circuit. Either clockwise or counterclockwise will work equally well.

2. Trace around the circuit in the chosen direction. If the positive side of a voltage drop, or voltage rise, is encountered first, consider that voltage drop, or rise, to be positive.

3. If the negative side of a voltage drop, or voltage rise, is encountered first, consider that voltage drop, or rise, to be negative.

For example starting at point A in Figure 7-17B, trace counterclockwise as shown recording each voltage encountered. The first voltage is E_B. Because the positive side of the battery is encountered first, the voltage is recorded as $+10$ V. Next E_{R_2} is encountered. This is recorded as -7 V because you arrive at the negative side of the resistor first. E_{R_1} is recorded as -3 V for the same reason. Thus, the sum of the voltages are:

$$+ 10\,V - 7\,V - 3\,V = 0\,V$$

Or stated as an equation:

$$E_B - E_{R_2} - E_{R_1} = 0\,V$$

As you can see, the sum of the voltage drops around the loop is zero.

In this example, the loop was traced in the counterclockwise direction. However, tracing in the clockwise direction, you'll find that the sum is still zero.

Using Kirchhoff's Law

Look at the circuit shown in Figure 7-18A. Assume that you wish to find the current at all points in the circuit and the voltage dropped by each resistor. If you attempt to solve this problem using only Ohm's Law, you run into insurmountable difficulties. However, if you use Kirchhoff's Law with Ohm's Law, the solution can be easily found.

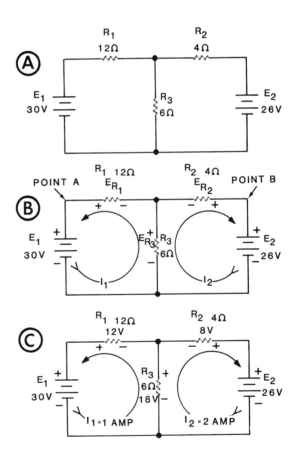

Figure 7-18 Using Kirchhoff's Law.

The first step in applying Kirchhoff's Law is to assume a direction for current flow through each loop. It makes no difference if the assumed direction is incorrect. With the batteries connected as shown it appears that the loop currents will be in the direction shown by the arrow in Figure 7-18B. Let's assume that this is the direction of current flow.

The second step is to mark the polarity of the voltage drops across the resistors. You do this by marking negative polarity where current enters the resistor and positive polarity where current leaves the resistor. Using this procedure, with the assumed direction of current flow, the polarity of voltage drops are marked as shown in Figure 7-18B.

The third step is to write an equation for each loop using Kirchhoff's Voltage Law. To do this, you start at a given point tracing around the loop in the assumed direction of current flow. You record each voltage rise and voltage drop following the procedure outlined earlier. Finally, you assume that the sum of all voltage drops and rises is equal to zero.

Starting at point A in Figure 7-18B, the equation is:

$$+ E_1 - E_{R_3} - E_{R_1} = 0$$

Notice that E_1 is positive because its positive terminal is encountered first. In the same way, the voltage drops across R_3 and R_1 are negative since their negative termi-

nals are encountered first. The sum of the three terms are equal to zero in accordance with Kirchhoff's Law.

Using this same procedure an equation is developed for the loop through which I_2 flows. If you start at point B and follow the direction of current flow, the equation becomes:

$$+ E_2 - E_{R_3} - E_{R_2} = 0$$

At this point you have two equations that describe the operation of the circuit. They are:

$$E_1 - E_{R_3} - E_{R_1} = 0$$

$$E_2 - E_{R_3} - E_{R_2} = 0$$

Notice that each equation contains a voltage rise and two voltage drops. The value of the voltage rises, E_1 and E_2, are given in Figure 7-18. Substituting 30 volts for E_1 and 26 volts for E_2 the equations become:

$$30\,V - E_{R_3} - E_{R_1} = 0$$

$$26\,V - E_{R_3} - E_{R_2} = 0$$

The next step is to manipulate these equations using Ohm's Law and some of the other values given in Figure 7-18. You can start with the equation:

$$30\,V - E_{R_3} - E_{R_1} = 0$$

The term E_{R_1} is the voltage drop across R_1. Since this voltage drop is caused by I_1 through R_1, using Ohm's Law:

$$E_{R_1} = R_1 \times I_1 \text{ or } R_1 I_1$$

Thus, the terms $R_1 I_1$ can be substituted for E_{R_1} in your equation. The equation becomes:

$$30 \text{ V} - E_{R_3} - R_1 I_1 = 0$$

The term E_{R_3} is the voltage drop across R_3. It is caused by currents I_1 and I_2. Thus:

$$E_{R_3} = R_3 \times (I_1 + I_2) \text{ or } R_3 (I_1 + I_2)$$

Once again substituting, the equation becomes:

$$30 \text{ V} - R_3(I_1 + I_2) - R_1 I_1 = 0$$

Next, you substitute the values of R_3 and R_1:

$$30 \text{ V} - 6\,\Omega\,(I_1 + I_2) - 12\,\Omega\,I_1 = 0$$

You eliminate the parentheses by multiplying the -6 times each term within the parentheses:

$$30 \text{ V} - 6\,\Omega\,I_1 - 6\,\Omega\,I_2 - 12\,\Omega\,I_1 = 0$$

Combining $-6\,\Omega\,I_1$ and $-12\,\Omega\,I_1$ you have:

$$30 \text{ V} - 18\,\Omega\,I_1 - 6\,\Omega\,I_2 = 0$$

At this point, it is convenient to have the voltage rise on one side of the equation and the voltage drops on the other. You do this by subtracting 30 V from both sides of the equation. This leaves:

$$- 18\,\Omega\,I_1 - 6\,\Omega\,I_2 = - 30 \text{ V}$$

Leave this equation for a moment and go back to the equation for the second loop. Recall that the equation is:

$$26 \text{ V} - E_{R_3} - E_{R_2} = 0$$

If you manipulate this equation as you did the first, the steps look like this:

$$26 \text{ V} - R_3 (I_1 + I_2) - R_2 I_2 = 0$$

Substitute values of R_3 and R_2:

$$26 \text{ V} - 6\,\Omega(I_1 + I_2) - 4\,\Omega\,I_2 = 0$$

Remove the parentheses:

$$26 \text{ V} - 6\,\Omega\,I_1 - 6\,\Omega\,I_2 - 4\,\Omega\,I_2 = 0$$

Combine I_2 terms:

$$26 \text{ V} - 6\,\Omega\,I_1 - 10\,\Omega\,I_2 = 0$$

Subtract 26 V from both sides:

$$- 6\,\Omega\,I_1 - 10\,\Omega\,I_2 = - 26 \text{ V}$$

Thus, your two original equations are now:

$$- 18\,\Omega\,I_1 - 6\,\Omega\,I_2 = - 30 \text{ V}$$

$$- 6\,\Omega\,I_1 - 10\,\Omega\,I_2 = - 26 \text{ V}$$

Up to this point you have manipulated the two equations using what you know about Ohm's Law and some basic algebra. Now, it is time to solve for the unknown values, I_1 and I_2.

Notice that each equation has two unknowns, I_1 and I_2. The solution to either of these equations depends on the other equation. In other words, to solve either equation, you must use both equations. Equations of this type are called **simultaneous** equations. There are several methods for solving simultaneous equations. One of the easiest methods involves cancelling or eliminating one of the unknowns. This method works for two reasons:

1. You can do almost anything you like to one side of an equation as long as you do the same thing to the other side. For example, you can add, subtract, multiply, or divide both sides of an equation by a number without changing the equality.

2. You can add two simultaneous equations together without upsetting the equality.

Consider your two simultaneous equations again:

$$-18\,\Omega\,I_1 - 6\,\Omega\,I_2 = -30\,V$$

$$-6\,\Omega\,I_1 - 10\,\Omega\,I_2 = -26\,V$$

At this point, you want to eliminate one of the unknowns from the equations. To do

this, you can add the equations but first you must manipulate one of the equations so that one of the terms will drop out when the addition takes place. You can do this by multiplying both sides of the second equation by -3 so that your equations now become:

$$-18\,\Omega\,I_1 - 6\,\Omega\,I_2 = -30\,V$$

$$+18\,\Omega\,I_1 + 30\,\Omega\,I_2 = +78\,V$$

Notice that by multiplying the bottom equation by -3, you have changed the term containing I_1 in the bottom equation to the same magnitude, but opposite sign, as the term containing I_1 in the top equation. Now, if you add the two equations, the I_1 terms cancel:

$$-18\,\Omega\,I_1 - 6\,\Omega\,I_2 = -30\,V$$

$$+18\,\Omega\,I_1 + 30\,\Omega\,I_2 = +78\,V$$

$$\overline{0 + 24\,\Omega\,I_2 = +48\,V}$$

Thus, you end up with a single equation:

$$+24\,\Omega\,I_2 = +48\,V$$

Now, you can solve for I_2 by dividing both sides of the equation by $24\,\Omega$:

$$I_2 = \frac{+48\,V}{+24\,\Omega}$$

$$I_2 = 2\,A$$

This positive current value tells you that your assumed direction of current flow is correct. If the current value had been negative, then you would know that your assumed current flow direction was incorrect.

Now you can find I_1 by substituting $+2$ A for I_2 in either of the above equations. That is:

$$-18\,\Omega\,I_1 - 6\,\Omega\,I_2 = -30\,V$$

Substitute $+2$ A for I_2:

$$-18\,\Omega\,I_1 - 6\,\Omega\,(+2\,A) = -30\,V$$

$$-18\,\Omega\,I_1 - 12\,V = -30\,V$$

Add 12 V to both sides:

$$-18\,\Omega\,I_1 = -18\,V$$

Divide by $-18\,\Omega$:

$$I_1 = \frac{-18\,V}{-18\,\Omega}$$

$$I_1 = +1\,A$$

Thus, the currents in the circuit are as shown in Figure 7-18C. Once the currents are known, the voltage drops can be determined using Ohm's Law. When computing the voltage drop across R_3, remember that both I_1 and I_2 flow through the resistor. Thus:

$$E_{R_3} = R_3\,(I_1 + I_2)$$

$$E_{R_3} = 6\,\Omega\,(1\,A + 2\,A)$$

$$E_{R_3} = 6\,\Omega\,(3\,A)$$

$$E_{R_3} = 18\,V$$

Verify that the other voltage drops shown in Figure 7-18C are correct.

Kirchhoff's Current Law

Another form of Kirchhoff's Law involves current rather than voltage. Kirchhoff's current law can be stated in several different ways. One form states that in parallel circuits, the total current is equal to the sum of the branch currents. Stated another way, the current entering any point in a circuit is equal to the current leaving that same point.

Figure 7-19 illustrates that these are simply two different ways of saying the same thing. Two branch currents of 1 A each are flowing in the circuit. Thus, the total current is 2 A. Now look at point A. Notice that 2 A flow into this point. Consequently, 2 A must flow out of this point. One-half of the current flows through R_1 while the other half flows through R_2. Once again, an important law is simply common sense. Nevertheless, this law can be used in much the same way as the voltage law to evaluate networks. However, because Kirchhoff's voltage law is generally easier to use, the current law will not be used in this unit.

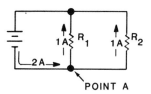

Figure 7-19 The current leaving point A is equal to the current entering point A.

27. Figure 7-20 shows another network that can be solved using Kirchhoff's Voltage Law. Two loops are shown. Start at point A and trace clockwise around the first loop. The equation for this loop is:

_____ .

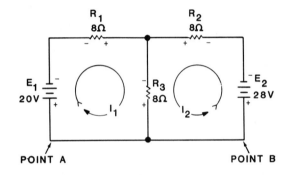

Figure 7-20 Solve with Kirchhoff's Law.

28. Substituting the known values from Figure 7-20 into the equation, the equation becomes: _____ .

29. Simplify the equation by getting rid of the parenthesis. The equation is now:

_____ .

30. Combining like terms the equation becomes: _____ .

31. Move 20 V to the right side of the equation and it becomes: _____ .

32. Starting at point B in Figure 7-20 and tracing in a counterclockwise direction, the equation is:

_____ .

33. Substituting the values given and the unknown currents, the equation becomes: _____ .

34. Getting rid of the parentheses, the equation is: _____ .

35. Combining like terms, you get:

_____ .

36. Moving 28 V to the right side of the equation you get: _____ .

37. Change the equation in the previous problem so that the I_1 term in the equations will cancel when the equations are added. The second equation becomes: _____ .

38. Now, add your two equations. The result is: _____ .

39. Solving for I_2 you find that $I_2 =$

_____ .

40. Use the value of I_2 and solve your first equation. $I_1 =$ _____ .

41. Now that you know I_1 and I_2, solve for the following:

$E_{R_1} =$ _____ .

$E_{R_2} =$ _____ .

$E_{R_3} =$ _____ .

Superposition Theorem

The superposition theorem is the most logical of the network theorems and it is widely used in physics, engineering, and even economics. It is used to analyze systems in which several forces act simultaneously to cause a net effect. It gives you a simple logical method for determining the net effect.

The logic behind the superposition theorem is that the net effect of several causes can be determined by finding the individual effect of each cause acting alone and then adding all the individual effects together. For example, suppose you have two batteries that are both forcing current to flow through a resistor. The net current can be determined by finding the individual current caused by each battery and then adding the individual currents together.

In more formal terms, the superposition theorem states: **In a linear, bilateral network containing more than one voltage source, the current at any point is equal to the algebraic sum of the currents produced by each voltage source acting separately**.

A linear circuit is one in which the current is directly proportional to the voltage. If the voltage doubles, so does the current. Bilateral means that the circuit conducts equally well in either direction. The resistive networks that you have been studying are both linear and bilateral so they lend themselves to the superposition theorem.

The easiest way to see how this theorem works is to consider an example. Figure 7-21A is a series circuit containing two voltage sources and two resistors. The 50 V battery attempts to force current in a counterclockwise direction while the 75 V battery attempts to force current in a clockwise direction. The problem is to find the net current in the circuit.

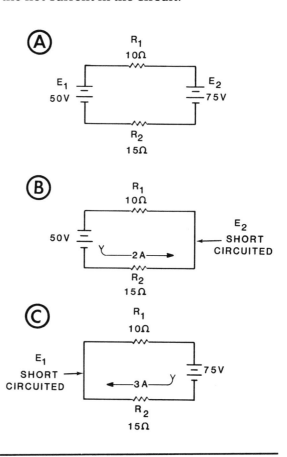

Figure 7-21 Using the superposition theorem.

The first step is to consider only the current produced by the 50 V battery. To do this, you must mentally short circuit the 75 V battery. This leaves the circuit shown in Figure 7-21B. Here the current is:

$$I = \frac{E}{R_T}$$

$$I = \frac{50 \text{ V}}{25 \text{ }\Omega}$$

$$I = 2 \text{ A}$$

This current flows in the counterclockwise direction as shown.

Next you must consider the current produced by the 75 V battery. Again, you mentally short circuit the 50 V battery as shown in Figure 7-21C. The current is:

$$I = \frac{E}{R_T}$$

$$I = \frac{75 \text{ V}}{25 \text{ }\Omega}$$

$$I = 3 \text{ A}$$

This current flows in the clockwise direction as shown.

As you can see, the 50 V battery attempts to force 2 A in the counterclockwise direction. Simultaneously, the 75 V battery attempts to force 3 A of current in the clockwise direction. Obviously then, the net current is 1 A in the clockwise direction.

Now, consider a slightly more complex network. Figure 7-22A shows the circuit that you analyzed earlier using Kirchhoff's Law. The superposition theorem can also be used to find the currents in the various parts of this circuit.

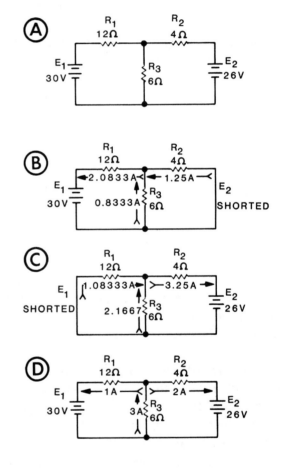

Figure 7-22 Applying the superposition theorem to a more complex network.

The first step is to redraw the circuit as shown in Figure 7-22B. Here you are interested in the current produced by E_1. Therefore, E_2 is shorted. The total resistance in this circuit is:

$$R_T = R_1 + \frac{R_2 \times R_3}{R_2 + R_3}$$

$$R_T = 12\,\Omega + \frac{4\,\Omega \times 6\Omega}{4\,\Omega + 6\,\Omega}$$

$$R_T = 12\,\Omega + \frac{24\,\Omega}{10\,\Omega}$$

$$R_T = 14.4\,\Omega$$

Thus, the total current produced by E_1 is:

$$I = \frac{E_1}{R_T}$$

$$I = \frac{30\,V}{14.4\,\Omega}$$

$$I = 2.08333\,A$$

With this amount of current, the voltage drop across R_1 is:

$$E_{R_1} = I \times R_1$$

$$E_{R_1} = 2.08333\,A \times 12\,\Omega$$

$$E_{R_1} = 25\,V$$

This leaves 5 V across R_2 and R_3. Thus, the current through R_2 is:

$$I_{R_2} = \frac{E_{R_2}}{R_2}$$

$$I_{R_2} = \frac{5\,V}{4\,\Omega}$$

$$I_{R_2} = 1.25\,A$$

And, the current through R_3 is:

$$I_{R_3} = \frac{E_{R_3}}{R_3}$$

$$I_{R_3} = \frac{5\,V}{6\,\Omega}$$

$$I_{R_3} = 0.8333\,A$$

The currents produced by E_1 are as shown in Figure 7-22B.

Next, consider the currents produced by E_2 with E_1 shorted. The circuit is shown in Figure 7-22C. Here the total resistance is:

$$R_T = R_2 + \frac{R_1 \times R_3}{R_1 + R_3}$$

$$R_T = 4\,\Omega + \frac{12\,\Omega \times 6\,\Omega}{12\,\Omega + 6\,\Omega}$$

$$R_T = 4\,\Omega + \frac{72\,\Omega}{18\,\Omega}$$

$$R_T = 4\,\Omega + 4\,\Omega$$

$$R_T = 8\,\Omega$$

Thus, the total current is:

$$I_T = \frac{E_2}{R_T}$$

$$I_T = \frac{26\ V}{8\ \Omega}$$

$$I_T = 3.25\ A$$

With this current, the voltage drop across R_2 is:

$$E_{R_2} = I \times R_2$$

$$E_{R_2} = 3.25\ A \times 4\ \Omega$$

$$E_{R_2} = 13\ V$$

This leaves 13 V across R_1 and R_3. Thus, the current through R_1 is:

$$I_{R_1} = \frac{E_{R_1}}{R_1}$$

$$I_{R_1} = \frac{13\ V}{12\ \Omega}$$

$$I_{R_1} = 1.08333\ A$$

Also, the current through R_3 is:

$$I_{R_3} = \frac{E_{R_3}}{R_3}$$

$$I_{R_3} = \frac{13\ V}{6\ \Omega}$$

$$I_{R_3} = 2.1667\ A$$

Thus, the currents produced by E_2 are as shown in Figure 7-22C.

The final step is to superimpose the two circuits. In Figure 7-22B, the current through R_1 is 2.0833 A flowing to the left. In Figure 7-22C, the current through R_1 is 1.0833 A flowing to the right. Obviously then, the net current is 1 A to the left. Combining the other individual currents in the same way, you find the net currents are as shown in Figure 7-22D. Also, if you refer back to Figure 7-18C, you will see that these are the same values computed earlier using Kirchhoff's law.

Self-Test Review

In the following questions, you will use the superposition theorem to analyze the circuit shown in Figure 7-23A.

42. When you short out E_2 you get the circuit shown in Figure 7- 23B. What is the total resistance of this circuit? _____ Ω.

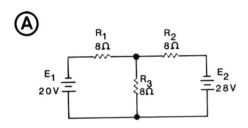

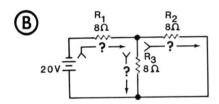

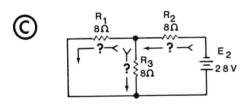

Figure 7-23 Analyze this network using the superposition theorem.

43. Therefore, the total current in the circuit is
_____ A.

44. The current through R_2 is
_____ A.

45. Likewise, the current through R_3 is
_____ A.

46. To determine the current produced by E_2 you redraw the circuit as shown in Figure 7-23C. Here the total resistance is _____ .

47. Therefore the total current is
_____ amperes.

48. This entire current flows through R_2 but is split evenly between R_1 and R_3. Thus, the current through R_3 is
_____ A.

49. Now, the net current through R_1 is
_____ A to the (left/right).

50. The net current through R_2 is
_____ A to the (right/left).

51. The net current through R_3 is
_____ A.

Thevenin's Theorem

Another important and powerful tool for simplifying and analyzing networks is Thevenin's theorem. Unlike the laws and theorems discussed earlier, the reasons why Thevenin's theorem works are not all that obvious. Fortunately, you can use this theorem without understanding why it works.

This theorem allows you to replace any two-terminal network of voltage sources and resistors, no matter how they are interconnected, with a single voltage source in series with a single resistor. A two-terminal network is simply a network that has two output terminals. For example, a two-terminal network such as the one shown in Figure 7-24A can be replaced by an equivalent circuit like that shown in Figure 7-24B.

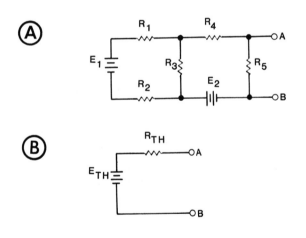

Figure 7-24 Complex networks can be represented by a single source (E_{TH}) in series with a single resistor (R_{TH}).

More formally, Thevenin's theorem states: **Any network of resistors and voltage sources, if viewed from any two terminals in the network, can be replaced with an equivalent voltage source (E_{TH}) and an equivalent series resistance (R_{TH}).** Of course, there are definite rules concerning the values assigned to E_{TH} and R_{TH}.

Perhaps the best way to understand this theorem is to consider an example. Figure 7-25A shows a circuit that can be easily analyzed using Ohm's Law. In this example, R_3 is the load while the remaining circuitry is considered to be the source. Use Ohm's law to determine the current through R_3. Do not read further until you have calculated the value of I_{R_3}. Now let's find the same current using Thevenin's theorem.

The first step is to mentally disconnect the load R_3 from the rest of the circuit as shown in Figure 7-25B. Notice that the circuit to the left of terminals A and B now has the same general form as those circuits shown in Figure 7-24A. Thus, this two-terminal network can be replaced with a "Thevenin equivalent" like the one shown earlier in Figure 7-24B. The only problem is to find the proper value of E_{TH} and R_{TH}.

E_{TH} is the voltage that can actually be measured between points A and B when R_3 is disconnected as shown in Figure 7-25B. This is called the **open circuit voltage**. Remember, it is the voltage between points A and B when the load is disconnected from these points. The circuit to be "thevenized"

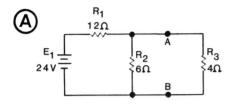

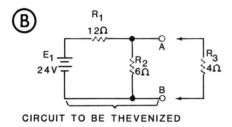

CIRCUIT TO BE THEVENIZED

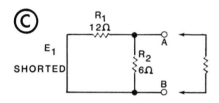

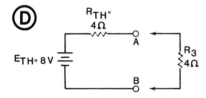

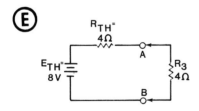

Figure 7-25 Using Thevenin's theorem.

is the original circuit less the load. Since E_1, R_1, and R_2 now form a series circuit, the voltage between points A and B can be easily computed. First, you find the circuit current:

$$I = \frac{E}{R_T}$$

$$I = \frac{24 \text{ V}}{18 \text{ }\Omega}$$

$$I = 1.333 \text{ A}$$

Notice that the voltage between points A and B is the voltage drop across R_2 or E_{R_2}. This is the Thevenin voltage. Thus:

$$E_{TH} = I \times R_2$$

$$E_{TH} = 1.333 \text{ A} \times 6 \text{ }\Omega$$

$$E_{TH} = 8 \text{ V}.$$

Now, determine the value of R_{TH}. R_{TH} is the measurable resistance between terminals A and B when the voltage source is shorted. Using an ohmmeter, check the resistance between points A and B with the voltage source shorted. This measures the Thevenin resistance. When E_1 is shorted as shown in Figure 7-25C, the resistance between points A and B is:

$$R_{TH} = \frac{R_1 \times R_2}{R_1 + R_2}$$

$$R_{TH} = \frac{12 \text{ }\Omega \times 6 \text{ }\Omega}{12 \text{ }\Omega + 6 \text{ }\Omega}$$

$$R_{TH} = 4 \text{ }\Omega$$

How come the parallel network equations are used to solve a circuit that is apparently connected in series? Look again at Figure 7-25C. Imagine an ohmmeter connected between points A and B. With a short across E_1, the battery in the ohmmeter acts as a voltage source for the circuit. Now, imagine a battery connected between points A and B. As you can see, if this is the case then resistors R_1 and R_2 form a parallel branch.

Thus, the network shown in Figure 7-25B can be represented by the Thevenin equivalent shown in Figure 7-25D. Now, reconnect R_3 between Terminals A and B as shown in Figure 7-25E. Notice that the series-parallel network has been redrawn as a series equivalent circuit. That is, the portion of the circuit consisting of R_1 and R_2 has the same relationship to R_3 as a single 4 Ω equivalent resistance. At any rate, now that you have simplified the circuit and have a series circuit, the current through R_3 can be easily determined:

$$I = \frac{E}{R_T}$$

$$I = \frac{8\ V}{8\ \Omega}$$

$$I = 1\ A$$

The current through R_3 is 1 A. This should be the same value that you computed using Ohm's Law.

You may wonder why Thevenin's theorem is used at all on an elementary circuit such as the one shown in Figure 7-25A. After all, you can find E_{R_3} and I_{R_3} using only Ohm's Law. However, there are times when this theorem is extremely valuable even with simple circuits like this one. Suppose, for example, that you had to compute E_{R_3} and I_{R_3} for 100 different values of R_3. Using only Ohm's Law, you must compute 100 different series-parallel problems. Using Thevenin's theorem, you still work one hundred problems. However, because the Thevenin equivalent is the same for all problems, the problems are the comparatively simple series circuit type rather than the more complex series-parallel type.

Thevenin's theorem also allows you to solve complex networks that cannot be analyzed using only Ohm's Law. For example, Figure 7-26A shows the circuit that you have already analyzed using Kirchhoff's Law and the superposition theorem. Now, try Thevenin's theorem to see if you arrive at the same answers.

First, find the current through R_3. You do this by thevenizing the entire circuit except for R_3. Thus, the first step is to remove R_3, the load, from the circuit by opening points A and B. The resulting circuit is shown in Figure 7-26B. Notice that in this circuit, E_1 tries to force current counterclockwise while E_2 tries to force current clockwise. In effect, these batteries are connected in a series opposing configuration and the net voltage causing current flow is:

$$E_T = E_1 - E_2$$

$$E_T = 30\ \text{V} - 26\ \text{V}$$

$$E_T = 4\ \text{V}.$$

The total resistance is:

$$R_T = R_1 + R_2$$

$$R_T = 12\ \Omega + 4\ \Omega$$

$$R_T = 16\ \Omega$$

Thus, the current is:

$$4\ \text{V} \div 16\ \Omega = 0.25\ \text{A}$$

in the counterclockwise direction. Verify that the voltage drops across R_1 and R_2 are the polarity and magnitude shown.

You can now determine E_{TH}. This can be done in two ways. You can look at the circuit to the right or to the left of points A and B. Starting at points A and B and looking to the left, you see the circuit shown in Figure 7-26C. Since 30 V is supplied to the circuit and 3 V is dropped across R_1, the remainder must be dropped between points A and B. Notice that the voltage between A and B is 30 V − 3 V = 27 V. Thus, looking at the circuit in this way you determine that V_{TH} is 27 V.

You may wonder what value of E_{TH} you will find if you look to the right of terminals A and B as shown in Figure 7-26D. Notice that the polarity of the voltage drop across R_2 is the same as the polarity of E_2. The voltage is 1 V + 26 V = 27 V. In both cases, the value of E_{TH} is the same.

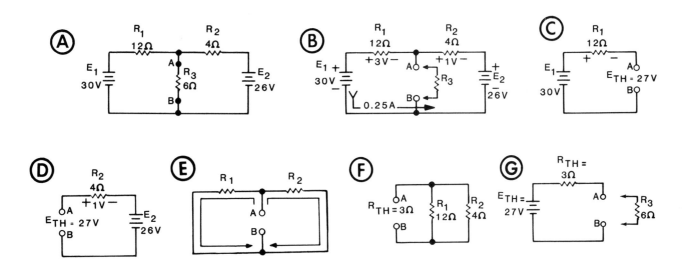

Figure 7-26 Using Thevenin's theorem.

Next, you find R_{TH} by determining the resistance between points A and B when the two voltage sources are short circuited. Looking at the circuit from points A and B, you can see that there are two parallel current paths through resistors R_1 and R_2 as indicated in Figure 7-26E. This circuit can be redrawn as shown in Figure 7-26F. Now, it can easily be seen that the resistance between points A and B is the value of R_1 and R_2 in parallel. Thus:

$$R_{TH} = \frac{R_1 \times R_2}{R_1 + R_2}$$

$$R_{TH} = \frac{12\,\Omega \times 4\,\Omega}{12\,\Omega + 4\,\Omega}$$

$$R_{TH} = 3\,\Omega$$

Thus, the Thevenin equivalent is the circuit shown in Figure 7-26G.

The final step is to reconnect R_3 to points A and B and then determine the current:

$$I = \frac{E}{R_T}$$

$$I = \frac{27\,V}{9\,\Omega}$$

$$I = 3\,A$$

This agrees with your earlier findings for the current through R_3.

Desk-Top Experiment 5
Thevenin's Theorem

Introduction

In this experiment, you will use Thevenin's Theorem to analyze a bridge circuit that consists of 4 resistors and a DC motor. The following list of steps will help you when you are thevenizing each circuit.

1. Mentally remove the load from the circuit.

2. Find the current through the circuit that remains once the load is removed. In effect, removing the load presents you with an entirely new circuit.

3. Use the current through the circuit to determine V_{TH}. This is done by using Ohm's Law to determine the voltage at the circuit outputs.

4. Mentally short the circuit's voltage source then determine the circuit's resistance as it would be measured from the outputs. This is R_{TH}.

Objectives

1. To gain experience using Thevenin's Theorem to analyze DC circuits.

2. To increase your understanding of how a bridge circuit operates and how it can be used as a motor control circuit.

Procedure

1. Using what you know about Thevenin's Theorem, analyze the circuit shown in Figure 7-27. First, draw the appropriate current paths on the figure.

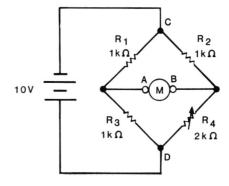

Figure 7-27 Circuit for Desk-Top Experiment 5.

2. In order to determine E_{TH}, you must first know the current through and the voltage dropped by the various components in the circuit. Therefore, calculate the following:

I_{R_1} = _____ A. I_{R_3} = _____ A.

E_{R_1} = _____ V. E_{R_3} = _____ V.

I_{R_2} = _____ A. I_{R_4} = _____ A.

E_{R_2} = _____ V. E_{R_4} = _____ V.

3. Now, using the calculations from step 2 and the circuit diagram, determine the Thevenin voltage between points A and B.

$$E_{TH} = \underline{\hspace{2cm}} V.$$

4. Determine the Thevenin resistance, R_{TH}, for the circuit in Figure 7-27.

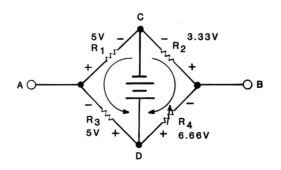

Figure 7-28 Finding V_{TH}.

Discussion

To make the explanation somewhat easier to understand, the circuit shown in Figure 7-27 is redrawn as shown in Figure 7-28. If you compare this with Figure 7-27 you will see that the current flows in the direction shown. In this case, the Thevenin voltage is the algebraic sum of the voltage drops between points A and B. That is, the Thevenin voltage is the algebraic sum of either the voltage drops across R_1 and R_2 or across R_3 and R_4. Note that the polarity of the voltage drops across the resistors is opposite. Thus, the sum of either of the resistor pairs is 1.6 V.

When solving for R_{TH}, you must first mentally short out the voltage source. This is done pictorially in Figure 7-29A. Notice that the circuit now consists of two parallel branches in series with one another. This is once again redrawn in Figure 7-29B for simplicity. R_{TH}, therefore, is 1166.66 Ω.

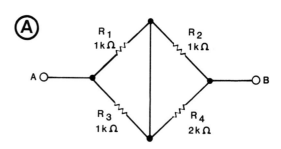

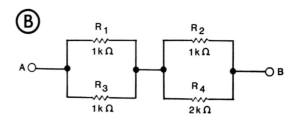

Figure 7-29 Finding R_{TH}.

Procedure (Cont.)

5. In the space provided, draw the Thevenin equivalent of the original bridge circuit given in Figure 7-27.

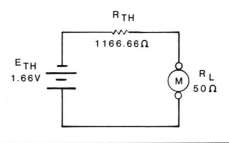

Figure 7-30 Thevenin equivalent circuit.

Discussion

The Thevenin equivalent for the circuit shown in Figure 7-27 is given in Figure 7-30. Here, the Thevenin voltage becomes the source voltage and the Thevenin resistance is connected in series with the load. Note that the Thevenin voltage and resistance are constant values for a given circuit. They are independent of the load.

Using Ohm's Law and the values given, it is easy to determine a load current of ≈ 1.37 mA. This current through a 50 Ω load produces a load voltage of 0.068 V.

6. Assuming that the DC motor has a resistance of 50 Ω, calculate the load current, I_L and the load voltage E_L.

$$I_L = \text{_____} \text{mA.}$$

$$E_L = \text{_____} \text{V.}$$

Self-Test Review

In the following questions, you will analyze a circuit step by step using Thevenin's theorem. The appropriate illustrations for this analysis are in Figure 7-31.

52. When finding the current flow through R_3 in Figure 7-31, the first step is to disconnect the _____ from the circuit.

53. This leaves the circuit shown in Figure 7-31B. The net voltage in the circuit is $E_2 - E1 =$ _____.

54. Because the total resistance is 16 ohms, the net voltage causes a current of _____ A.

55. In this circuit, the current flows in a _____ direction.

56. R_1 and R_2 each drop _____ V.

57. Examining the circuit on the left side of terminals A and B, you find that E_{TH} is _____ V.

58. Examining the voltage in the circuit to the right of terminals A and B, you find that E_{TH} is _____ V.

In order to determine R_{TH}, you short out the voltage sources and end up with the circuit shown in Figure 7-31C.

59. From Figure 7-31C, $R_{TH} =$ _____ Ω.

60. The current in the Thevenin equivalent circuit shown in Figure 7-31D is _____ A.

61. The voltage drop across R_3 in the Thevenin equivalent is _____ V.

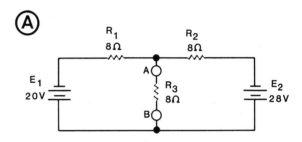

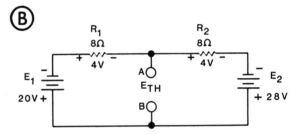

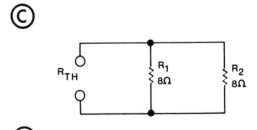

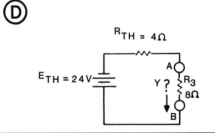

Figure 7-31 Solve for I_{R_3} using Thevenin's theorem.

Norton's Theorem

Using Thevenin's theorem, you found that a circuit like that in Figure 7-32A can be represented by the equivalent circuit shown in Figure 7-32B. Norton's theorem gives you a slightly different way of representing the same circuit. Thevenin's theorem uses an equivalent **voltage** source (E_{TH}) in series with an equivalent resistance (R_{TH}). On the other hand, Norton's theorem uses an equivalent **current** source (I_N) in **parallel** with an equivalent resistance (R_N). Thus, the circuit in Figure 7-32A can also be represented by the Norton equivalent shown in Figure 7-32C.

Current Sources and Voltage Sources

At this point, some words of explanation are in order. The idea of a voltage source is easy to visualize. An ideal voltage source is a device that produces the same output voltage regardless of the current drawn from it. As used in most electronic devices, a battery can be considered a nearly ideal voltage source.

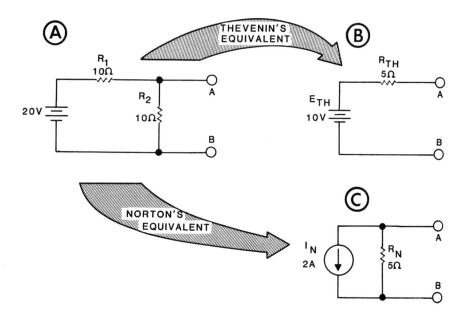

Figure 7-32 Comparing Norton's and Thevenin's equivalent circuits.

A large 12 V battery will produce an output of approximately 12 V whether the load current is 0 A, 1 A or even 10 A. The reason for this is that the resistance of the battery is very low compared to the load resistance connected to it. An ideal voltage source has an internal resistance of 0 Ω. In most electronic devices, the internal resistance of the battery or power supply is negligible compared to other circuit resistances. Thus, a battery can generally be considered as a nearly ideal voltage source. In Thevenin's theorem, E_{TH} is considered to be an ideal voltage source having 0 Ω resistance. Thus, you represent the voltage source with a short when determining R_{TH}.

The idea of a current source is similar. Whereas a voltage source has a certain voltage rating, the current source has a certain current rating. An ideal current source will deliver its rated current regardless of the value of the load resistance connected across it. Figure 7-32 illustrates this point. The voltage source (E_{TH}) in Figure 7-32B produces exactly 10 V regardless of what resistance value is connected across terminals A and B. In the same way, the current source in Figure 7-32C produces 2 A regardless of the resistance value connected across terminals A and B.

A current source can be visualized as a voltage source with an enormously high internal resistance. Consider, for example, the circuit shown in Figure 7-33A. Here a 10-volt battery is shown in series with a 1 MΩ resistor. If points A and B are shorted, the current in the circuit is:

$$I = \frac{E}{R}$$

$$I = \frac{10 \text{ V}}{1,000,000 \text{ }\Omega}$$

$$I = 10 \text{ }\mu A$$

If a 10 Ω resistor is placed across A and B, the current will still be 10 μA for all practical purposes. Even a 1 kΩ resistor would not cause a noticeable drop in current. Thus, this circuit acts as a 10 μA current source depicted in Figure 7-33B. Of course, this is not an ideal current source because if a large enough resistance is placed between points A and B the current will decrease. An ideal current source would have an infinite resistance and the current output would be constant regardless of the load resistance.

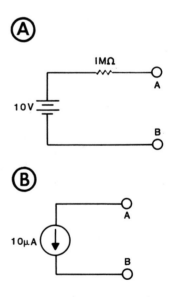

Figure 7-33 The current source.

Notice that the symbol for the current source is a circle with an arrow. In this course, the arrow will point in the direction of electron flow through the current source.

Finding the Norton Equivalent

Norton's theorem allows you to **represent** a circuit containing voltage sources and resistors as a current source, I_N, in parallel with an equivalent resistance, R_N. Thus, although an ideal current source is impossible to build, you can represent the most elementary or the most complex circuit as an ideal current source and a parallel resistor. As with Thevenin's theorem, there are strict rules that tell you what the value of I_N and R_N must be to represent a specific circuit.

The value of the current source (I_N) is equal to the current that flows through the terminals of the network when they are shorted. As an example, refer back to Figure 7-32A. The first step in converting this circuit to its Norton equivalent is to short terminals A and B to determine the short circuit current. Notice that doing this will short out R_2. Thus, the total resistance in the circuit is the 10 Ω or the resistance of R_1. Consequently, the value of the current source is:

$$I_N = \frac{E}{R}$$

$$I_N = \frac{20\,V}{10\,\Omega}$$

$$I_N = 2\,A$$

The size of the parallel resistor, R_N, is equal to the resistance between terminals A and B with the voltage sources shorted. Thus, in Figure 7-32A, the resistance is that of R_1 and R_2 in parallel or 5 ohms. Notice that the method for finding the resistance value is the same in both Thevenin's and Norton's theorems. The difference is that in the case of Norton's theorem the resistor is placed in parallel with the current source. Using these rules, the circuit in Figure 7-32A reduces to the Norton equivalent in Figure 7-32C.

With nothing connected between terminals A and B, the entire 2 A flows through R_N. However, if a load resistor is connected across terminals A and B, the current will split between R_N and the load resistor. The amount of current that each resistor conducts is inversely proportional to its resistance. If the load resistor has the same value as R_N, each will pass 1 A. If the load resistor is larger, it will pass proportionately less current.

Figure 7-34A is the circuit that you have evaluated with each of the network theorems. To illustrate Norton's theorem, use it and solve for the current through R_3. Since you are interested in the current through R_3, you want to find a Norton equivalent for the circuit that connects to R_3.

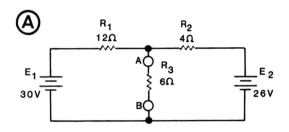

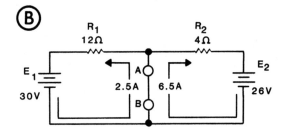

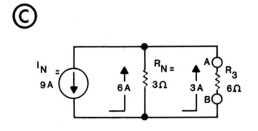

Figure 7-34 Using Norton's theorem.

First, to find the current source, I_N, you must imagine a short circuit across terminals A and B as shown in Figure 7-34B. The current from B to A caused by E_1 is:

$$I = \frac{E_1}{R_1}$$

$$I = \frac{30 \text{ V}}{12 \text{ }\Omega}$$

$$I = 2.5 \text{ A}$$

Also, E_2 causes a current to flow from B to A:

$$I = \frac{E_2}{R_2}$$

$$I = \frac{26 \text{ V}}{4 \text{ }\Omega}$$

$$I = 6.5 \text{ A}$$

Thus, the total calculated current from B to A is 2.5 A + 6.5 A = 9 A. This is the value of the current source, I_N, as shown in Figure 7-34C.

Next you find the shunt resistance (R_N) by mentally shorting E_1 and E_2 and measuring the resulting resistance. Obviously, the resistance is equal to R_1 and R_2 in parallel. Thus:

$$R_N = \frac{R_1 \times R_2}{R_1 + R_2}$$

$$R_N = \frac{12 \text{ }\Omega \times 4 \text{ }\Omega}{12 \text{ }\Omega + 4 \text{ }\Omega}$$

$$R_N = \frac{48 \text{ }\Omega}{16 \text{ }\Omega} \text{ or } 3 \text{ }\Omega$$

Thus, the circuit shown in Figure 7-34A can be redrawn as shown in Figure 7-34C. Notice that everything except R_3 has been reduced to I_N and R_N.

Finally, you can find the current through R_3 by determining how the 9 A from the current source is distributed between R_N and R_3. Obviously, R_N will draw more of the current since it is smaller. In fact, R_N will draw twice as much current since it is one-half the size of R_3. Thus, two-thirds of the current will flow through R_N while only one-third will flow through R_3. The current through R_N is 2/3 × 9 A = 6 A while that through R_3 is 1/3 × 9 A = 3 A. A handy equation for finding the current through R_3 is:

$$I_{R_3} = \frac{R_N}{R_N + R_3} \times I_N$$

$$I_{R_3} = \frac{3}{3 + 6} \times 9\,A$$

$$I_{R_3} = \frac{3}{9} \times 9\,A$$

$$I_{R_3} = 3\,A$$

This equation is used to determine the current distribution between the two resistors, R_N and R_3. While this equation is especially useful when applying Norton's theorem, it can be used to determine the current distribution between any two parallel resistors.

This procedure ends when you find that 3 amps of current is flowing through R_3. Earlier, you solved this same problem in other ways and arrived at the same answer.

Norton-Thevenin Conversions

It may have occurred to you that there are striking similarities between Norton's theorem and Thevenin's theorem. Norton's theorem represents a circuit as a current source and a shunt resistor, while Thevenin's theorem represents the same circuit as a voltage source in series with a resistor. Since a given circuit can be represented in either form, there must be some way of converting directly from a Norton equivalent to a Thevenin equivalent and vice versa.

Figure 7-35A shows a two-terminal network that can be represented as the Thevenin equivalent shown in Figure 7-35B or as the Norton equivalent in Figure 7-35C. You can convert the Thevenin form directly to the Norton form simply by applying Norton's theorem to the Thevenin equivalent circuit. If you short points A and B, the current will be:

$$I_N = \frac{E_{TH}}{R_{TH}}$$

$$I_N = \frac{6\,V}{4\,\Omega}$$

$$I_N = 1.5\,A$$

Next, you find R_N by shorting out E_{TH} and measuring the resistance between points A and B. Obviously, R_N will be the same as R_{TH}. Thus, you derive the Norton equivalent shown in Figure 7-35C.

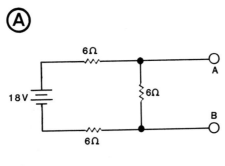

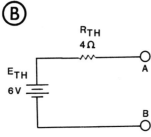

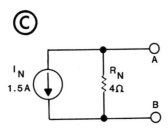

Figure 7-35 Norton-Thevenin conversions.

Conversion in the opposite direction is just as easy. You simply apply Thevenin's theorem to the Norton equivalent. The open circuit voltage between A and B is:

$$E_{TH} = I_N \times R_N$$

$$E_{TH} = 1.5 \text{ A} \times 4 \text{ }\Omega$$

$$E_{TH} = 6 \text{ V}$$

Now, to find R_{TH}, you must know how to handle a current source. Recall that an ideal voltage source has no resistance and, thus, is replaced with a short when finding R_{TH} or R_N. However, as you have seen, an ideal current source has infinite resistance. Thus, when finding R_{TH} or R_N, a current source is considered an open circuit. Thus, if you open the current source, the resistance between points A and B is 4 Ω. As before:

$$R_{TH} = R_N$$

To summarize, you can convert from the Thevenin form to the Norton form by applying two simple equations:

$$I_N = \frac{E_{TH}}{R_{TH}}$$

and:

$$R_N = R_{TH}$$

Likewise, you can convert from the Norton form to the Thevenin form by applying the equations:

$$E_{TH} = I_N \times R_N$$

and:

$$R_{TH} = R_N$$

The other thing you must remember is that in the Thevenin form R_{TH} is in series while in the Norton form R_N is in shunt.

62. With Norton's theorem, a two-terminal network is represented by a _____ source and an equivalent resistance.

63. The equivalent resistance, R_N, is always in (series/parallel) with the current source.

64. Whereas an ideal voltage source has no resistance, an ideal current source has _____ resistance.

65. The value of the current source is the current that flows through the output terminals when they are (shorted/open).

66. The size of R_N is determined by the same method used to find R_{TH} with _____ theorem.

Use Norton's theorem to solve for the current through R_3 in the circuit shown in Figure 7-36A.

67. The first step is to short out R_3 and determine the current from point A to B as shown in Figure 7-32B. The current produced by E_1 is _____ A.

68. The current caused by E_2 is _____ A.

69. The value of the current source (I_N) is _____ A.

70. The value of R_N is _____ Ω.

71. The circuit may be redrawn as shown in Figure 7-36C. Now you can determine the current through R_3 by using the equation:

$$I_{R_3} = \underline{\hspace{2cm}}$$

72. The current through R_3 is _____ A.

73. It is sometimes useful to be able to convert from a Norton equivalent to a Thevenin equivalent. This is done by using the two equations _____ and _____.

74. You can convert from a Thevenin form to a Norton form by using the two equations: _____ and _____.

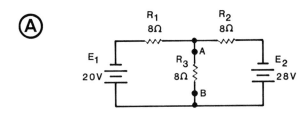

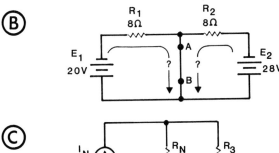

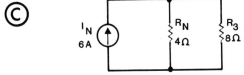

Figure 7-36 Solve for I_{R_3} by using Norton's Theorem.

Summary

In a series circuit, the total resistance is found by adding the individual resistance values:

$$R_T = R_1 + R_2 + R_3 + \ldots$$

Also in a series circuit, the current is the same at all points in the circuit and the sum of the voltage drops is equal to the applied voltage.

In parallel circuits, the total resistance is less than that of any branch. With two branches:

$$R_T = \frac{R_1 \times R_2}{R_1 + R_2}$$

With more than two branches:

$$R_T = \frac{1}{\dfrac{1}{R_1} + \dfrac{1}{R_2} + \dfrac{1}{R_3} + \ldots}$$

Again in a parallel circuit, the voltage is the same across all branches and the total current is the sum of the branch currents.

Simple series-parallel circuits can usually be reduced to simpler forms by combining resistors using one or more of the above formulas.

A voltage divider is used to produce two or more output voltages from a common higher voltage.

A series dropping resistor is used to control the value of current and voltage applied to a load.

A bridge circuit generally consists of four resistances connected together so that there are two input terminals and two output terminals. Resistor values can be selected so that the bridge is balanced. In this condition, the voltage between the two output terminals is 0 V. The bridge can be used with a meter to measure resistance or temperature.

Kirchhoff's Law provides a way of analyzing circuits that cannot be analyzed using Ohm's Law alone. Kirchhoff's Voltage Law states that the sum of the voltages around a closed loop is 0. When a circuit has two or more loops, an equation can be written for each loop. The equations can then be combined in such a way that only one unknown is left. The unknown quantity can then be determined.

Kirchhoff's Current Law states that the current entering a point is equal to the currents leaving that point. It too can be used to analyze complex circuits.

The superposition theorem gives you a logical way for analyzing circuits that have more than one voltage source. The effect of each voltage source is considered one at a time with all other voltage sources shorted out. The individual effects are then combined to determine the net effect of all voltage sources.

Thevenin's theorem is a handy tool for analyzing networks because it allows you to represent a complex two-terminal network as a single voltage source in series with a single resistor.

Norton's theorem is equally handy because it allows you to represent a complex two-terminal network as a single current source in parallel with a single resistor.

Unit 8
Inductance and Capacitance

Contents

Introduction

Inductors and capacitors are generally considered to be AC devices. However, they do have some important DC characteristics which you should know about. This unit will serve as an introduction to these components.

When you have completed this unit, you will be able to:

1. Define the following terms: Induction, inductance, counter EMF, capacitance, RC time constant, RL time constant, farad, henry, self induction, steady-state condition, transient-state condition, and dielectric.

2. Identify the schematic symbol for the inductor and the capacitor.

3. State the three physical factors that determine capacitance.

4. Name two factors that will increase the inductance of an inductor.

5. State how to determine the direction of an EMF that is induced in a conductor.

6. Given the values of resistance and inductance, determine the RL time constant for a circuit.

7. Given the values of resistance and capacitance, determine the RC time constant for a circuit.

8. Calculate total capacitance in series, parallel, and series-parallel.

9. Calculate total inductance in series, parallel, and series- parallel.

In an earlier unit on magnetism, you learned two rules that are quite important to the study of inductance. First, you learned that when current flows through a conductor, a magnetic field builds up around the conductor. Second, you found that when a conductor is subjected to a moving magnetic field, a voltage is induced into the conductor. These two rules form the basis for a phenomenon called **self-induction**.

Self-Induction

Before you learn about self-induction, you must first differentiate between two conditions that can exist in any DC circuit. The first is called the **steady-state** condition while the other is called the **transient-state** condition. Up to this point, you have considered only the steady-state condition.

Most DC circuits reach the steady-state condition within a fraction of a second after power is applied. In this condition, the current in the circuit has reached the value computed by Ohm's Law. That is, the current in the circuit equals the voltage applied to the circuit divided by the resistance of the circuit. However, because of other characteristics of the circuit, the current does not reach the steady-state value instantaneously. There is a brief period called the **transient time** in which the current builds up to its steady-state value. Thus, the transient condition exists for an instant after power is applied to a circuit.

In circuits containing only resistors, the transient condition exists for such a short period of time, that it can be detected only with sensitive instruments. However, if inductors or capacitors are used in the circuit, the transient condition may be extended so that it is readily apparent.

During the transient time, when the current is changing from zero to some finite value, the phenomenon called **self-induction** occurs. Recall that a magnetic field builds up around any conductor when current flows through that conductor. Also, when a moving magnetic field crosses a conductor, a voltage is induced into the conductor. Keeping these two facts in mind, consider what happens during the transient time in the DC circuit shown in Figure 8-1. When S_1 is closed, current begins to flow and a magnetic field builds up around the conductor as shown. However, the magnetic field does not just suddenly appear, it must build up from the center of the wire. If you look at a cross section of the wire as shown in Figures 8-1B and 8-1C, you see illustrated the gradual expansion of the magnetic field.

As the magnetic field expands from the center of the wire, its lines of force cut across the wire. This fulfills the requirements for inducing a voltage into the wire; the relative motion between a magnetic field and a conductor. Thus, the sequence of events is as follows:

1. The switch is closed.

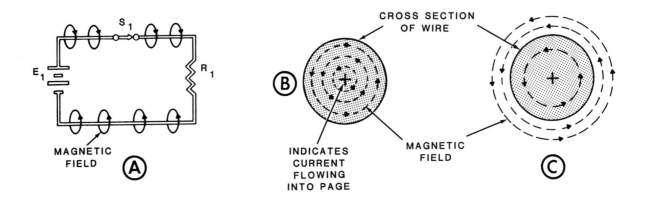

Figure 8-1 Self-induction.

2. Current begins to flow through the wire.

3. A magnetic field begins to build up around the wire.

4. The moving magnetic field expanding from within the wire induces a voltage into the wire.

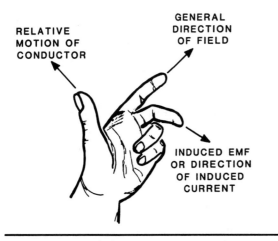

Figure 8-2 Left-hand generator rule.

By using the left-hand generator rule discussed earlier, you can determine the polarity of the induced voltage and the direction of the induced current. Figure 8-2 shows the left-hand generator rule again to refresh your memory. Remember, the index finger points in the direction of the magnetic field, the thumb points in the direction of relative motion, and the middle finger points in the direction of the induced voltage or current.

In Figure 8-3A, the tail of the arrow indicates that current is flowing into the page. From the left-hand rule for conductors you know that the direction of the magnetic field is counterclockwise around the wire. Consequently, on the right side of the wire the general direction of the field is as shown in Figure 8-3A. Also, as the magnetic field expands outward on the right, the relative motion is the same as if the conductor had moved to the left. Apply the left-hand rule by pointing your thumb and forefinger as shown. Notice that your middle finger which indicates the direction of the induced current points out of the page. Thus, the induced current flows in the opposite direction to the original current.

Figure 8-3B shows that the same result is found if the left-hand rule is applied to the left side of the conductor. While it is true that the general direction of the field is reversed at this point, the relative motion of the conductor is also reversed so that the induced current still flows out of the page.

Figure 8-3C shows the relationship of the original current and the induced current. The original current induces a lower reverse current. These currents flow in opposite directions and the net result is that the original current is initially less than can be accounted for by Ohm's Law. That is, at least when power is first applied, there is more opposition to current flow than just the resistance of the circuit.

The induced current is caused by an induced EMF. The induced EMF attempts to force current counter to the original current. For this reason the induced EMF is often called a **counter EMF**.

The counter EMF exists during the period of time that the magnetic field is expanding. Thus, it exists from the time that the switch is closed until the instant that the current reaches its steady state. As stated previously, in DC circuits the period that it takes for the current to build to its steady state is called transient time. It is during transient time that the counter EMF occurs.

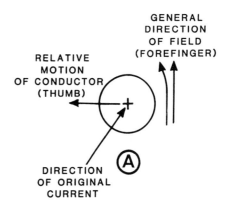

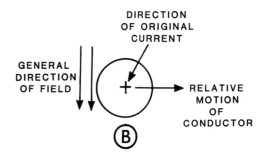

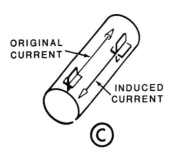

Figure 8-3 Determining the direction of the induced current.

In DC circuits, a transient condition also exists when the switch is reopened. When the circuit is broken, the original current attempts to stop flowing. This causes the magnetic field to collapse. As the field collapses, it again induces an EMF into the conductor. Using the left-hand rule, you can determine the direction of the resulting induced current. Refer to Figure 8-3A again. The general direction of the magnetic field remains the same. As the field collapses inward, the conductor is cut by the flux lines as they move to the left. Thus, the relative motion is the same as if the conductor were moving to the right. Applying the left-hand rule, you find that the induced current is now in the same direction as the original current.

Of course, current cannot flow in an open circuit. Nevertheless, an EMF is induced that attempts to keep current flowing in the same direction. In some cases, the induced EMF is high enough to ionize the air between the switch contacts causing an arc or spark. In very high current circuits, the arc-over caused by the induced EMF can actually damage the switch contacts.

The process by which the induced EMF is produced is called **self-induction**. The effect of self-induction is to oppose changes in current flow. If the original current attempts to increase, self-induction opposes the increase. If the original current attempts to decrease, self-induction opposes the decrease. Self-induction may also be defined as **the action of inducing an EMF into a conductor when there is a change of current in the conductor**.

Inductance

Inductance is the ability of a device or circuit to oppose a change in current flow. Inductance may also be defined as the ability to induce an EMF when there is a change in current flow. **Induction** and **inductance** are easily confused, therefore it is necessary to discuss the difference between them.

Induction is the **action** of inducing an EMF when there is a change in current. Obviously then, induction exists only when a change in current occurs. Inductance is different. It is the **ability** to cause an induced voltage when a change in current occurs. If a circuit, or device, has this ability, it has it with or without current flow. Thus, inductance is a physical property. Like resistance, inductance exists whether current is flowing or not.

The unit of measurement for inductance is the **henry** (H). It is named in honor of Joseph Henry; a nineteenth century physicist who did important research in this area of science. A henry is the amount of inductance that causes EMF of 1 V to be induced into a conductor when the current through the conductor changes at the rate of 1 A per second. In most electronic's applications, the henry is an inconveniently large quantity. For this reason, the quantities **millihenry** (mH) and **microhenry** (μH) are more commonly used.

The symbol for inductance is **L**. Thus, the statement "the inductance is 10 milli-henrys" can be written as an equation:

$$L = 10\,mH$$

Inductors

Because a magnetic field forms around any conductor when current flows through it, every conductor has a certain value of inductance. However, with short lengths of wire, the inductance value is so small that it can be measured only with very sensitive instruments. Many times in electronics, a specific amount of inductance is required in a circuit. A device that is designed to have a specific value of inductance is called an **inductor**.

Inductors come in a variety of values from microhenries to several henries. The construction of the inductor is extremely simple. It consists of a length of wire coiled around some type of core. For this reason, the inductor is often called a coil.

Figure 8-4 shows why the inductance of a wire increases when the wire is wound into a coil. In Figure 8-4A, a single loop is shown. As the magnetic field expands or contracts, it cuts this single turn of wire and a small value of counter EMF is induced. Figure 8-4B shows what happens when two loops are wound together. Notice that the field is twice as strong and that both turns are cut by the entire field. Since both the

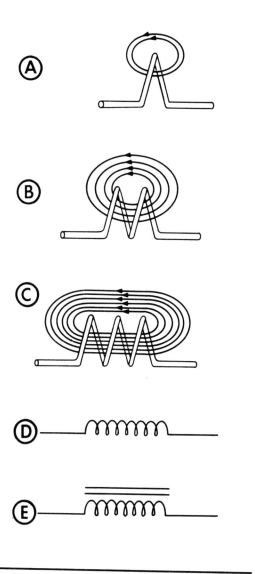

Figure 8-4 The inductor.

field strength and the number of turns are doubled, the induced EMF increases by a factor of 4. Thus, the inductance is four times as great. Figure 8-4C shows three turns that produce a field strength three times as high as before. Now, three times the number of flux lines cut three times the number of turns. Thus, the inductance and the induced EMF increase by a factor of 3 × 3 or 9. These examples show that the inductance of the coil varies as the number of turns squared.

Another way to dramatically increase the inductance is to wind the coil on a core material that has a high permeability. For example, a coil wound on a soft iron core will have many times the inductance of an air-core coil.

Figure 8-4D shows the schematic symbol for the air-core inductor while Figure 8-4E shows the symbol for the iron-core inductor. Although not indicated by the symbols, every inductor has a certain amount of resistance because the wire from which it is constructed has resistance.

Time Constant of an Inductor

You have learned that current does not rise to its maximum value instantly when an inductance is present in a circuit. The transient time depends on the value of the inductance and the value of any series resistance. For a given value of resistance, the time required for the current to build to its maximum value is directly proportional to the value of inductance. The higher the inductance, the greater the amount of time required for the current to reach maximum value. On the other hand, for a given value of inductance, the time is inversely proportional to the resistance. The larger the resistance, the shorter the transient time.

Mathematically, this relationship can be expressed with the equation:

$$T = L/R$$

In a circuit that consists of a 5 mH inductor and a 1 kΩ resistor, the time constant is:

$$T = \frac{.005\ H}{1000\ \Omega}$$

$$T = .000005 \text{ seconds or } 5\ \mu s$$

For this circuit, 5 μs is the length of time that it takes for the current through the inductor to reach 63.2% of its maximum value. During each succeeding time constant, the current increases another 63.2% of the remaining difference between the present value and its maximum value.

If the maximum current through the circuit is 100 A, the current after one time constant is:

$$100\ A \times .632 = 63.2\ A$$

and the current must increase another 36.8 amperes before it reaches maximum value.

During the second time constant, the current increases by 63.2% of the remaining 36.8 A. The calculations look like this:

$$36.8 \text{ A} \times .632 = 23.25 \text{ A}$$

The 23.25 A is the amount of increase in current that occurs during the second time constant. To determine the current through the circuit after two time constants, you must add the second current increase to the preceding current increase. Now:

$$63.2 \text{ A} + 23.25 \text{ A} = 86.45 \text{ A}$$

This is the current through the inductor after two time constants.

During each succeeding time constant, the current continues to approach its maximum value. Theoretically, the current through the circuit never reaches its maximum value. However, for all practical purposes after five time constants the current through the inductor is considered to be at its maximum value.

Later, you will be introduced to time constant curves as a method of determining the percent of current or voltage after a given time constant.

Inductors in Combination

Inductors, like other components, can be connected in series, parallel, or series-parallel combinations. No matter what the combination, there are times when it is necessary to determine the total inductance of a circuit. The next two sections explain how this is done.

Inductors in Series

If two inductors, each with 100 windings, are connected in series, they have the same overall effect on the circuit as one inductor with 200 windings. As the number of windings increases, the amount of inductance in the circuit increases. The inductance of the inductors is additive. That is, the inductance of any number of inductors in series can be determined by using the formula:

$$L_T = L_1 + L_2 + L_3.....$$

As you can see, inductors in series are treated mathematically the same as resistors in series. The total inductance is equal to the sum of the individual inductances.

Inductors in Parallel

A single inductor in a circuit will have a given amount of inductance or opposition to a change in current flow. If another inductor of the same size is placed in parallel with the first inductor, the amount of inductance in the circuit decreases. The reason for this is relatively simple. Each of the inductors still opposes the change in current through the circuit. However, because there are now two current paths, there is an overall decrease in opposition to current flow.

The formulas used to determine inductance in parallel are essentially the same equations used to determine resistance in parallel. They are:

$$L_T = \frac{L_1 \times L_2}{L_1 + L_2}$$

or:

$$L_T = \frac{1}{\dfrac{1}{L_1} + \dfrac{1}{L_2} + \dfrac{1}{L_3} + ...}$$

or, for equal inductances in parallel:

$$L_T = \frac{\text{Value of one inductor}}{\text{Number of inductors in parallel}}$$

Inductors in Series-Parallel

If a number of inductors are connected in a series-parallel circuit, the total inductance is calculated in the same way as the total resistance in a resistive circuit. First, the inductance of any parallel inductors is determined. Then, this is added to the inductance of any portion of the circuit in series with the parallel inductance. If you have any difficulty understanding this concept, refer back to the discussion of resistors in series-parallel given in Unit 3.

1. In a DC circuit, the normal or _____ - _____ condition exists after the current has reached its maximum value.

2. In a DC circuit, the time between when the switch is closed and the time that the current reaches its maximum value is called the _____ time.

3. During this time, the current is increasing and a _____ _____ is building up around the conductors in the circuit.

4. The EMF induced by the changing magnetic field tries to push current through the conductor in the (same/opposite) direction.

5. The EMF induced in a DC circuit is sometimes called a _____ EMF.

6. When the switch is reopened, the magnetic field collapses and induces an EMF which (aids/opposes) the original current.

7. The induced EMF always tends to oppose any _____ in current.

8. The action of inducing an EMF when there is a change in current is called _____.

9. The ability or physical characteristic of a conductor or coil to oppose a change in current is called _____.

10. The unit of measurement for inductance is the _____.

11. One henry is the value of inductance which will induce an EMF of one _____ when the current changes at the rate of one ampere per second.

12. A device designed to have a specific inductance is called an _____.

13. The length of time required for the current in a circuit to reach its maximum value is determined by both the _____ and the _____ in the circuit's components.

14. The length of time that it takes for current to reach its maximum increases if the _____ increases.

15. The length of time that it takes for the circuit current to reach its maximum increases if the resistance _____.

Capacitance

Capacitance is the property of a circuit or device that enables it to store electrical energy by means of an **electrostatic** field. A device especially designed to have a certain value of capacitance is called a **capacitor**. The capacitor has the ability to store electrons and release them at a later time. The number of electrons that it can store for a given applied voltage is determined by the capacitor's **capacitance**.

Capacitors

In the early days of electronics, the word **condenser** was used instead of capacitor. However, today the word condenser is rarely used except in special cases. An automobile mechanic may still call the capacitor in an ignition system a condenser but the more correct and accepted term is capacitor.

Figure 8-5 shows the principle parts of a capacitor. These are two metal plates that are separated by a nonconducting material called a **dielectric**. Often metal foil is used for the plates while the dielectric may be paper, glass, ceramic, mica, or some other type of good insulator.

The actual construction of the capacitor looks quite different from that shown in Figure 8-5. For example, Figure 8-6 shows how a paper dielectric capacitor is constructed. Two thin sheets of metal foil are separated by a sheet of paper. Additional sheets of paper are placed on the top and bottom of the foil sheets. Then the sheets are wound

into a compact cylinder. Leads are attached to each of the foil sheets. Finally, the entire unit is sealed into a permanent package by the addition of a wax or plastic case.

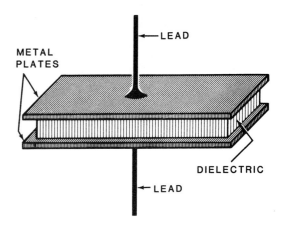

Figure 8-5 The capacitor.

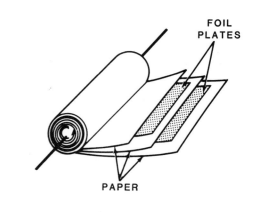

Figure 8-6 Construction of the paper capacitor.

Charging the Capacitor

One characteristic of the capacitor is its ability to store an electrical charge. Figure 8-7 illustrates the charging action. For simplicity the capacitor is shown as two metal plates separated by an air dielectric. In Figure 8-7A the capacitor is not charged. This means that there are the same number of free electrons in both plates. Naturally then, there is no difference of potential between the two plates and a voltmeter connected across the plates will indicate 0 volts. No current is flowing in the circuit because switch S_1 is open.

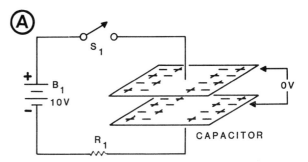

Figure 8-7B shows what happens when S_1 is closed. With S_1 closed, the positive terminal of the battery is connected to the upper plate of the capacitor. The positive charge of the battery attracts the free electrons in the upper plate. Thus, these electrons flow out of the upper plate to the positive terminal of the battery. At the same instant, the positive upper plate of the capacitor attracts the free electrons in the negative plate. However, because the two plates are separated by an insulator, no electrons can flow to the upper plate from the lower plate. Nevertheless, the attraction of the positive charge on the upper plate pulls free electrons into the lower plate. Thus, for every electron that leaves the upper plate and flows to the positive terminal of the battery another electron leaves the negative terminal and flows into the bottom plate.

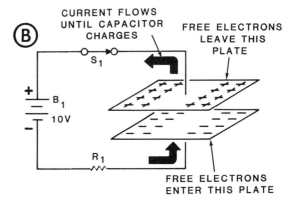

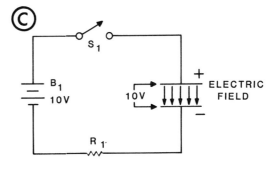

Figure 8-7 Charging the capacitor.

As the capacitor charges, a difference of potential begins to build up across the two plates. Also, an electric field is established in the dielectric material between the plates. The capacitor continues to charge until the difference of potential between the two plates is the same as the voltage across the battery. In the example shown, current flows until the charge on the capacitor builds up to 10 V. Once the capacitor has the same EMF as the battery, no additional current can flow because there is no longer a difference of potential between the battery and the capacitor.

It should be emphasized again that although current flows in the circuit while the capacitor is charging, **current does not flow through the capacitor**. Electrons flow out of the positive plate and into the negative plate. However, electrons cannot flow through the capacitor because of the insulating dielectric. Moreover, if electrons did flow through the dielectric, the capacitor would not develop a charge in the first place. It would simply produce a voltage drop in the same way as a resistor.

Figure 8-7C shows that once the capacitor is charged, the switch can be opened and the capacitor will retain its charge. A good capacitor can retain a charge for a long period of time.

Discharging the Capacitor

Theoretically, all of the energy stored in a capacitor can be recovered. Thus, a perfect capacitor will dissipate no power. It simply stores energy and later releases the energy. While a perfect capacitor cannot be built, you can approach this condition. The act of storing the energy is called **charging** the capacitor. The act of recovering the energy is called **discharging** the capacitor.

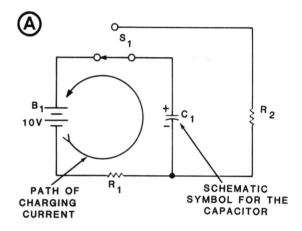

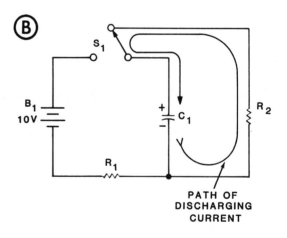

Figure 8-8 Discharging the capacitor.

Figure 8-8 illustrates the charge and discharge cycle. In Figure 8-8A, the arm of S_1 is positioned so that capacitor C_1 is placed directly across the battery. Notice the schematic symbol that is used to represent the capacitor. A current flows as shown; charging the capacitor to the applied voltage, 10 V.

When the arm of S_1 is moved to its other position, as shown in Figure 8-8B, this removes C_1 from across the battery and places C_1 across resistor R_2. When this happens, the free electrons on the negative plate rush through R_2 to the positively charged plate. The flow of electrons continues until the two plates are once again at the same potential. At this time, the capacitor is said to be discharged and current flow in the circuit stops.

As the capacitor discharges, the voltage across it decreases. When completely discharged the voltage across the capacitor is once again 0 volts. At this time all the energy which was initially stored has been released. The power consumed by R_2 is provided by the battery with C_1 acting as a temporary storage medium.

16. That property of a circuit or device which enables it to store energy by means of an electric field is called _capacitance_

17. A device designed to have a certain value of capacitance is called a _capacitor_.

18. The capacitor consists of two _charged_ _plates_ separated by an insulator.

19. The insulator in a capacitor is called a _dielectric_.

20. When a battery is connected across a capacitor, electrons flow from one plate of the capacitor to the _positive_ terminal of the battery.

21. At the same time, electrons flow from the _negative_ terminal of the battery to the other capacitor plate.

22. Current will flow in the circuit until the capacitor becomes completely _charged_.

23. When completely charged, the voltage across the capacitor is equal to the voltage across the _battery source_.

24. If the capacitor is disconnected from the battery and connected across a resistor, it will _discharge_ through the resistor.

25. The discharge will continue until the EMF across the capacitor is _0_ volts.

Because of its ability to store an electrical charge and its relatively low cost, in many types of electronic equipment the capacitor is used more often than any other type of component except the resistor. Thus, it is important that you learn as much as possible about these devices.

Unit of Capacitance

Capacitance is a measure of the amount of charge that a capacitor can store for a given applied voltage. The unit of capacitance is the **farad**, abbreviated F. This unit of measure gets its name from Michael Faraday; a scientist who did a great amount of research with capacitance.

One farad is the amount of capacitance that will store a charge of one coulomb of electrons when an EMF of one volt is applied. The farad is an extremely large value of capacitance. For this reason, the unit microfarad, μF, meaning one millionth of a farad, is more often used. Even the microfarad is frequently too large. In these cases the unit micro-microfarad, μμF, is used. The more modern name for the micro-microfarad is the picofarad, pF.

To summarize, the farad is the amount of capacitance that will store one coulomb of charge when one volt is applied. The microfarad is one millionth of a farad. The picofarad is one millionth of a microfarad or

$$\frac{1}{1,000,000,000,000}$$

of a farad. Using powers of ten, the microfarad is 10^{-6} farad while the picofarad is 10^{-12} farad.

There is a formula that expresses capacitance in terms of charge and voltage. The formula is:

$$C = \frac{Q}{E}$$

C is the capacitance in farads; Q is the charge in coulombs; and E is the EMF in volts.

Factors Determining Capacitance

Capacitance is determined by three factors:

1. The area of the capacitor's plates.

2. The spacing between the plates.

3. The nature of the dielectric.

This is illustrated in Figure 8-9. Figure 8-9A shows a capacitor made up of two 1-inch square plates separated by 0.001 inch of air. The air acts as the dielectric in this case. Such a device has a capacitance of 225 pF. Using this capacitor as a reference, see what happens when the area of the plates, the spacing of the plates, or the nature of the dielectric changes.

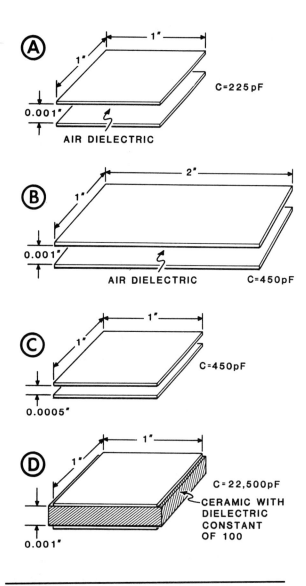

Figure 8-9 Factors that determine capacitance.

Figure 8-9B illustrates what happens when the area of the plates is doubled but all other factors remain the same. If a voltage source is applied to this capacitor, there is a larger plate area to hold electrons that come from

the source as well as a larger plate area to supply electrons to the positive side of the source. This means that there is now twice as much area in which the electrostatic field can exist. As a result, the capacity or capacitance of the device doubles. The capacitance value is now 450 pF. Thus, capacitance is directly proportional to the area of the plates. As the plate area increases, the capacitance also increases.

Figure 8-9C shows that the capacitance can also be doubled by reducing the spacing between the plates to one half its former distance. The path of the electrostatic lines of force is reduced by one-half. This doubles the strength of the field which, in turn, doubles the capacitance. Thus, capacitance is inversely proportional to the spacing between the plates. As the space between the plates decreases, the capacitance increases.

Finally, Figure 8-9D shows that the capacitance can be greatly increased by changing the dielectric. By its nature, air is a very poor dielectric. Most insulators support electrostatic lines of force more easily than air. The ease with which an insulator supports electrostatic lines of force is indicated by its **dielectric constant**. Air is used as a reference. It is arbitrarily given a dielectric constant of 1. Most insulators have a higher dielectric constant. For example, a sheet of waxed paper has a dielectric constant of about 3. This means that a sheet of 0.001 inch waxed paper placed between the plates would triple the capacitance of the example capacitor.

Some typical dielectric constants for common types of insulators are given in Table 8-1.

Material	Dielectric Constant (K)
Air	1
Vacuum	1
Waxed Paper	3 – 4
Mica	5 – 7
Glass	4 – 10
Rubber	2 – 3
Ceramics	10 – 5000

Table 8-1

The capacitance value of the capacitor shown in Figure 8-9D can be increased by a factor of 100 simply by using an insulator with a dielectric constant of 100. Thus, capacitance is directly proportional to the dielectric constant. As the dielectric constant increases, the capacitance of the capacitor also increases.

There is a formula that combines the three factors just discussed. It is:

$$C = 0.225\,K \left(\frac{A}{d} \right)$$

In this formula, C is the capacitance in picofarads; K is the dielectric constant; and A is the area (in square inches) of one plate; and d is the distance (in inches) between the two plates.

Types of Capacitors

Capacitors are available in many different shapes and sizes. However, all capacitors can be placed in one of two categories: variable and fixed. The next section discusses these two categories in more detail.

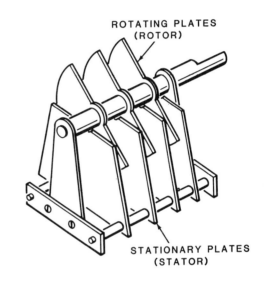

Figure 8-10 The variable capacitor.

Variable Capacitors

Figure 8-10 shows the construction of an air-dielectric variable capacitor. The capacitance value of this type of capacitor can be changed by rotating the shaft. The capacitor plates are attached to the shaft. As the shaft is turned, the rotating plates change position in relation to the stationary plates. The rotating and stationary plates are electrically connected and each forms one plate of the capacitor. The rotating plates and staticnary plates mesh together but do not touch. By moving the shaft, the area of the plates across from each other can be changed from maximum when fully meshed to minimum when fully open. As you have seen, this changes the capacitance of the device.

Fixed Capacitors

Most fixed capacitors are constructed as shown earlier in Figure 8-6. They consist of alternate layers of metal foil (plates) and insulators (dielectric).

Capacitors are often named for the material used as their dielectric. Thus, there are paper, ceramic, mica, and electrolytic capacitors. Sometimes capacitors are classified according to their shape. Thus, there are disc capacitors and tubular capacitors.

One of the most popular types of fixed capacitor is the electrolytic capacitor. Its construction is illustrated in Figure 8-11. Sheets of metal foil are separated by a sheet of paper or gauze that is saturated with a chemical paste called an electrolyte. The electrolyte is a good conductor and therefore the paper is not the dielectric. Actually, the dielectric is formed during the manufacturing process. A DC voltage is applied across the foil plates. As current flows, a thin layer of aluminum oxide builds up on the plate that is connected to the positive side of the DC voltage source. As shown in Figure 8-11C, the oxide layer is extremely thin. Because the oxide is a fairly good in-

sulator it acts as a dielectric. The upper foil becomes the positive plate; the oxide becomes the dielectric; and the electrolyte becomes the negative plate. Notice that the bottom layer of foil simply provides a connection to the electrolyte.

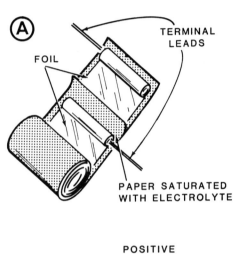

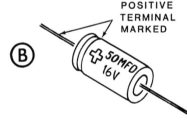

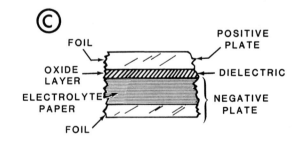

Figure 8-11 The electrolytic capacitor.

Recall that capacitance is inversely proportional to the spacing between plates. Because the oxide layer is extremely thin, very high values of capacitance are possible with this technique. While most other capacitors have capacitances below 1 μF, the electrolytic capacitor may have capacitance values ranging from about 5 μF up to thousands of microfarads.

Because of its construction, the electrolytic capacitor is **polarized**. This means that the capacitor has a negative and a positive lead. When connected in a circuit, the positive lead must be connected to the more positive point. As shown in Figure 8-11B, the positive lead is marked on the electrolytic capacitor. At other times, the marking on the capacitor may indicate the negative lead.

CAUTION must be exercised when working with **polarized capacitors.**

When proper polarity is **NOT** observed, a polarized capacitor may explode. When a capacitor explodes it can cause extensive damage to your circuit, but more importantly it is very dangerous to you and anyone who is nearby. An exploding capacitor sounds like a gun shot and has the same devastating results if anyone is in the line of fire.

Always check capacitors for polarity markings and proper installation, prior to applying power to a newly constructed circuit.

An important characteristic of the electrolytic, or any other capacitor is its voltage rating. The voltage rating indicates the maximum voltage that the capacitor can withstand without the dielectric breaking down or arcing over. With electrolytic capacitors this value is generally printed on the capacitor along with its capacitance value.

Self-Test Review

26. The unit of capacitance is the _____ .

27. One farad is the amount of capacitance that will store a charge of one _____ when an EMF of one _____ is applied.

28. Because the farad is so large, the units _____ (meaning millionth of a farad) and _____ (meaning millionth of a millionth of a farad) are used.

29. A formula that expresses capacitance in terms of charge and EMF is C = _____ .

30. One of the factors that determines capacitance is the _____ of the two plates of the capacitor.

31. The larger the area, the (higher/lower) the value of the capacitor will be.

32. Another factor is the _____ between the plates of the capacitor.

33. The greater the distance between the plates, the (higher/lower) the value of capacitance.

34. The third factor that determines capacitance is the nature of the _____.

35. The higher the dielectric constant, the (higher/lower) the capacitance will be.

36. One form of variable capacitor employs rotary plates that are meshed with stationary plates. This type of capacitor uses _____ as a dielectric.

37. In the electrolytic capacitor, the _____ is a very thin layer of aluminum oxide.

38. Because of its unique construction, the electrolytic capacitor is _____.

RC Time Constants

When a capacitor is connected across a DC voltage source, it charges to the applied voltage. If the charged capacitor is then connected across a load, it will discharge through the load. The length of time required for a capacitor to charge or discharge can be computed if certain circuit values are known.

There are two factors that determine the charge or discharge time for a capacitor. These are the value, or capacitance, of the capacitor and the value of the resistance through which the capacitor must charge or discharge. The time that it takes for the capacitor to charge or discharge is directly proportional to both resistance and capacitance. To understand the relationship between resistance, capacitance, and time, you must consider the idea of an RC **time constant**.

A time constant is the time required for a capacitor to charge to 63.2 percent of the applied voltage. If the capacitor is being discharged, a time constant is the length of time required for the EMF stored in the capacitor to drop by 63.2 percent.

The time constant can be expressed as an equation:

$$T = R \times C$$

Here T is the time constant expressed in seconds; R is the resistance in ohms; and C is the capacitance in farads. As mentioned earlier the farad is too large a value to be practical and capacitance is most often expressed

in microfarads. In the above equation, if C is in microfarads and R is in ohms, then T will be in microseconds. If C is in microfarads and R is in kilohms, then T will be in milliseconds. Finally, if C is in microfarads and R is in megohms, then T will be in seconds.

Some examples may help illustrate this.

If C = 1 μF and R = 100 Ω; then:

$$T = R \times C$$

$$T = 100\ \Omega \times 1\ \mu F$$

$$T = 100\ \mu s$$

If C = 1 μF and R = 10 kΩ; then:

$$T = R \times C$$

$$T = 10\ k\Omega \times 1\ \mu F$$

$$T = 10\ ms$$

If C = 1 μF and R = 2 MΩ; then:

$$T = R \times C$$

$$T = 2\ M\Omega \times 1\ \mu F$$

$$T = 2\ s$$

As you study these examples, remember that the time constant (T) is **not** the time required to fully charge or discharge the capacitor. Rather, it is the time required to charge the capacitor to 63.2 percent of the applied voltage. To see how a capacitor charges, consider the following example.

Figure 8-12 shows a 1 µF capacitor connected in series with a 1 MΩ resistor. Thus, the time constant, R × C, is 1 second. Initially, the capacitor is completely discharged and the voltage across it is 0 volts. When the arm of the switch is moved up so that the 100 V power supply is connected to the R-C network, the capacitor attempts to charge to the level of the applied voltage. However, the capacitor does not charge instantaneously. It takes a specific amount of time that depends on the circuit capacitance and resistance. In fact, it takes 5 time constants before the capacitor is considered to be fully charged. The time constant of the circuit is:

$$T = R \times C$$

$$T = 1\,M\Omega \times 1\,\mu F$$

$$T = 1\ second$$

Thus, after 1 second, which is the time constant, the capacitor will have charged to 63.2 percent of the applied voltage or to 63.2 volts.

Figure 8-13 shows two curves that are helpful when working with time constants. Curve A shows how a capacitor charges. Initially, the capacitor charges rapidly, charging to 63.2 percent of the applied voltage during the first time constant. However, as time passes, the capacitor begins to charge more slowly.

During the second time constant, the capacitor charges to 63.2 percent of the remaining voltage. In the example, the remaining voltage after 1 time constant is 100 V − 63.2 V = 36.8 V. Now, 63.2 percent of 36.8 V is about 23.3 V. Thus, at the end of the second time constant, the voltage on the capacitor has risen to:

$$63.2\,V + 23.3\,V = 86.5\,V.$$

This is 86.5 percent of the applied voltage.

During the third time constant, the capacitor once again charges to 63.2 percent of the remaining voltage. Therefore, after 3 time constants, the capacitor has charged to 95 percent of the applied voltage. Once again, during the 4th time constant the capacitor charges to 63.2 percent of the remaining voltage. Thus, after 4 time constants, it has charged to 98.2 percent; and, finally, after 5 time constants to more then 99 percent of the source voltage.

For most purposes, the capacitor is considered fully charged after five time constants. You may recognize this mathematical progression from the previous discussion of inductors. The percentages on the curves shown in Figure 8-13 are the same with inductors. Therefore, this Figure can be applied to current calculations with inductors.

Because of its shape, curve A is called an exponential curve. The capacitor does not charge at the same rate each second but, rather, it charges at a rate governed by a power of a given factor. The capacitor, then, is said to charge exponentially.

Curve B of Figure 8-13 shows the rate at which the capacitor discharges. At the first instant the capacitor is fully charged. During the first time constant, the voltage drops by 63.2 percent to 36.8 percent of its original value. During the second time constant, the voltage drops an additional 63.2 percent or to only 13.5 percent of its original value. The voltage drops to about 5 percent at three time constants and to only 1.8 percent after four. After five time constants, the charge is less than 1 percent of its original value. For all practical purposes, the capacitor is considered fully discharged after five time constants.

In Figure 8-12A the capacitor is charged to approximately 100 V in 5 seconds. Figure 8-12B shows the capacitor being discharged. According to curve B, the charge on the capacitor will be:

100 V initially;

36.8 volts after 1 time constant (1 second);

13.5 volts after 2 time constants (2 seconds);

5 volts after 3 time constants (3 seconds);

1.8 volts after 4 time constants (4 seconds);

0.7 volts after 5 time constants (5 seconds).

As you can see, 0.7 V is such a small fraction of the original 100 V that, after five time constants, the capacitor can be considered as discharged.

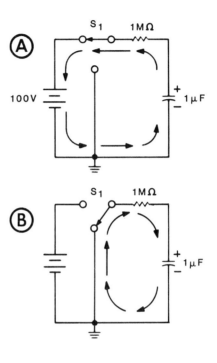

Figure 8-12 Working with time constants.

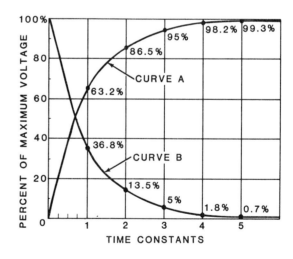

Figure 8-13 Time constant curves.

Desk-Top Experiment 6
Time Constants

Introduction

Thus far in this unit you have learned about both inductive and capacitive time constants. You have studied a bit about the relationship between inductance, capacitance, and current flow in a DC circuit. It is now time for you to take a closer look at these relationships.

Objectives

1. To learn to calculate both inductive and capacitive time constants.

2. To observe these relationships by constructing your own time constant curves.

Procedure

1. Figure 8-14A shows an inductor connected in series with a resistor. What is the LR time constant for this circuit?

    _____ s

2. What is the maximum current through this circuit?

    _____ A

3. How long will it take for the current through the circuit to reach its maximum value?

    _____ s

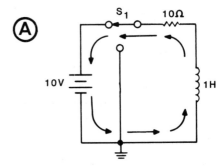
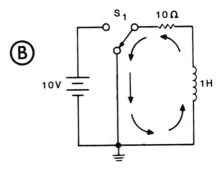

Figure 8-14

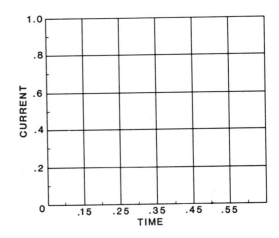

Figure 8-15

4. In Figure 8-15, plot the current through the inductor against the time for the first 5 time constants after the circuit shown in Figure 8-14A is turned on.

5. Again, in Figure 8-15, plot the current through the inductor shown in Figure 8-14B for the first 5 time constants.

6. When switch S_1 is as shown in Figure 8-14B, what is the direction of current flow in the circuit? _____.

7. According to Kirchoff's Law, the sum of the voltage drops in a circuit will equal the sum of the voltage rises. After 1 time constant what is the voltage dropped across the resistor in Figure 8-14A?

_____ V

Where is the remainder of the applied voltage dropped in this circuit after 1 time constant? _____.

Discussion

In the circuit shown in Figure 8-14A, the time constant is .1 seconds. This is calculated using the formula:

$$T = \frac{L}{R}$$

Since it takes 5 time constants for the current through the circuit to reach its maximum value, it takes .5 seconds for the current in the circuit in Figure 8-14 to reach its maximum value of 1 A.

Figure 8-16 contains the current curves for the circuit in Figure 8-14A and 8-14B. When switch S_1 is positioned as shown in Figure 8-14A, the current through the circuit is initially 0 A. This is because at the first instant the inductor offers maximum opposition to a change in current flow. Thus, the current is initially 0 A. However, the current gradually increases until after 5 time constants it is equal to 99.3% of the maximum circuit current.

When switch S_1 is moved to the position shown in Figure 8-14B, the current in the circuit will continue to flow in the counterclockwise direction for 5 time constants. This happens because the inductor opposes a change in current. As the lines of force collapse across the inductor, an EMF is produced that moves current in a counterclockwise direction. This current curve is also shown in Figure 8-16.

You can determine the voltage drop across the resistor once you know the current through the circuit after 1 time constant. In this case, the voltage drop across the resistor is 6.32 V. The remainder of the voltage applied to the circuit is dropped across the inductor. To be more specific, the inductor produces 3.68 V of counter EMF after 1 time constant. This counter EMF acts like an additional voltage source connected in a series opposing configuration with the 10 V battery.

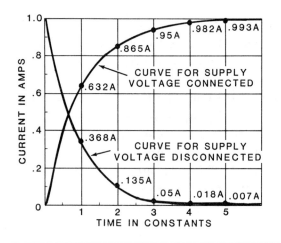

Figure 8-16

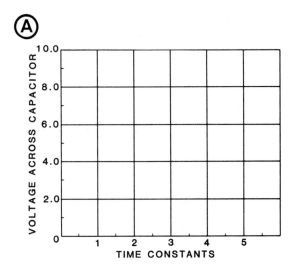

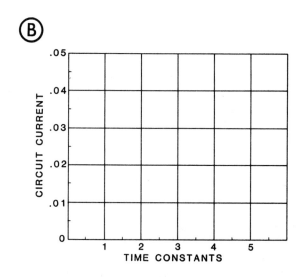

Figure 8-17

Procedure (Cont.)

8. In the space provided, draw a circuit with an RC time constant of .2 seconds for the capacitor charge and .5 seconds for the capacitor discharge. Use a 200 kΩ resistor, in the charging portion of the circuit and a 10 V battery as a voltage source.

9. What is the current through the charging portion of the circuit after 3 time constants?

 A

10. Does current flow through the circuit in the same direction when the switch is in the charge and discharge positions?

_____

11. In Figure 8-17A, plot the voltage across the capacitor in the charge circuit. In Figure 8-17B plot the current through the charge circuit.

Discussion

Your circuit should look something like the circuit shown in Figure 8-18. Since you know the value of the resistor in the charge path and the length of the time constant, you manipulate the RC time constant formula and get:

$$C = \frac{T}{R}$$

$$C = \frac{.2 \text{ s}}{200 \text{ k}\Omega}$$

$$C = 1 \text{ } \mu F$$

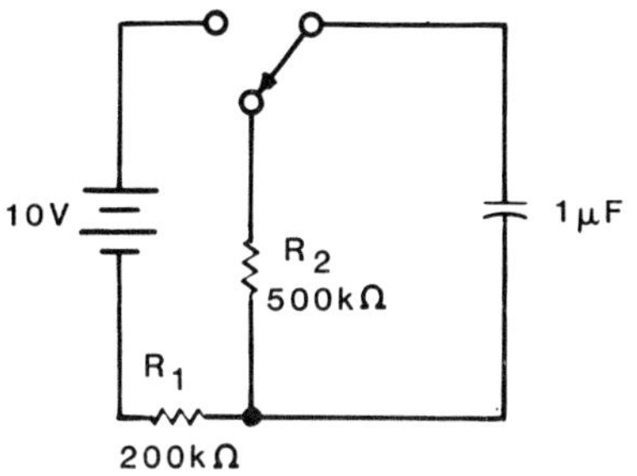

Figure 8-18 Circuit for steps 8 to 11.

Now that you have the value of the capacitor used in the circuit, once again manipulate the RC time constant formula and verify the discharge circuit:

$$R = \frac{T}{C}$$

$$R = \frac{.5 \text{ s}}{1 \text{ } \mu F}$$

$$R = 500 \text{ k}\Omega$$

The maximum current through the charging portion of the circuit is .05 mA.

The current in the discharge circuit flows in the opposite direction of the current in the charge circuit. Remember, current does not flow through a capacitor. Thus, the only way for a capacitor to discharge is in the opposite manner to its charge path.

Figure 8-19A shows the voltage curve for the capacitor in the charge circuit. Notice that as time increases, the voltage across the capacitor increases. In Figure 8-19B, you see that as time increases, the current through the circuit decreases. With an inductor, just the opposite occurs. When voltage is applied to an inductor initially the current is 0 and the voltage across the inductor is maximum.

Looking again at Figure 8-19 you see that when the voltage is minimum the current is maximum. For this reason, it is said that current **leads** voltage in a capacitive circuit.

In an inductive circuit, voltage is maximum when current is minimum. Therefore, it is said that current **lags** voltage in the inductive. The relationship between voltage and current in capacitive and inductive circuits is extremely important and you will cover it in greater detail in your study of AC electronics.

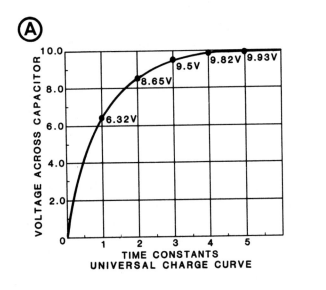

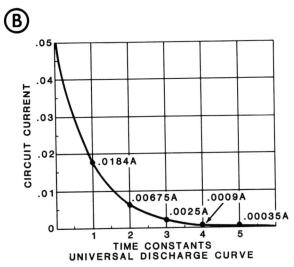

Figure 8-19

39. The time required for a capacitor to charge or discharge is determined by the value of the _____ and the value of any _____ through which it must discharge.

40. The time that it takes to charge a capacitor to 63.2 percent of the applied voltage is referred to as a _____.

41. The formula for computing the time constant is T = _____.

42. In a circuit, if R is in megohms and C is in microfarads, T will be in _____.

43. On the other hand, if R is in kilohms and C is in microfarads, T will be in _____.

44. If R is in ohms and C is in microfarads, T will be in _____.

45. Refer to Figure 8-20A. The RC time constant for this circuit is _____ s.

46. Assume the capacitor is fully discharged. In Figure 8-20A, the charge on the capacitor will be _____ V after 1 time constant.

47. After 0.4 seconds, the charge on the capacitor will be _____ V.

48. For all practical purposes, the voltage across the capacitor will be 10 volts after _____ time constants.

49. In Figure 8-20B, the total resistance in the discharge path is _____.

50. The discharge time constant for Figure 8-20B is _____ s.

51. After 1 second, the charge on the capacitor will be _____ V.

52. The voltage will drop to 0.5 volts after _____ s.

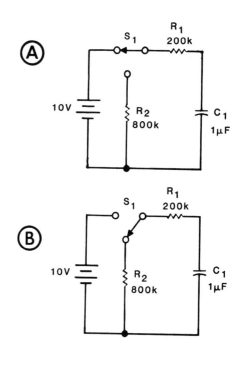

Figure 8-20 Solving time constants.

Capacitors in Combination

Like other electronic components, capacitors can be connected in a variety of configurations. Thus, you should know how capacitors behave when connected together in different ways. Although the quantities differ, you will recognize the formulas used to calculate capacitance values.

Capacitors in Parallel

Figure 8-21A shows the dimensions of the 225 pF capacitor discussed earlier. In Figure 8-21B, two of these capacitors are connected in parallel. Of the three factors that determine capacitance, only one has changed. The dielectric constant and the spacing between the plates are the same as before. However, the effective area of the two plates has increased. In fact the area has doubled. Recall that capacitance is directly proportional to the area of the plates. Therefore, since the total area of the plates has doubled, the total capacitance is twice that of the single capacitor.

This shows that connecting capacitors in parallel is equivalent to adding the plate areas. Consequently, the total capacitance is equal to the sum of the individual capacitance values. If three capacitors are connected in parallel, the total capacitance, (C_T) is found by adding the individual values:

$$C_T = C_1 + C_2 + C_3$$

If $C_1 = 5$ μF, $C_2 = 10$ μF, and $C_3 = 1$ μF; then $C_T = 16$ μF. Notice that capacitors in parallel add like resistors in series.

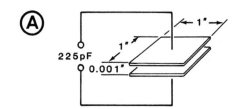

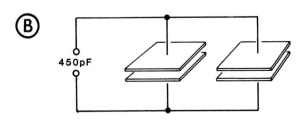

Figure 8-21 Connecting capacitors in parallel increases capacitance.

Capacitors connected in parallel will all charge to the same voltage. Remember the voltage is the same across every section of a parallel network.

Capacitors In Series

Figure 8-22 compares a single 225 pF capacitor with two 225 pF capacitors connected in series. As shown, this is equivalent to doubling the thickness of the dielectric. That is, two series capacitors act like a single capacitor that has a dielectric thickness equal to the sum of the individual dielectric thickness. Since capacitance is inversely proportional to the spacing between the plates, doubling the thickness of the dielectric cuts the total capacitance value to one half that of the single capacitor.

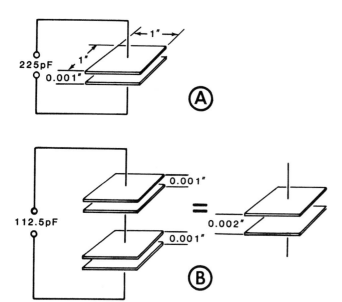

Figure 8-22 Connecting capacitors in series decreases capacitance.

The total capacitance of a group of series capacitors is calculated in the same way as the total resistance of parallel resistors. Or stated more simply, capacitors in series combine in the same way as resistors in parallel. The total capacitance of two capacitors in series can be calculated by the formula:

$$C_T = \frac{C_1 \times C_2}{C_1 + C_2}$$

Notice that this equation has the same form as the equation for calculating two resistors in parallel.

When more than two capacitors are connected in series, the following formula is used:

$$C_T = \frac{1}{\dfrac{1}{C_1} + \dfrac{1}{C_2} + \dfrac{1}{C_3} + \ldots}$$

Here again, the equation has the same form as the one shown earlier for calculating total resistance in parallel circuits.

Figure 8-23 shows two capacitors connected in series across a 12 V battery. An interesting thing about capacitors in series is the way in which the applied voltage is distributed across the capacitors. If both capacitors have the same value, then the applied voltage is distributed evenly between the two. In Figure 8-23A, each capacitor charges to one half the applied voltage or to 6 V.

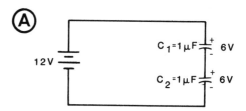

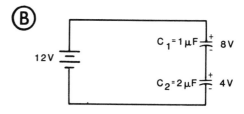

Figure 8-23 Voltage distribution across capacitors in series.

However, when the capacitors have different values an interesting thing happens. The smaller capacitor charges to a higher voltage than the larger capacitor. In Figure 8-23B, C_2 is twice as large as C_1. Therefore C_1 charges to twice the voltage. Since the total voltage across both capacitors must be 12 volts, C_1 must drop 8 volts while C_2 drops only 4 volts.

To understand why the voltage is distributed in this way, you must recall an earlier equation that expressed capacitance in terms of charge and voltage. The equation is:

$$C = \frac{Q}{E}$$

Where C is capacitance in farads, Q is the charge in coulombs, and E is in volts. This equation can be rearranged:

$$E = \frac{Q}{C}$$

In this form, the equation states that the voltage across the capacitor is directly proportional to the charge on the capacitor but inversely proportional to the size of the capacitor. In Figure 8-23B, the two capacitors are in series. Consequently, the charging current is the same at all points in the circuit. For this reason, the two capacitors must always have equal charges. Since the charges are equal, the voltage is determined solely by the value of the capacitor. Furthermore, since the voltage is inversely proportional to the capacitance value, the smaller capacitor charges to a higher voltage.

53. The formula for determining the total capacitance of three capacitors in parallel is _____.

54. If the three capacitors in parallel are all 6 μF, the total capacitance is _____.

55. If three 6 μF capacitors are connected in series, the total capacitance is _____.

56. The formula used to determine the total capacitance in series is _____.

57. When two capacitors having different values are connected in series, the (smaller/larger) capacitor will charge to the higher voltage.

Summary

When current flows through a conductor a magnetic field builds up around the conductor. As the magnetic field builds up, a voltage is induced into the conductor. The induced voltage opposes the applied voltage and is called a counter EMF. The process by which the counter EMF is produced is called self-induction.

Counter EMF is always of a polarity that opposes changes in current. It opposes the increase in current that occurs when power is applied to a circuit. It also opposes the decrease in current that occurs when power is removed. The ability of a device to oppose a change of current is called inductance. The unit of inductance is the Henry.

A device designed to have a specific inductance is called an inductor. The inductor consists of turns of wire wrapped around a core. The greater the number of turns and the higher the permeability of the core, the greater will be the value of the inductance.

The capacitor consists of two metal plates separated by an insulator called a dielectric. It has the ability to store an electrical charge. This ability to store a charge is called capacitance. When connected to a voltage source, the capacitor charges to the value of the applied voltage. If the charged capacitor is then connected across a load, it will discharge through the load.

The unit of capacitance is the farad; although the microfarad and the picofarad are more commonly used. Three factors determine the value of a capacitor. They are: the area of the plates, the spacing between the plates, and the dielectric constant.

There are many different types of capacitors. They are generally classified by their dielectric. The most popular types are air, paper, mica, ceramic, and electrolytic.

The length of time required for a capacitor to charge is determined by the capacitance and the resistance in the circuit. A time constant is the length of time required for a capacitor to charge to 63.2 percent of its applied voltage. The formula for finding the time constant is:

$$T = R \times C$$

The time constant chart is used when working with time constants. It shows the manner in which capacitors charge and discharge. It plots the number of time constants against the percent of the applied voltage.

Capacitors may be connected in series or in parallel. When connected in parallel, the total capacitance is equal to the sum of the individual capacitor values. The formula is:

$$C_T = C_1 + C_2 + C_3 + \ldots$$

When connected in series, the total capacitance is determined by the following formula:

$$C_T = \cfrac{1}{\dfrac{1}{C_1} + \dfrac{1}{C_2} + \dfrac{1}{C_3} + \ldots}$$

Appendix A

Appendix A

Scientific Notation

In electronics, it is common to deal with both very large and very small numbers. An example of a very large number is the speed at which electricity travels. It travels at the speed of light which is approximately 1,000,000,000 feet per second or about 300,000,000 meters per second. As for very small numbers, consider the size and weight of an electron. It is believed that the electron has a diameter of approximately 0.000 000 000 0022 inch and a weight of about 0.000 000 000 000 000 000 000 000 0009 gram. Sometimes, we perform arithmetic with numbers such as these. To simplify such arithmetic, a shorthand method has been developed to express numbers. This shorthand method is called *scientific notation*. The following programmed instruction sequence will serve as an introduction to scientific notation.

---

1. As mentioned above, scientific notation is a shorthand method of expressing numbers. While any number can be expressed in scientific notation, this technique is particularly helpful in expressing very large and very _____ numbers.

---

2. (small) Scientific notation is based on a concept called powers of ten. Thus, in order to understand scientific notation we should first learn what is meant by powers of _____.

---

3. (ten) In mathematics, a number is raised to a power by multiplying the number times itself one or more times. Thus, we raise 5 to the second power by multiplying 5 times itself. That is, 5 to the second power is $5 \times 5 =$_____.

---

4. (25) Also, 5 to the third power is the same as saying $5 \times 5 \times 5 =$ _____.

---

5. (125) Thus, 5 can be raised to any power simply by multiplying it times itself the required number of times. For example, 5 × 5 × 5 × 5 = 625. Consequently, 5 raised to the _____ power is equal to 625.

6. (fourth) The above examples use powers of five. However, any number can be raised to a power by the technique of multiplying it times itself the required number of times. Thus, the powers of two would look like this:

2 to the second power equals 2 × 2 = 4

2 to the third power equals 2 × 2 × 2 = 8

2 to the fourth power equals 2 × 2 × 2 × 2 = 16

2 to the fifth power equals 2 × 2 × 2 × 2 × 2 = 32

2 to the sixth power equals 2 × 2 × 2 × 2 × 2 × 2 = _____

7. (64) In mathematics, the number which is raised to a power is called the *base*. If 5 is raised to the third power, 5 is considered the _____.

8. (base) The power to which the number is raised is called the *exponent*. If 5 is raised to the third power, then the exponent is 3. In the same way, if 2 is raised to the sixth power, then 2 is the base while 6 is the _____.

9. (exponent) There is a shorthand method for writing "2 raised to the sixth power." It is:

$$2^6$$

Notice that the exponent is written as a small number at the top right of the base. Remember <u>this</u> number is the base while <u>this</u> number is the exponent.

$$2^6$$

Therefore in the example 3^4, 3 is the _____ while 4 is the _____.

10. (base, exponent) The number 3^4 is read "3 raised to the fourth power." It is equal to:

$$3 \times 3 \times 3 \times 3 = 81.$$

The number 4^6 is read _____ .

11. (4 raised to the sixth power) Scientific notation uses powers of ten. Several powers of ten are listed below:

$$10^2 = 10 \times 10 = 100$$
$$10^3 = 10 \times 10 \times 10 = 1000$$
$$10^4 = 10 \times 10 \times 10 \times 10 = 10,000$$
$$10^5 = 10 \times 10 \times 10 \times 10 \times 10 = 100,000$$
$$10^6 = 10 \times 10 \times 10 \times 10 \times 10 \times 10 = \text{_____} .$$

12. (1,000,000) Multiplication by 10 is extremely easy since all we have to do is add one zero for each multiplication. Another way to look at it is that multiplication by ten is the same as moving the decimal point one place to the right. Thus, we can find the equivalent of 10^2 by multiplying $10 \times 10 = 100$; or, simply by adding a 0 after 10 to form 100; or by moving the decimal point one place to the right to form 10.0. = 100. In any event, 10^2 is equal to

_____ .

13. (100) There is a simple procedure for converting a number expressed as a power of ten to its equivalent number. We simply write down a 1 and after it write the number of zeros indicated by the exponent. For example, 10^6 is equal to 1 with 6 zeros after it. In the same way 10^{11} is equal to 1 with _____ zeros after it.

14. (11) This illustrates one of the advantages of power of ten. It is easier to write and remember 10^{21} than its equivalent number: 1,000,000,000,000,000,000,000. Try it yourself and see if it isn't easier to write 10^{35} than to write its equivalent number of:

_____ .

15. (100,000,000,000,000,000,000,000,000,000,000,000). In the above examples, we converted a number expressed in powers of ten to its equivalent number. Now let's see how we convert in the opposite direction. Remember the number must be expressed using 10 as the base with the appropriate exponent. The exponent is determined simply by counting the zeros which fall on the right side of the 1. Thus, 1,000,000 becomes 10^6 because there are 6 zeros in the number. In the same way, 10,000,000,000 is expressed as _____.

16. (10^{10}) To be sure you have the right idea, study each of the groups below. Which group contains an error? _____.

Group A	Group B	Group C
$10^6 = 1,000,000$	$1000 = 10^3$	$10^7 = 10,000,000$
$10^2 = 100$	$10,000 = 10^4$	$10^9 = 1,000,000,000$
$10^9 = 1,000,000,000$	$100 = 10^2$	$10^{11} = 10,000,000,000$

17. (Group C) There are two special cases of powers of ten which require some additional explanation. The first is 10^1. Here the exponent of 10 is 1. If we follow the procedure developed in Frame 13 we find that $10^1 = 10$. That is, we put down a 1 and add the number of zeros indicated by the exponent. Thus $10^1 = $ _____.

18. (10) The other special case is 10^0. Here the exponent is 0. Once again we follow the procedure outlined in Frame 13. Here again we write down a 1 and add the number of zeros indicated by the exponent. However, since the exponent is 0, we add no zeros. Thus, the equivalent number of 10^0 is 1. That is $10^0 = $ _____.

19. (1) Any base number with an exponent of 1 is equal to the base number. Any base number with an exponent of 0 is equal to 1. Thus, $X^1 = $ _____ and $X^0 = $ _____.

20. (X, 1) In the examples given above, the exponents have been positive numbers. For simplicity the plus sign has been omitted. Therefore, 10^2 is the same as 10^{+2}. Also, 10^6 is the same as

_____.

21. (10^{+6}) Positive exponents represent numbers larger than 1. Thus, numbers such as 10^2, 10^7, and 10^{15} are greater than 1 and require _____ exponents.

22. (positive) Numbers smaller than 1 are indicated by negative exponents. Thus, numbers like 0.01, 0.0001, and 0.00001 are expressed as negative powers of ten because these numbers are less than

_____.

23. (1) Some of the negative powers of ten are listed below:

$10^{-1} = 0.1$
$10^{-2} = 0.01$
$10^{-3} = 0.001$
$10^{-4} = 0.0001$
$10^{-5} =$ _____.

24. (0.00001) A brief study of this list will show that this is simply a continuation of the list shown earlier in frame 11. If the two lists are combined in a descending order, the result will look like this:

$10^6 =$ 1,000,000.
$10^5 =$ 100,000.
$10^4 =$ 10,000.
$10^3 =$ 1,000.
$10^2 =$ 100.
$10^1 =$ 10.
$10^0 =$ 1.
$10^{-1} =$ 0.1
$10^{-2} =$ 0.01
$10^{-3} =$ 0.001
$10^{-4} =$ 0.0001
$10^{-5} =$ _____

25. (0.00001) We can think of the negative exponent as an indication of how far the decimal point should be moved to the left to obtain the equivalent number. Thus, the procedure for converting a negative power of ten to its equivalent number can be developed. The procedure is to write down the number 1 and move the decimal point to the left the number of places indicated by the negative exponent. For example, 10^{-4} becomes:

$$0.0001. \text{ or } 0.0001$$

Notice that the -4 exponent indicates that the decimal point should be moved ＿＿＿＿＿＿ places to the ＿＿＿＿＿＿.

26. (4, left) Up to now we have used powers of ten to express only those numbers which are exact multiples of ten such as 100, 1000, 10,000, etc. Obviously, if these were the only numbers which could be expressed as powers of ten, this method of writing numbers would be of little use. Actually, any ＿＿＿＿＿＿ can be expressed in powers-of-ten notation.

27. (number) The technique by which this is done can be shown by an example. If 1,000,000 can be represented by 10^6, then 2,000,000 can be represented by 2×10^6. That is, we express the quantity as a number multiplied by the appropriate power of ten. As another example, $2,500,000 = 2.5 \times 10^6$. Also, $3,000,000 =$ ＿＿＿＿＿＿.

28. (3×10^6) In the same way, we can write 5,000 as 5×10^3. Some other examples are:

$$200 = 2 \times 10^2$$
$$1500 = 15 \times 10^2$$
$$22,000 = 22 \times 10^3$$
$$120,000 = 12 \times 10^4$$
$$1,700,000 = 17 \times 10^5$$
$$9,000,000 = \underline{\hspace{1.5cm}}$$

29. (9×10^6) By the same token, we can convert in the opposite direction. Thus, 2×10^5 becomes $2 \times 100,000$ or $200,000$. Also, $2.2 \times 10^3 = 2.2 \times 1000 = 2,200$. And, $66 \times 10^4 = $ _____.

30. ($660,000$) You may have noticed that when we use powers of ten there are several different ways to write a number. For example, $25,000$ can be written as 25×10^3 because 25×1000 equals $25,000$. However; it can also be written as 2.5×10^4 because $2.5 \times 10,000$ equals $25,000$. It can even be written as 250×10^2 since $250 \times 100 = 25,000$. In the same way, 4.7×10^4, 47×10^3, and 470×10^2 are three different ways of writing the number _____.

31. ($47,000$) Numbers smaller than one are expressed as negative powers of ten in much the same way. Thus, $.0039$ can be expressed as 3.9×10^{-3}, 39×10^{-4}, or $.39 \times 10^{-2}$. Also, 6.8×10^{-5}, 68×10^{-6}, and $.68 \times 10^{-4}$ are three different ways of expressing the number _____.

32. ($.000068$) As you can see there are several different ways in which a number can be written as a power of ten. Scientific notation is a way of using powers of ten so that all numbers can be expressed in a uniform way. To see exactly what scientific notation is, consider the following examples of numbers written in scientific notation:

$$6.25 \times 10^{18}$$
$$3.7 \ \times 10^6$$
$$4.0 \ \times 10^2$$
$$6.8 \ \times 10^{-4}$$
$$3.9 \ \times 10^{-6}$$
$$2.2 \ \times 10^{-12}$$

Notice that the numbers range from a very large number to an extremely small number. And yet, all these numbers are written in a uniform way. This method of writing numbers is called scientific _____.

33. (notation) The rules for writing a number in scientific notation are quite simple. First, the decimal point is always placed after the first digit on the left which is not a zero. Therefore, the final number will appear in this form: 6.25, 7.3, 9.65, 8.31, 2.0 and so forth. It must never appear in a form such as: .625, 73, 96.5, .831 or 20. Thus, there is always one and only one digit on the _____ side of the decimal point.

34. (left) The second rule involves the sign of the exponent. If the original number is greater than 1, the exponent must be positive. If the number is less than 1, the exponent must be negative. Thus, 67,000 requires a positive exponent but 0.00327 requires a _____ exponent.

35. (negative) Finally, the magnitude of the exponent is determined by the number of places that the decimal point is moved. For example, 39,000.0 is expressed as 3.9×10^4 because the decimal point must be moved 4 places in order to have only one digit to the left of it. Using this rule, 6,700,000,000 is expressed as $6.7 \times$ _____ .

36. (10^9) The number 0.00327 is expressed as 3.27×10^{-3}. Here the decimal point is moved 3 places in order to have one digit which is not zero to the left of the decimal. Likewise 0.00027 is expressed as $2.7 \times$ _____ .

37. (10^{-4}) To be sure you have the idea look at the groups of numbers below. Which of the following groups contains a number that is not expressed properly in scientific notation? _____

Group A	Group B	Group C
6.25×10^{18}	1.11×10^{11}	6.9×10^{10}
3.75×10^{-9}	-3.1×10^2	3.4×10^7
4.20×10^1	-3.1×10^{-2}	39.5×10^2
7.93×10^0	2.00×10^2	6.0×10^4

38. (Group C) The number 39.5×10^2 is not written in scientific notation because there are two digits on the left side of the decimal point. The minus signs in Group B may have confused you. Although, it has not been mentioned, negative numbers can also be expressed in scientific notation. Thus, a number like $-6,200,000$ becomes -6.2×10^6. All the rules previously stated hold true except that now a _____ sign is placed before the number.

39. (minus) Small negative numbers are handled in the same way. Thus -0.0092 becomes -9.2×10^{-3}. The minus sign before the number indicates that this is a negative number. The minus sign before the exponent indicates that this number is less than _____ .

40. (1) Listed below are numbers which are converted to scientific notation. Which one of these groups contains an error? _____ .

Group A	Group B	Group C
$2,200 = 2.2 \times 10^3$	$119,000 = 1.19 \times 10^5$	$119 = 1.19 \times 10^2$
$32,000 = 3.2 \times 10^4$	$1,633,000 = 1.633 \times 10^6$	$93 = 9.3 \times 10^1$
$963,000 = 9.63 \times 10^5$	$937,000 = 9.37 \times 10^4$	$7.7 = 7.7 \times 10^0$
$660 = 6.6 \times 10^2$	$6,800 = 6.8 \times 10^3$	$131.2 = 1.312 \times 10^2$

41. (Group B) 937,000 converts to 9.37×10^5 and not to 9.37×10^4. Which of the groups below contains an error?_____ .

Group A	Group B	Group C
$0.00037 = 3.7 \times 10^{-4}$	$0.44 = 4.4 \times 10^{-1}$	$.37 = 3.7 \times 10^{-1}$
$0.312 = 3.12 \times 10^{-1}$	$0.0002 = 2.0 \times 10^{-4}$	$.0098 = 9.8 \times 10^{-3}$
$0.068 = 6.8 \times 10^{-2}$	$0.0798 = 7.98 \times 10^{-2}$	$.00001 = 1.0 \times 10^{-5}$
$0.0092 = 9.2 \times 10^3$	$0.644 = 6.44 \times 10^{-1}$	$0.0075 = 7.5 \times 10^{-3}$

42. (Group A) The final number in group A requires a negative exponent. Which of the groups below contains an error?_____ .

Group A	Group B	Group C
$3,700,000 = 3.7 \times 10^6$	$9440 = 9.44 \times 10^3$	$20 = 2.0 \times 10^1$
$-5,500 = -5.5 \times 10^3$	$-110 = -1.1 \times 10^2$	$0.02 = 2.0 \times 10^{-2}$
$0.058 = 5.8 \times 10^{-2}$	$0.0062 = 6.2 \times 10^{-4}$	$-200,000 = -2.0 \times 10^5$
$-0.0034 = -3.4 \times 10^{-3}$	$-0.0123 = -1.23 \times 10^{-2}$	$-0.000200 = -2.0 \times 10^{-4}$

43. (Group B) 0.0062 is equal to 6.2×10^{-3}. Match the following:

1.	16	a.	1.6×10^{-3}
2.	.0016	b.	1.6×10^4
3.	160,000	c.	1.6×10^0
4.	1.6	d.	1.6×10^1
5.	.016	e.	1.6×10^{-2}
6.	16,000	f.	1.6×10^5

44. (1-d, 2-a, 3-f, 4-c, 5-e, 6-b). Another concept that goes hand in hand with powers of ten and scientific notation is metric prefixes. These are prefixes such as *mega* and *kilo* which when placed before a word change the meaning of the word. For example, the prefix *kilo* means *thousand*. When kilo and meter are combined the word kilometer is formed. This word means 1000 meters. In the same way, the word kilogram means _____ grams.

45. (1,000) Since kilo means 1,000 we can think of it as multiplying any quantity times 1000 or 10^3. Thus, kilo means 10^3. Another popular metric prefix is *mega*. *Mega* means *million*. Thus a mega-ton is one million tons or 10^6 tons. In the same way one million volts is referred to as a _____volt.

46. (mega) One thousand watts can be called a kilowatt. Also one million watts can be called a _____.

47. (megawatt) A kilowatt is equal to 10^3 watts while a megawatt is equal to _____ watts.

48. (10^6) Often it is convenient to convert from one prefix to another. For example, since a megaton is 10^6 tons and a kiloton is 10^3 tons, a megaton equals 1000 kilotons. And, since a megaton is one thousand times greater than a kiloton, the kiloton is equal to .001 megaton. Now, consider the quantity 100,000 tons. This is equal to 100 kilotons or _____ megatons.

49. (0.1) Kilo is often abbreviated k. Thus, 100 kilowatts may be expressed as 100 k watt. Mega is abbreviated M. Therefore 10 megawatts may be expressed as _____ watts.

50. (10M) The quantity 5 k volts is 5 kilovolts or 5000 volts. Also, 5 M volts is 5 megavolts or _____ volts.

51. (5,000,000) There are also prefixes which have values less than one. The most used are:

milli   which means *thousandth* (.001) or 10^{-3}, and
micro   which means *millionth* (.000 001) or 10^{-6}.

One thousandth of an ampere is called a milliampere. Also, one thousandth of a volt is called a _____.

52. (millivolt) If a second is divided into one million equal parts each part is called a microsecond. Also, the millionth part of a volt is called a _____.

53. (microvolt) One volt is equal to 1000 millivolts or 1,000,000 microvolts. Or, 1 volt equals 10^3 millivolts and 10^6 microvolts. Expressed another way, 1 millivolt equals .001 volt while 1 microvolt equals .000001 volt. Thus, 1 millivolt equals 10^{-3} volts while 1 microvolt equals _____ volt.

54. (10^{-6}) Powers of ten allow us to express a quantity using whichever metric prefix we prefer. For example, we can express 50 millivolts as 50×10^{-3} volts simply by replacing the prefix milli with its equivalent power of ten. In the same way 50 microvolts is equal to $50 \times$ _____ volts.

55. (10^{-6}) When writing abbreviation for the prefix milli the letter small m is used. A small m is used to distinguish it from mega which used a capital M. Obviously, the abbreviation for micro cannot also be m. To represent micro the Greek letter μ (pronounced mu) is used. Thus, 10 millivolts is abbreviated 10 m volts while 10 microvolts is abbreviated 10 μ volts. Remember, m means 10^{-3} while μ means _____.

56. (10^{-6}) Match the following:

1.	M watt	a.	10^{-3} watts
2.	k watt	b.	10^{-6} watts
3.	m watt	c.	500×10^{-3} watts
4.	μ watt	d.	10^6 watts
5.	.5 watt	e.	.5k watts
6.	500 watts	f.	10^3 watts
7.	500,000 watts	g.	.5 M watts
8.	.00005 watts	h.	.05 k watts
9.	50 watts	i.	5 m watts
10.	.005 watts	j.	50 μ watts

57. (1-d, 2-f, 3-a, 4-b, 5-c, 6-e, 7-g, 8-j, 9-h, 10-i) Additional aspects of powers of ten, scientific notation, and metric prefixes will be discussed later.

Appendix B

Finding The Square Root Of A Number

The easiest way to find the square root of a number is to use a calculator which has a square root key. If your calculator does not have a square root key, you may still be able to compute square roots using a procedure described in the instruction manual supplied with your calculator. For those without a calculator, a slide rule is the next easiest method. Tables or logarithms may also be used. In spite of all these aids, you may on some occasion find it necessary to use the old-fashioned, long-hand method of computing the square root of a number. The following programmed instruction sequence explains this method of computing square roots.

1. The square root of a given number is the number which when multiplied by itself equals the given number. For example, the square root of 25 is 5 because $5 \times 5 =$ _____.

2. (25) The symbol which is used in mathematics to indicate that the square root is to be taken is the radical sign ($\sqrt{}$). Thus, $\sqrt{25} =$ _____.

3. (5) Some examples are so simple that we intuitively know the answer. For example, $\sqrt{9} = 3$, $\sqrt{100} = 10$, $\sqrt{64} =$ _____.

4. (8) However, when the number is very long such as 53,545.96 the square root is found by a long (but relatively simple) procedure. Let's find the square root of the number by using this procedure.

   The first step is to write the number in groups of two digits starting at the decimal point. For example, if we were taking the square root of 6,314.313 we would group the digits like this:

   $$63 \quad 14 \quad . \quad 31 \quad 30$$

   However, in our example the number is 53,545.96. Therefore, the number is written in groups of two digits like this: _____.

5. (5 35 45 . 96) Notice that 5 must be written by itself in this example because there are an odd number of digits to the left of the decimal point. Since we are taking the square root of this number, it should be placed under a radical sign like this: _____.

6. ($\sqrt{5}$ 35 45 . 96) We are now ready to find the first number in the answer. We do this by examining the first group of numbers on the left. In this case, the "group" consists of the single number 5. On the line above the 5, we place a number which when multiplied by itself will come close to equalling, but will not exceed 5. In this case we use 2 because $2 \times 2 = 4$. This is as close as we can get to 5 without exceeding 5. Thus, the first digit in the answer is _____.

7. (2) Our work to this point looks like this:

$$
\begin{array}{r}
2 \\
\sqrt{5\ \ 35\ \ 45\ .\ \ 96}
\end{array}
$$

Next we multiply 2 by itself and place the product under 5 and subtract. Thus, our work becomes:

$$
\begin{array}{r}
2 \\
\sqrt{5\ \ 35\ \ 45\ .\ \ 96} \\
\underline{4 } \\
1
\end{array}
$$

At this point, the next group of two digits is brought down and placed beside the 1. The next two digits are _____.

8. (35) Thus, our work looks like this:

$$
\begin{array}{r}
2 \\
\sqrt{5\ \ 35\ \ 45\ .\ \ 96} \\
\underline{4 } \\
1\ \ 35
\end{array}
$$

The next step is to double the number above the radical sign and place the result in front of the 135 like this:

$$
\begin{array}{c}
\quad\; 2 \\
\sqrt{5\;\;35\;\;45\;\;.\;\;96} \\
\quad\; 4 \\
4\;\big/\overline{1\;\;35}
\end{array}
$$

Notice that a space is left here for another number. The second digit of the answer is now computed and placed above the second group of numbers. This number is found by trial and error. For example, let's guess that the next digit is 4. We place the new 4 here and here.

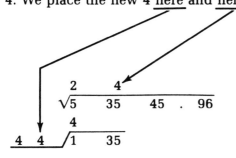

To check our guess, we multiply this digit times this number and place the product here.

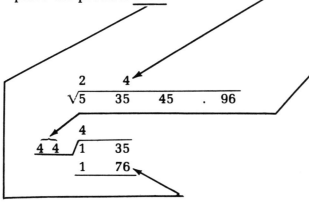

Notice that the product (176) is larger than 135, this tells us that our guess is too high. Thus, we must erase the numbers shown above because they are incorrect. Then we must make a new guess for the second digit of the answer. This new guess should be _____ than the first guess.

<u>lower/higher</u>

9. (lower) Let's try 3 as the second digit of the answer. Thus, our problem becomes:

$$
\begin{array}{r}
2 \qquad 3 \\
\sqrt{5 \quad 35 \quad 45 \quad . \quad 96} \\
\\
4 \\
43\overline{)1 \quad 35}
\end{array}
$$

Now we multiply 3 times 43 and place the product under the 135. If the product is smaller than 135 we subtract:

$$
\begin{array}{r}
2 \qquad 3 \\
\sqrt{5 \quad 35 \quad 45 \quad . \quad 96} \\
\\
4 \\
4\ 3\overline{)1 \quad 35} \\
1 \quad 29 \\
\hline
6
\end{array}
$$

This number tells us that our guess is correct. If this number is greater than 43, our guess is too low. On the other hand we saw in Frame 8 what happens if our guess is too high. Thus, at this point, we know that the first two digits in the answer are _____.

10. (23) In the next step we bring down the next two digit group of numbers so that our work looks like this:

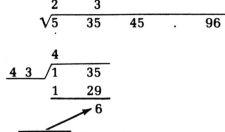

$$
\begin{array}{r}
2 \qquad 3 \\
\sqrt{5 \quad 35 \quad 45 \quad . \quad 96} \\
\\
4 \\
4\ 3\overline{)1 \quad 35} \\
1 \quad 29 \\
\hline
6 \quad 45
\end{array}
$$

As before the number above the radical sign (23) is doubled to 46. This 46 is placed in front of the 645. A space is left open after the 46 for the next trial answer:

```
          2     3
       √5   35    45    .    96

             4
       43 /1   35

              1    29
       46  ╱       6    45
         space
```

We guess at the third digit in the answer and place our guess above the third group of numbers and in front of the 46 on the bottom line. By trial and error you will soon find that the proper number for this third digit is _____.

11. (1) Thus, the problem becomes:

```
          2      3      1
       √5    35     45    .    96

              4
      4 3 /1     35
             1    29
     4 6 1 ╱       6    45
```

Next, we multiply 1 × 461, place the product under 645, and subtract:

```
          2      3      1
       √5    35     45    .    96

              4
      4 3 /1     35

              1    29
     4 6 1 ╱       6    45
                  4    61
                  1    84
```

The next step is to bring down the final group of two numbers so that the number on the bottom line becomes _____.

12. (1 84 96) The decimal point in the answer is always immediately above the decimal point in the number under the radical sign. Thus, by placing the decimal point in the answer our work looks like this:

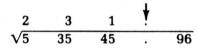
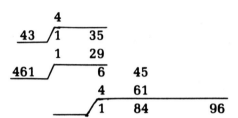

To find the next digit of the answer, we double our partial answer (231) to get 462. We place this number in front of the 1 84   96   leaving a space for our trial number:

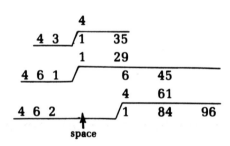

Again by trial and error, we find that the final digit must be
_____.

13. (4) Thus, we place 4 in the answer and after the 462. Next we multiply
4 × 4624 so that our final work looks like this:

```
              2      3      1    .    4
          √5      35     45    .    96

                  4
          43   /1      35
               1      29
          461  /       6      45

                       4      61
          4624 /       1      84     96
                       1      84     96
                       ————————————————
                                      0
```

Notice that the answer comes out even. This tells us that the square
root of 53,545. 96 is exactly _____.

14. (231.4) We can easily prove this by multiplying 231.4 by itself.

```
Thus:       231.4
         ×  231.4
         ——————————
            925 6
           2314
           6942
          4628
         ——————————
         53,545.9 6
```

To be sure you have the idea, an additional example is given below. Study each step carefully starting with Step 1 and ending with Step 23.

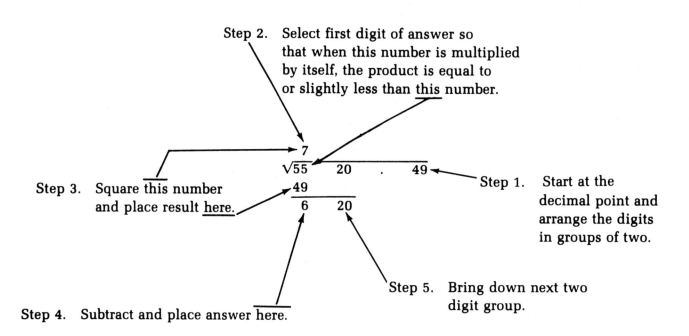

Step 2. Select first digit of answer so that when this number is multiplied by itself, the product is equal to or slightly less than this number.

Step 1. Start at the decimal point and arrange the digits in groups of two.

Step 3. Square this number and place result here.

Step 4. Subtract and place answer here.

Step 5. Bring down next two digit group.

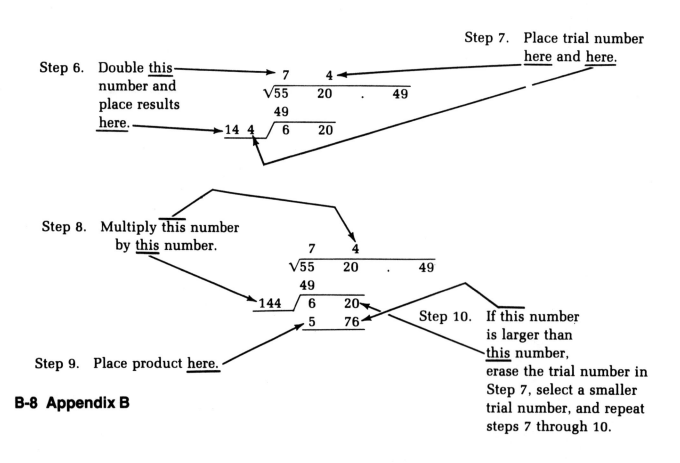

Step 6. Double this number and place results here.

Step 7. Place trial number here and here.

Step 8. Multiply this number by this number.

Step 9. Place product here.

Step 10. If this number is larger than this number, erase the trial number in Step 7, select a smaller trial number, and repeat steps 7 through 10.

B-8 Appendix B

Step 14. Place decimal point in answer here.

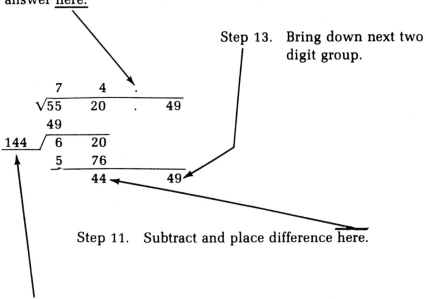

Step 13. Bring down next two digit group.

Step 11. Subtract and place difference here.

Step 12. If difference is larger than this number, erase the trial number in Step 7, select a larger trial number and repeat steps 7 through 12.

Step 15. Double this number and place result here.

Step 16. Place trial number here and here.

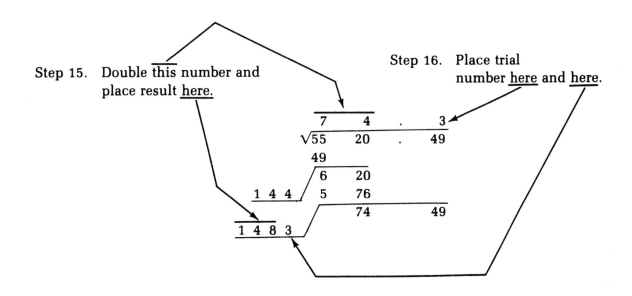

Step 17. Multiply this number by this number.

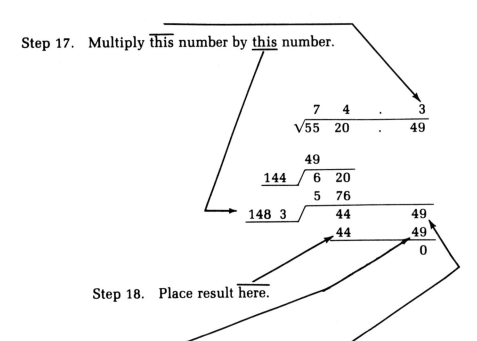

Step 18. Place result here.

Step 19. If this number is larger than this number, erase the trial number in Step 16, select a smaller trial number and repeat steps 16 through 19.

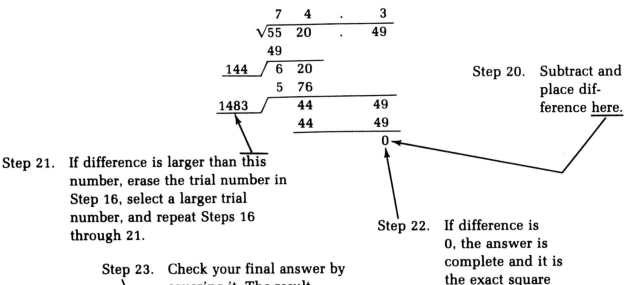

Step 20. Subtract and place difference here.

Step 21. If difference is larger than this number, erase the trial number in Step 16, select a larger trial number, and repeat Steps 16 through 21.

Step 22. If difference is 0, the answer is complete and it is the exact square root of the number. If difference is not 0, additional accuracy can be obtained by bringing down 00 and continuing with the procedure.

Step 23. Check your final answer by squaring it. The result should be the original number.

```
        74.3
        74.3
      _____
       222 9
      2972
      5201
      _____
      5520. 49
```

INDEX

Electromagnetic field, 5-5
Electromagnetic induction, 5-25
Electromotive force, 2-5
Electron, 1-7
Electron, free, 1-14
Electron, stray, 1-14
Electron, valence, 1-19
Electrostatic field, 1-10
Electrostatic force, 1-10
Element table, 1-6
Elements, 1-6
EMF, 2-5
EMF, counter, 8-7

Farad, 8-19
Faraday's law, 5-26
Ferromagnetic, 5-8
Field, 5-5
Field, electromagnetic, 5-5
Field, electrostatic, 1-10
Field intensity, 5-19
Flux, 5-18
Flux density, 5-19
Flux lines, 5-7
Foot pound, 2-10
Free electron, 1-14
Friction, charging by, 1-15
Friction, voltage produced by, 2-15

Generator, AC, 5-27
Generator, DC, 5-29
Generator, left-hand rule, 5-26, 5-27
Ground, 2-36

Heat, voltage produced by, 2-17
Henry, 8-8

Inaccuracy, measurement, 6-34
Induced voltage, 5-25
Inductance, 8-8
Induction, charging by, 1-15
Induction, electromagnetic, 5-25
Induction, magnetic, 5-24
Induction self-, 8-5
Inductor, 8-9
Inductor time constant, 8-10
Ion, 1-13
Ionization, 1-14

Joule, 2-10

Kirchhoff's current law, 7-29
Kirchhoff's law, 7-25
Kirchhoff's voltage law, 7-24

Left-hand rule for conductors, 5-14
Left-hand rule for generators, 5-27
Light, voltage produced by, 2-16
Lines of flux, 5-7
Loading, voltmeters, 6-21
Loudspeaker, 5-34

Magnetic domains, 5-11
Magnetic field rule, 5-5
Magnetic field rule, left-hand, 5-14
Magnetic induction, 5-24
Magnetic tape, 5-35
Magnetic unit table, 5-21
Magnetics, Ohms' law for, 5-20
Magnetism, 2-12
Magnetism, theory of, 5-10
Magnetism, voltage produced by, 2-12
Magnetizing force, 5-19

Magneteolectricity, 2-12

Magnetomotive force, 5-19

Magnet, 5-5

Matter, 1-5

Measurement inaccuracies, 6-34

Memory, core, 5-40

Meter accuracy, ammeter, 6-14

Meter construction, 6-5

Meter Movement, 6-5

Meter movement, taut-band, 6-8

Meter movement, theory of 6-5

Microampere, 1-32

Mks, 5-21

mmf, 5-19

Model, of atom, Bohr, 1-7

Molecule, 1-6

Motor, DC, 5-36

Motor rule, right-hand, 5-37

Multimeters, electrical, 6-34

Multimeters, electronic, 6-34

Multiplier, resistor for voltmeter, 6-21

Negative temperature coefficient, 3-9

Network theorem, Kirchhoff's current law, 7-29

Network theorem, Kirchhoff's voltage law, 7-24

Network theorem, Norton's theorem, 7-45

Network theorem, Norton-Thevenin conversions, 7-49

Network theorem, Superposition theorem, 7-31

Network theorem, Thevenin's theorem, 7-36

Neutron, 1-7

Norton's theorem, 7-45

Norton-Thevenin conversions, 7-49

Nucleus, 1-7

Ohm, 3-5

Ohmmeter, series, 6-25

Ohmmeter, shunt, 6-31

Ohm's law, current, 4-5

Ohm's law, power, 4-20

Ohm's law, resistance, 4-10

Ohm's law, voltage, 4-8

Ohm's law for magnetics, 5-20

Ohms per volt, 6-20

Open circuit voltage, 7-36

Orbital shells, 1-18

Parallax, 6-36

Parallel connection of batteries, 2-28

Parallel resistance, 3-20

Parallel resistors, current distribution, 7-6

Paramagnetic, 5-8

Permeability, 5-19

Photoelectric effect, 2-16

Piezoelectric effect, 2-17

Positive temperature coefficient, 3-8

Potential difference, 2-6

Potentiometer, 3-16

Power, 4-20

Power, Ohm's law for, 4-20

Power transfer theorem, maximum power, 4-22

Powers of ten, Appendix A

Pressure, voltage produced by, 2-17

Primary cell, 2-20

Proton, 1-7

RC time constant, 8-25

Record pickup, 5-34

Reed relay, 5-33

Reluctance, 5-19